Linear Algebra

HARBRACE COLLEGE MATHEMATICS SERIES

Salomon Bochner and W. G. Lister, EDITORS

Volumes on the following topics are now in preparation: Functions, Calculus, Multivariate Calculus, Discrete Probability, and Theory of Functions of Several Variables.

Linear Algebra

ROSS A. BEAUMONT
UNIVERSITY OF WASHINGTON

Harcourt, Brace & World, Inc.
New York/Chicago/Burlingame

LIBRARY OF CONGRESS CATALOG CARD NUMBER: 65-17515

PRINTED IN THE UNITED STATES OF AMERICA

Foreword

The Harbrace College Mathematics Series has been undertaken in response to the growing demands for flexibility in college mathematics curricula. This series of concise, single-topic textbooks is designed to serve two primary purposes: First, to provide basic undergraduate text materials in compact, coordinated units. Second, to make available a variety of supplementary textbooks covering single topics.

To carry out these aims, the series editors and the publisher have selected as the foundation of the series a sequence of six textbooks covering functions, calculus, linear algebra, multivariate calculus, theory of functions, and theory of functions of several variables. Complementing this sequence are a number of other planned volumes on such topics as probability, statistics, differential equations, topology, differential geometry, and complex functions.

By permitting more flexibility in the construction of courses and course sequences, this series should encourage diversity and individuality in curricular patterns. Furthermore, if an instructor wishes to devise his own topical sequence for a course, the Harbrace College Mathematics Series provides him with a set of books built around a flexible pattern from which he may choose the elements of his new arrangement. Or, if an instructor wishes to supplement a full-sized textbook, this series provides him with a group of compact treatments of individual topics.

An additional and novel feature of the Harbrace College Mathematics Series is its continuing adaptability. As new topics gain emphasis in the curricula or as promising new treatments appear, books will be added to the series or existing volumes will be revised. In this way, we will meet the changing demands of the instruction of mathematics with both speed and flexibility.

SALOMON BOCHNER
W. G. LISTER

April 1965

Preface

This book is a concise treatment of the essential topics of linear algebra that are prerequisites for many advanced mathematics courses. For this reason, the book is constructed around the central theme of finite dimensional real vector spaces and their linear transformations. The field of real numbers is consistently used as the ground field of scalars, thus presenting the fundamental results of linear algebra in a form most useful in other undergraduate courses in mathematics, statistics, physics, and engineering. If more generality is desired, an instructor can, with a lecture or two on fields, adapt the text to a more general situation.

The background of the student using this text should include plane geometry, elementary coordinate geometry, and some three-dimensional geometry. The student should also be familiar with very elementary set theory and set notation and the concepts of a mapping and a one-to-one correspondence. The knowledge of the properties of the real number system and polynomials acquired in a modern elementary algebra course is sufficient algebraic preparation. Summation notation is used where it is convenient and may require explanation. In short, the formal prerequisites for this text are those now included in an up-to-date high school program.

The book is written largely in the formal style of an advanced mathematics text. After a leisurely beginning, the pace quickens as the basic notions of linear algebra are introduced. The generous supply of examples and exercises given in each section, which require both proofs and routine computations, should ameliorate (or at least diversify) the student's task. The proofs of some results stated in the text are left as exercises. The exercises that give additional results of unusual importance, as well as a few that contain definitions, are indicated by an asterisk (*).

This book is suitable for a one-semester course meeting three hours per week (or a one-quarter course meeting five hours per week) at the sophomore or junior level. It is particularly adaptable as a supplementary text in a calculus sequence in which the concepts of linear algebra are needed before a reasonable treatment of multivariate calculus or linear differential equations can be given. As an integral part of the Harbrace College Mathematics Series, this textbook is designed as the third book in a core sequence of six compact volumes. The first book in the sequence covers relations, functions, and elementary analytic geometry. The second book deals with elementary calculus, and the fourth book treats multivariate calculus and elementary differential equations. Thus an undergraduate course based on this book would generally follow a course in elementary calculus.

The task of writing this book has been considerably lightened by the confidence placed in the author by the editors of the Harbrace College Mathematics Series, Salomon Bochner and W. G. Lister, whose helpful suggestions are greatly appreciated. My special thanks are due to my colleague and friend H. S. Zuckerman, who carefully read the entire manuscript and made detailed and valuable comments. Finally, I owe my thanks to Miss Betsy Dent, Mrs. Judy Hickenbottom, and Mrs. Elizabeth Kurrle for their expert typing of the manuscript, and to the Department of Mathematics of the University of Washington for the services they provided.

ROSS A. BEAUMONT

Seattle, Washington
April 1965

Contents

CHAPTER ONE

Vector Methods in Geometry 1

1 Geometrical vectors 1

2 Vector operations 6

3 Coordinate systems on a line and in a plane 12

4 Coordinate systems in three-dimensional space 22

5 Applications to geometry 29

CHAPTER TWO

Real Vector Spaces 35

6 Linear dependence in $\mathcal{E}_3$ 35

7 Real vector spaces 38

8 Dimension of a vector space 45

9 Euclidean vector spaces 51

CHAPTER THREE

Systems of Linear Equations 57

10 Elementary transformations 57

11 Systems of equations in echelon form 62

12 Theory of linear systems; homogeneous systems 68

CHAPTER FOUR

Linear Transformations and Matrices 74

13 Linear transformations of $\mathcal{E}_2$ and $\mathcal{E}_3$ 74

14 Definition of a linear transformation 79

15 The algebra of linear transformations 85

16 The matrix of a linear transformation 89

17 The algebra of matrices 95

18 Applications to systems of linear equations 105

CHAPTER FIVE

Equivalence of Matrices 115

19 Change of basis 115

20 Matrices of linear transformations with respect to difference bases 119

21 Elementary transformation matrices 127

22 Rank of a matrix 135

23 Canonical form of a matrix under equivalence 137

CHAPTER SIX

Determinants 143

24 Definition of a determinant 143

25 Properties of determinants 148

26 Expansion of a determinant 153

27 Some applications of determinants 157

CHAPTER SEVEN

Similarity of Matrices 162

28 Characteristic values 162

29 Matrices similar to diagonal matrices 166

30 Orthogonal linear transformations and orthogonal matrices 172

CHAPTER EIGHT

Quadratic Forms 181

31 Bilinear and quadratic mappings 181

32 Orthogonal reduction of real symmetric matrices 187

33 Congruent reduction of real symmetric matrices 195

Answers to Selected Exercises 202

Index 214

CHAPTER ONE

Vector Methods in Geometry

1 Geometrical vectors

Many physical quantities, such as force, displacement, velocity, and acceleration, are described by a magnitude and a direction. Moreover, it follows from the laws of physics that such quantities can be combined or "added" by essentially similar rules; *vectors* in two- and three-dimensional space provide a mathematical model that describes these physical systems.

If a force F acts at a point P in space, then this force can be represented geometrically by a directed line segment with initial point at P, pointing in the direction in which the force acts, and with length equal to the magnitude of the force (Figure 1).

Consider a system of forces acting at a point P, and suppose that the given forces all act along a single line through P. We add the magnitudes of the forces acting in one direction, then add the magnitudes of the forces in the opposite direction, and subtract the smaller sum from the larger. Then a single force F whose magnitude is this difference, and which acts at P along the line in the direction of the larger sum, is physically equivalent to the system of forces acting at P (Figure 2). If a positive direction is chosen on the line, then a positive or negative real number that gives the magnitude

FIGURE 1

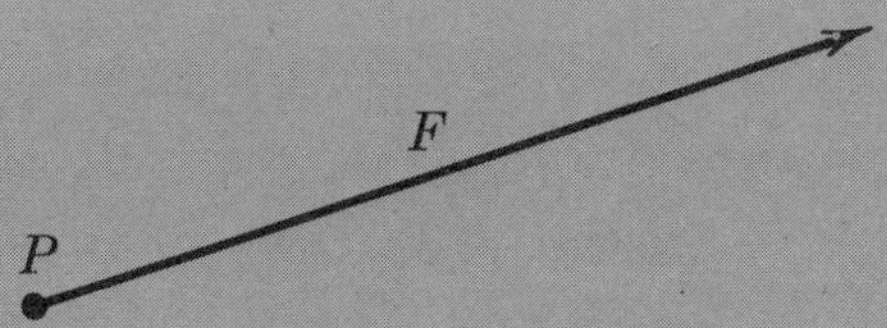

FIGURE 2

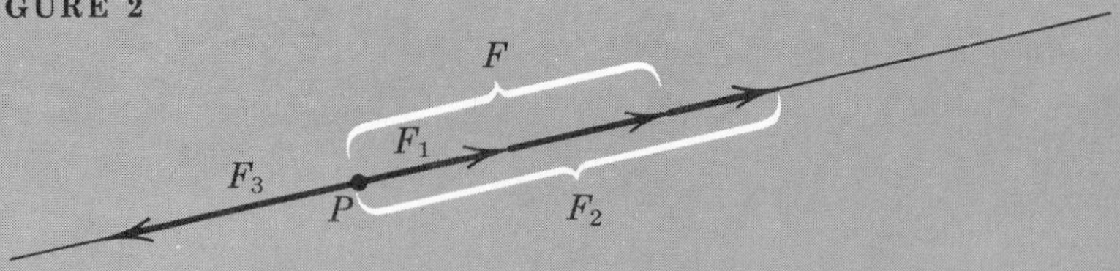

of the force can be assigned to each force, and the algebra of real numbers can be used to compute the *resultant force* F.

If the several forces at the point P do not all act along the same line, then the algebra of real numbers is not adequate to compute a resultant force acting at P. By the laws of physics, two forces F_1 and F_2 acting at P are equivalent to a single force F, which has the magnitude and direction of the diagonal of the parallelogram determined by the directed line segments representing F_1 and F_2 (Figure 3). If F_3 is a third force acting at P, then the directed line segments representing F_3 and F determine a parallelogram and F', the resultant force of F_3 and F, can be computed by the rule used to compute F (Figure 4). It can be shown that the directed line segment representing F' is the diagonal of the parallelopiped determined by F_1, F_2, and F_3. Hence, the same force F' would be obtained regardless of the order or grouping used to combine the three forces F_1, F_2, and F_3. Thus, the operation for combining forces enjoys some of the same algebraic properties as addition of real numbers.

The magnitude of a force F can be measured by a positive real number m. If k is any positive real number, then $k \cdot F$ is a force with magnitude km and the same direction as F, and $(-k) \cdot F$ is a force with magnitude km and direction opposite to F. If F acts at a point P, then any force acting at P along the line determined by F can be described as $r \cdot F$ for some positive or negative real number r.

Suppose that a force F_1, acting at a point P has the same magnitude and direction as a force F_2 acting at a different point Q. If P and Q are points

FIGURE 3

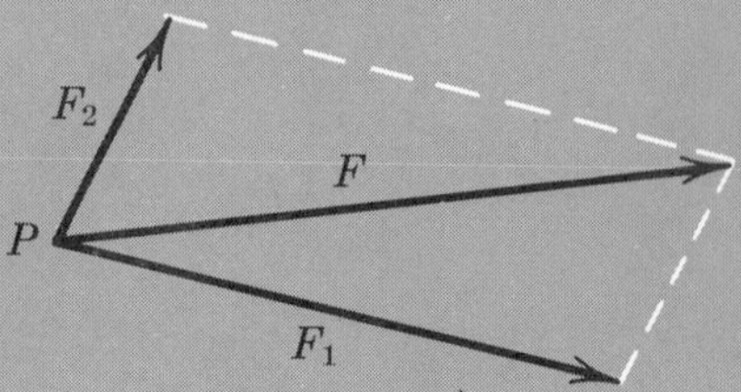

FIGURE 4

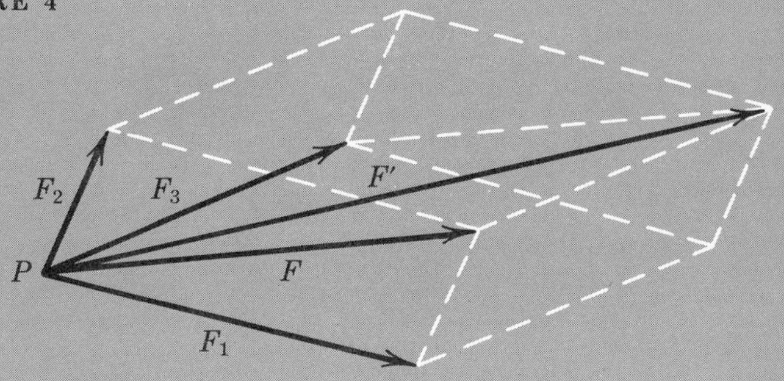

on some rigid body, the effect of the two forces on the motion of the body will not, in general, be the same. However, in applications, it is convenient to regard F_1 and F_2 as the same force acting at two different points. That is, two forces with the same magnitude and direction are equal.

We have observed that forces are combined or "added" by a parallelogram law and that a force can be "multiplied" by a real number. Moreover, we have seen that two forces are regarded as equal if they have the same magnitude and direction. The other physical quantities mentioned above (displacement, velocity, acceleration) are added by the parallelogram law, multiplied by real numbers, and have the same definition of equality. For example, let D_1 be a displacement from a point A to point B and D_2 be a displacement from the point B to a point C. Then the single displacement D from A to C, which is equivalent to the combination of the two given displacements, is found by the same rule as that for adding two forces (Figure 5).

Vectors form the appropriate mathematical model for these four physical systems. Our discussion of vectors will assume that the reader is familiar with the plane, three-dimensional space, and the concept of a directed line segment. This treatment of geometrical vectors will lead to interesting new ideas, useful mathematical tools, and important generalizations.

A directed line segment in three-dimensional space has length and direction. Each ordered pair of distinct points in space $\langle P, Q\rangle$ determines a directed line segment with initial point at P and terminal point at Q. Con-

FIGURE 5

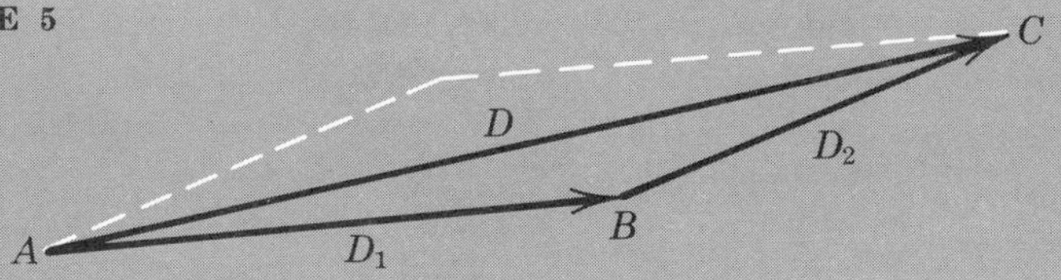

FIGURE 6

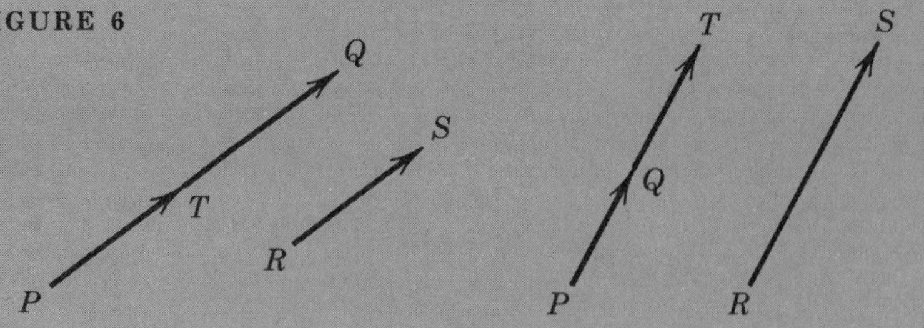

versely, each directed line segment determines an ordered pair of points. Thus, it is evident that there is a one-to-one correspondence between the set of all directed line segments and the set of ordered pairs of distinct points. It is customary to denote a directed line segment from a point P to a point Q by the symbol $\overrightarrow{PQ}$. The length of $\overrightarrow{PQ}$ is written $|PQ|$. It is convenient to extend this one-to-one correspondence to the set of all possible ordered pairs of points, including even those pairs $\langle P, P\rangle$ for which the first and second member are the same point. Let $\langle P, P\rangle$ correspond to the point P, which we write as the segment $\overrightarrow{PP}$. Thus, although $\overrightarrow{PP}$ has zero length and, strictly speaking, no direction, it is viewed as a directed line segment corresponding to $\langle P, P\rangle$. Such a segment $\overrightarrow{PP}$ is called a *zero directed line segment*. Consequently, a *nonzero directed line segment* is a segment $\overrightarrow{PQ}$, where P is different from Q.

Let $\overrightarrow{PQ}$ and $\overrightarrow{RS}$ be nonzero directed line segments. Translate the segment $\overrightarrow{RS}$ without rotation until its initial point falls on P, and denote its new terminal point by T. Then $\overrightarrow{PQ}$ and $\overrightarrow{RS}$ have the *same direction* if and only if either T lies on $\overrightarrow{PQ}$ or Q lies on $\overrightarrow{PT}$ (Figure 6). According to our earlier discussion, we should identify two directed line segments that have the same length and direction. Thus, we are led to the following definition.

(1.1) Definition. Two nonzero directed line segments $\overrightarrow{PQ}$ and $\overrightarrow{RS}$ are *equivalent* if they have the same length and direction. Any two zero directed line segments are equivalent. If $\overrightarrow{PQ}$ and $\overrightarrow{RS}$ are equivalent, we write $\overrightarrow{PQ} \sim \overrightarrow{RS}$.

Definition 1.1 defines a relation on the set of all directed line segments in space that satisfies these three basic conditions:

(1.2) (a) $\overrightarrow{PQ} \sim \overrightarrow{PQ}$ for every directed line segment $\overrightarrow{PQ}$.
(b) If $\overrightarrow{PQ} \sim \overrightarrow{RS}$, then $\overrightarrow{RS} \sim \overrightarrow{PQ}$.
(c) If $\overrightarrow{PQ} \sim \overrightarrow{RS}$ and $\overrightarrow{RS} \sim \overrightarrow{TU}$, then $\overrightarrow{PQ} \sim \overrightarrow{TU}$.

The conditions (a), (b), and (c) of 1.2 are called the *reflexive*, *symmetric*, and *transitive* laws, respectively. Any relation on an arbitrary set S that satisfies these three laws is called an *equivalence relation* (see Exercise 1.4). Ordinary equality of elements of a set has these properties, and an equivalence relation can be regarded as a generalization of equality. Equivalence relations occur, significantly, in all areas of contemporary mathematics. The principal facts concerning equivalence relations are developed in the exercises at the end of this section.

Let us denote by $[\overrightarrow{PQ}]$ the set of all directed line segments that are equivalent to $\overrightarrow{PQ}$. If $\overrightarrow{PQ}$ is not zero, then $[\overrightarrow{PQ}]$ is the set of all nonzero directed line segments with the same length and direction as $\overrightarrow{PQ}$. If $\overrightarrow{PQ}$ is zero (that is, $P = Q$), then $[\overrightarrow{PQ}]$ is the set of all zero directed line segments. The sets $[\overrightarrow{PQ}]$ are called *equivalence classes* of the equivalence relation defined by 1.1. We note that it follows from 1.2 that $[\overrightarrow{PQ}] = [\overrightarrow{RS}]$ (that is, $[\overrightarrow{PQ}]$ and $[\overrightarrow{RS}]$ are the same sets of directed line segments) if and only if $\overrightarrow{PQ} \sim \overrightarrow{RS}$ (see Exercise 1.5).

(**1.3**) **Definition.** A *vector* is a set $[\overrightarrow{PQ}]$ of all directed line segments that are equivalent to $\overrightarrow{PQ}$ according to Definition 1.1.

Thus, a vector $[\overrightarrow{PQ}]$ is the set of all directed line segments with the same length and direction as $\overrightarrow{PQ}$ (or else the set of all zero directed line segments). The vector $[\overrightarrow{PQ}]$ can be represented by any directed line segment that is a member of $[\overrightarrow{PQ}]$. That is, $[\overrightarrow{PQ}] = [\overrightarrow{RS}]$ if and only if $\overrightarrow{RS} \in [\overrightarrow{PQ}]$. For $\overrightarrow{RS} \in [\overrightarrow{PQ}]$ if and only if $\overrightarrow{PQ} \sim \overrightarrow{RS}$. If O is any point in space and $[\overrightarrow{PQ}]$ is any vector, then there is a directed line segment $\overrightarrow{OR}$ with initial point at O such that $\overrightarrow{OR} \sim \overrightarrow{PQ}$. Therefore, $[\overrightarrow{PQ}] = [\overrightarrow{OR}]$. Thus, every vector in three-dimensional space can be represented by a directed line segment with the same initial point O.

The *length* and *direction* of the vector $[\overrightarrow{PQ}]$ is the common length and direction of all directed line segments in $[\overrightarrow{PQ}]$, providing $\overrightarrow{PQ}$ is not zero. If $\overrightarrow{PQ}$ is zero, then $[\overrightarrow{PQ}]$ is called the *zero vector*. The zero vector has length zero, has no direction, and shall be denoted by $[\overrightarrow{0}]$.

Exercises

1.1 A jet plane has an air speed of 615 miles per hour, and the nose of the plane is pointed due west. There is a northwest wind of 100 miles per hour (a northwest wind is a wind from the northwest). Draw a diagram to illustrate this situation, showing the ground speed and direction of flight of the plane.

1.2 The forces shown in the accompanying figure all act in the same plane at a point P. Compute the resultant force at P graphically.

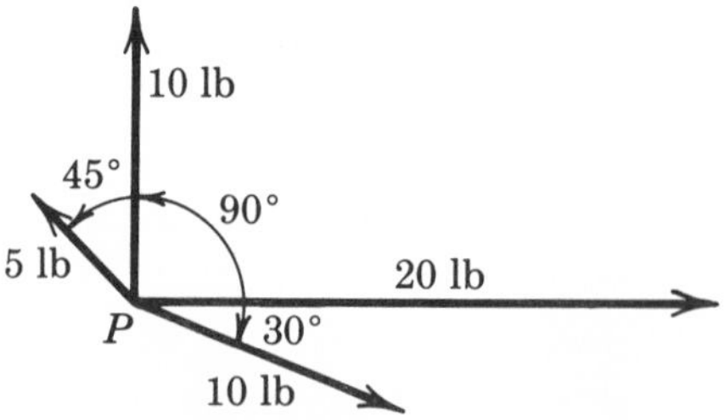

*__1.3__ Let $S = \{a, b, c, \ldots\}$ be any set. A *relation* on S is a set R of ordered pairs $\langle a, b\rangle$ of elements of S. For example, less than ($<$) is a relation on the set of all real numbers, and this relation is the set R of all ordered pairs $\langle x, y\rangle$ of real numbers such that $x < y$. For the relation $<$, which of the following ordered pairs are elements of R? $\langle 2, 5\rangle$, $\langle -1, -6\rangle$, $\langle 5.2, 3.7\rangle$; $\langle -1, \pi\rangle$; $\langle 2/3, 2/3\rangle$; $\langle 1/2, \sqrt{2}\rangle$.

*__1.4__ Let S be any set, and let R be a relation on S. Then R is an *equivalence relation* (a) if $\langle a, a\rangle \in R$ for all $a \in S$; (b) if $\langle a, b\rangle \in R$, then $\langle b, a\rangle \in R$; (c) if $\langle a, b\rangle \in R$ and $\langle b, c\rangle \in R$, then $\langle a, c\rangle \in R$. For directed line segments, we wrote $\overrightarrow{PQ} \sim \overrightarrow{RS}$ instead of $\langle \overrightarrow{PQ}, \overrightarrow{RS}\rangle \in R$ (see 1.2), and for a given relation R, it is customary to use a notation like $a\,R\,b$ or $a \sim b$ to stand for $\langle a, b\rangle \in R$. Which of the following relations are equivalence relations?

(i) Congruence of triangles ($\cong$) on the set of all triangles in the plane.
(ii) Less than or equal to ($\leq$) on the set of all real numbers.
(iii) $a - b$ is divisible by 5 on the set of all integers.
(iv) a divides b on the set of all positive integers.

*__1.5__ Let S be a set and let $\sim$ be an equivalence relation on S. For $a \in S$, denote by $[a]$ the set of all $x \in S$ such that $x \sim a$. In set notation,

$$[a] = \{x \in S \mid x \sim a\}.$$

The set $[a]$ is called the *equivalence class* of the element a with respect to the relation $\sim$. Prove the following properties of equivalence classes. Let $a \in S$ and $b \in S$. Then, (a) $a \in [a]$; (b) $[a] = [b]$ if and only if $a \sim b$; (c) either $[a] = [b]$ or else $[a]$ and $[b]$ have no elements in common.

1.6 Let Z be the set of all integers, and let m be a fixed positive integer. For $a, b \in Z$, define $\langle a, b\rangle \in R$ if and only if $a - b$ is divisible by m. Prove that R is an equivalence relation. Describe the equivalence classes of this relation.

2 Vector operations

The definition of the sum of two vectors is motivated by the examples of physical systems discussed in the preceding section.

* Exercises of unusual importance are indicated by an asterisk (*).

FIGURE 7

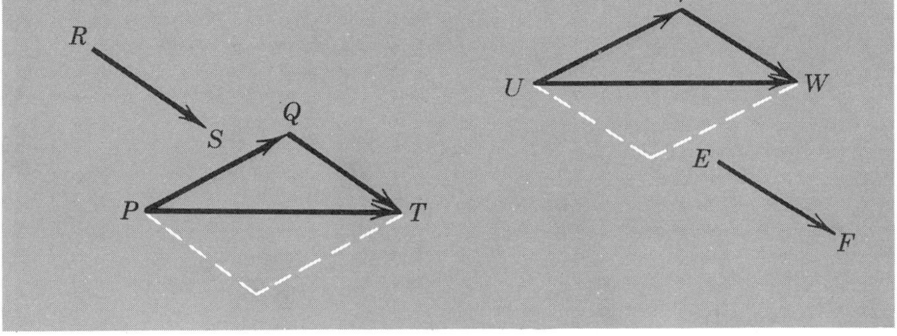

(2.1) Definition. Let $[\overrightarrow{PQ}]$ and $[\overrightarrow{RS}]$ be vectors, and let $\overrightarrow{QT}$ be a directed line segment with the same length and direction as $\overrightarrow{RS}$, so that $[\overrightarrow{RS}] = [\overrightarrow{QT}]$. Then

$$[\overrightarrow{PQ}] + [\overrightarrow{RS}] = [\overrightarrow{PQ}] + [\overrightarrow{QT}] = [\overrightarrow{PT}].$$

It is necessary to show that vector addition is well-defined; that is, we must prove that the vector $[\overrightarrow{PT}]$ is uniquely determined by the given vectors $[\overrightarrow{PQ}]$ and $[\overrightarrow{RS}]$. This proof consists of showing that if $[\overrightarrow{PQ}] = [\overrightarrow{UV}]$ and if $[\overrightarrow{RS}] = [\overrightarrow{EF}]$, then if $[\overrightarrow{UV}]$ and $[\overrightarrow{EF}]$ are added by the rule given in Definition 2.1 yielding a vector $[\overrightarrow{UW}]$, it follows that $[\overrightarrow{UW}] = [\overrightarrow{PT}]$. This geometrical argument (Figure 7) is left as an exercise.

Vector addition satisfies the same algebraic identities as addition of real numbers. Recalling that the zero vector $[\overrightarrow{0}]$ is the set of all line segments of zero length, Definition 2.1 yields the following formula:

(2.2) $[\overrightarrow{PQ}] + [\overrightarrow{0}] = [\overrightarrow{0}] + [\overrightarrow{PQ}] = [\overrightarrow{PQ}]$ for any vector $[\overrightarrow{PQ}]$.

Indeed, $[\overrightarrow{0}] = [\overrightarrow{QQ}]$, so that

$$[\overrightarrow{PQ}] + [\overrightarrow{0}] = [\overrightarrow{PQ}] + [\overrightarrow{QQ}] = [\overrightarrow{PQ}].$$

Similarly, $[\overrightarrow{0}] = [\overrightarrow{PP}]$, so that

$$[\overrightarrow{0}] + [\overrightarrow{PQ}] = [\overrightarrow{PP}] + [\overrightarrow{PQ}] = [\overrightarrow{PQ}].$$

The commutative law of addition can be easily verified:

(2.3) $[\overrightarrow{PQ}] + [\overrightarrow{RS}] = [\overrightarrow{RS}] + [\overrightarrow{PQ}]$ for any vectors $[\overrightarrow{PQ}]$, $[\overrightarrow{RS}]$.

If either $[\overrightarrow{PQ}]$ or $[\overrightarrow{RS}]$ is the zero vector, then 2.3 follows from 2.2. Thus, we may assume that neither vector is the zero vector. Let $[\overrightarrow{PQ}] = [\overrightarrow{SU}] =$

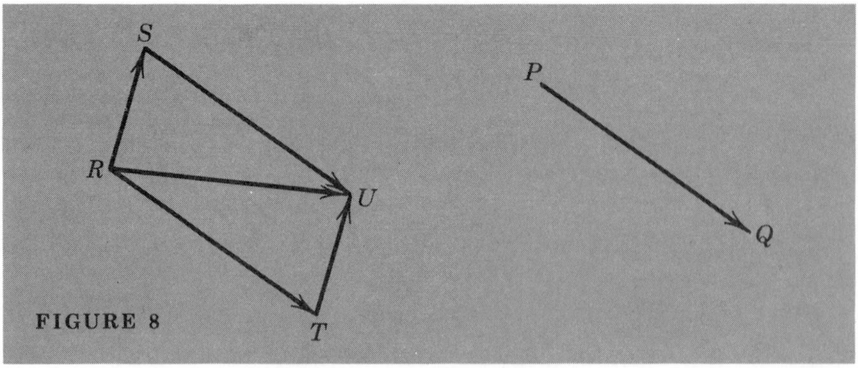

FIGURE 8

$[\overrightarrow{RT}]$ (Figure 8); then $[\overrightarrow{TU}] = [\overrightarrow{RS}]$. Therefore,

$$[\overrightarrow{PQ}] + [\overrightarrow{RS}] = [\overrightarrow{RT}] + [\overrightarrow{TU}] = [\overrightarrow{RU}]$$

and

$$[\overrightarrow{RS}] + [\overrightarrow{PQ}] = [\overrightarrow{RS}] + [\overrightarrow{SU}] = [\overrightarrow{RU}],$$

proving 2.3. Figure 8 shows the situation where $\overrightarrow{PQ}$ and $\overrightarrow{RS}$ do not determine parallel lines. The reader can draw the figure for the case where $\overrightarrow{PQ}$ and $\overrightarrow{RS}$ are parallel.

A second important algebraic identity satisfied by vector addition is the associative law:

(2.4) $([\overrightarrow{PQ}] + [\overrightarrow{RS}]) + [\overrightarrow{UV}] = [\overrightarrow{PQ}] + ([\overrightarrow{RS}] + [\overrightarrow{UV}])$ for any vectors $[\overrightarrow{PQ}]$, $[\overrightarrow{RS}]$, and $[\overrightarrow{UV}]$.

Let $[\overrightarrow{RS}] = [\overrightarrow{QT}]$ and $[\overrightarrow{UV}] = [\overrightarrow{TX}]$ (Figure 9). Then,

$$\begin{aligned}([\overrightarrow{PQ}] + [\overrightarrow{RS}]) + [\overrightarrow{UV}] &= ([\overrightarrow{PQ}] + [\overrightarrow{QT}]) + [\overrightarrow{TX}] \\ &= [\overrightarrow{PT}] + [\overrightarrow{TX}] = [\overrightarrow{PX}].\end{aligned}$$

Also,

$$\begin{aligned}[\overrightarrow{PQ}] + ([\overrightarrow{RS}] + [\overrightarrow{UV}]) &= [\overrightarrow{PQ}] + ([\overrightarrow{QT}] + [\overrightarrow{TX}]) \\ &= [\overrightarrow{PQ}] + [\overrightarrow{QX}] = [\overrightarrow{PX}].\end{aligned}$$

Figure 9 illustrates the general situation where $\overrightarrow{PQ}$, $\overrightarrow{RS}$, and $\overrightarrow{UV}$ are not all parallel to some plane.

As a consequence of 2.3 and 2.4, a sum of any number of vectors is independent of the order and grouping of the terms.

Let $[\overrightarrow{PQ}]$ be any vector. By Definition 2.1, $[\overrightarrow{PQ}] + [\overrightarrow{QP}] = [\overrightarrow{PP}] = [\overrightarrow{0}]$. The vector $[\overrightarrow{QP}]$ is called the *negative* of the vector $[\overrightarrow{PQ}]$, and we write

FIGURE 9

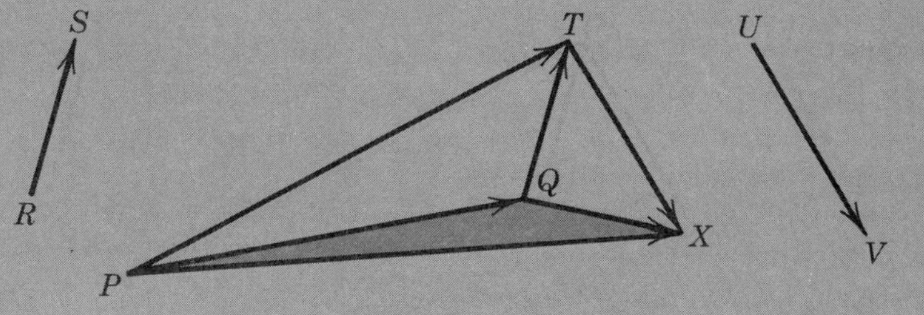

$[\overrightarrow{QP}] = -[\overrightarrow{PQ}]$. Since $[\overrightarrow{PQ}] = [\overrightarrow{TU}]$ implies $[\overrightarrow{QP}] = [\overrightarrow{UT}]$, it follows that the negative of a vector $[\overrightarrow{PQ}]$ is independent of the choice of the representative line segment $\overrightarrow{PQ}$. Suppose that $[\overrightarrow{RS}]$ is any vector such that $[\overrightarrow{PQ}] + [\overrightarrow{RS}] = [\overrightarrow{0}]$. Then

$$\begin{aligned}[\overrightarrow{RS}] &= [\overrightarrow{RS}] + [\overrightarrow{0}] = [\overrightarrow{RS}] + ([\overrightarrow{PQ}] + [\overrightarrow{QP}]) = ([\overrightarrow{RS}] + [\overrightarrow{PQ}]) + [\overrightarrow{QP}] \\ &= ([\overrightarrow{PQ}] + [\overrightarrow{RS}]) + [\overrightarrow{QP}] = [\overrightarrow{0}] + [\overrightarrow{QP}] = [\overrightarrow{QP}].\end{aligned}$$

Thus, $-[\overrightarrow{PQ}] = [\overrightarrow{QP}]$ is the only vector X that satisfies the vector equation $[\overrightarrow{PQ}] + X = [\overrightarrow{0}]$.

Subtraction of vectors is defined by

$$[\overrightarrow{PQ}] - [\overrightarrow{RS}] = [\overrightarrow{PQ}] + (-[\overrightarrow{RS}]).$$

Let $[\overrightarrow{RS}]$ be represented by a directed line segment $\overrightarrow{PT}$; that is, $[\overrightarrow{RS}] = [\overrightarrow{PT}]$. Then $[\overrightarrow{PQ}] - [\overrightarrow{RS}]$ is represented by $\overrightarrow{TQ}$ (Figure 10) since

$$\begin{aligned}[\overrightarrow{TQ}] &= [\overrightarrow{TP}] + [\overrightarrow{PQ}] = [\overrightarrow{PQ}] + [\overrightarrow{TP}] = [\overrightarrow{PQ}] + (-[\overrightarrow{PT}]) \\ &= [\overrightarrow{PQ}] + (-[\overrightarrow{RS}]) = [\overrightarrow{PQ}] - [\overrightarrow{RS}].\end{aligned}$$

The second vector operation suggested by the examples of Section 1 is *scalar multiplication*, a process by which a vector is multiplied by a real number to obtain another vector.

(2.5) Definition. Let r be a real number, and let $[\overrightarrow{PQ}]$ be a nonzero vector. The vector $r \cdot [\overrightarrow{PQ}]$ is represented by a directed line segment of length $|r|\,|PQ|$. If $r > 0$, $r \cdot [\overrightarrow{PQ}]$ has the same direction as $[\overrightarrow{PQ}]$. If $r < 0$, $r \cdot [\overrightarrow{PQ}]$ has the direction opposite to $[\overrightarrow{PQ}]$. If $r = 0$, $r \cdot [\overrightarrow{PQ}] = [\overrightarrow{0}]$. For any

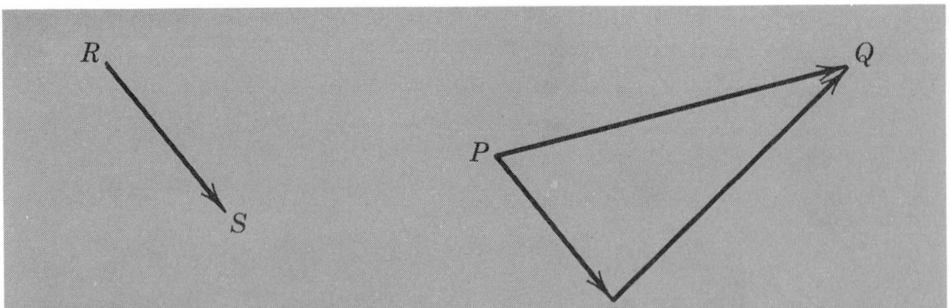

FIGURE 10

real number r, define $r \cdot [\overrightarrow{0}] = [\overrightarrow{0}]$. The vector $r \cdot [\overrightarrow{PQ}]$ is called the *scalar product* of $[\overrightarrow{PQ}]$ by r.

Thus, $r \cdot [\overrightarrow{PQ}]$ is represented by a directed line segment "r times as long as $\overrightarrow{PQ}$" with the same or opposite direction as $\overrightarrow{PQ}$, depending on whether r is positive or negative. If $[\overrightarrow{PQ}] = [\overrightarrow{RS}]$, then $r \cdot [\overrightarrow{PQ}] = r \cdot [\overrightarrow{RS}]$. Hence, scalar multiplication is well-defined. The reader should note that $r \cdot [\overrightarrow{PQ}] = -(|-r| \cdot [\overrightarrow{PQ}])$ when r is negative. Scalar multiplication satisfies several useful algebraic identities, which are listed in the following theorem.

(2.6) Theorem. Let $[\overrightarrow{PQ}]$ and $[\overrightarrow{RS}]$ be vectors, and let r and s be real numbers. Then

(a) $r \cdot (s \cdot [\overrightarrow{PQ}]) = s \cdot (r \cdot [\overrightarrow{PQ}]) = (rs) \cdot [\overrightarrow{PQ}]$;

(b) $(r + s) \cdot [\overrightarrow{PQ}] = r \cdot [\overrightarrow{PQ}] + s \cdot [\overrightarrow{PQ}]$;

(c) $r \cdot ([\overrightarrow{PQ}] + [\overrightarrow{RS}]) = r \cdot [\overrightarrow{PQ}] + r \cdot [\overrightarrow{RS}]$;

(d) $1 \cdot [\overrightarrow{PQ}] = [\overrightarrow{PQ}]$.

The proof of Theorem 2.6 is left as an exercise (Exercise 2.6).

A third vector operation is one in which two vectors are combined to obtain a real number. Let $[\overrightarrow{PQ}]$ and $[\overrightarrow{RS}]$ be nonzero vectors. Let $\overrightarrow{PT}$ be a directed line segment such that $[\overrightarrow{RS}] = [\overrightarrow{PT}]$. The angle θ, where $0° \leq \theta \leq 180°$, measured from the direction of $\overrightarrow{PT}$ to the direction of $\overrightarrow{PQ}$ is called the *angle between the vectors* $[\overrightarrow{PQ}]$ and $[\overrightarrow{RS}]$ (Figure 11). If either $[\overrightarrow{PQ}] = [\overrightarrow{0}]$ or $[\overrightarrow{RS}] = [\overrightarrow{0}]$, the angle θ between $[\overrightarrow{PQ}]$ and $[\overrightarrow{RS}]$ is defined as zero.

(2.7) Definition. Let $[\overrightarrow{PQ}]$ and $[\overrightarrow{RS}]$ be vectors, and let θ be the angle between them. The *inner product* of $[\overrightarrow{PQ}]$ and $[\overrightarrow{RS}]$ is the real number $|PQ|\,|RS| \cos\theta$, which is denoted by

$$[\overrightarrow{PQ}] \circ [\overrightarrow{RS}].$$

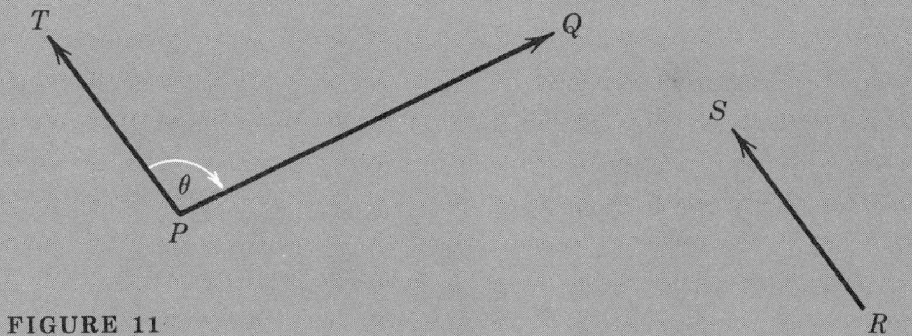

FIGURE 11

The inner product is independent of the representation of the vectors (see Exercise 2.9). It follows directly from Definition 2.7 that inner multiplication is commutative. That is,

(2.8) $[\overrightarrow{PQ}] \circ [\overrightarrow{RS}] = [\overrightarrow{RS}] \circ [\overrightarrow{PQ}]$.

The length of a vector can be expressed in terms of the inner product. By Definition 2.7, $[\overrightarrow{PQ}] \circ [\overrightarrow{PQ}] = |PQ|\,|PQ| \cos 0 = |PQ|^2$. Therefore,

(2.9) The length of the vector $[\overrightarrow{PQ}]$ is $([\overrightarrow{PQ}] \circ [\overrightarrow{PQ}])^{1/2}$.

Two nonzero vectors are said to be *orthogonal* if the angle between them is 90°. In other words, two nonzero vectors are orthogonal if and only if the directed line segments that represent them are perpendicular. It is convenient to regard every vector as being orthogonal to the zero vector. Orthogonality of vectors can be characterized in terms of the inner product:

(2.10) Theorem. The vectors $[\overrightarrow{PQ}]$ and $[\overrightarrow{RS}]$ are orthogonal if and only if $[\overrightarrow{PQ}] \circ [\overrightarrow{RS}] = 0$.

PROOF. If $[\overrightarrow{PQ}]$ and $[\overrightarrow{RS}]$ are orthogonal, then either at least one of the vectors is $[\overrightarrow{0}]$ or the angle θ between the vectors is 90°. In either case, $[\overrightarrow{PQ}] \circ [\overrightarrow{RS}] = |PQ|\,|RS| \cos\theta = 0$. Conversely, suppose that $[\overrightarrow{PQ}] \circ [\overrightarrow{RS}] = 0$. Then at least one of the three numbers $|PQ|$, $|RS|$, or $\cos\theta$ is zero. If $|PQ| = 0$ or $|RS| = 0$, then $[\overrightarrow{PQ}] = [\overrightarrow{0}]$ or $[\overrightarrow{RS}] = [\overrightarrow{0}]$. Thus, $[\overrightarrow{PQ}]$ and $[\overrightarrow{RS}]$ are orthogonal. Otherwise, $\cos\theta = 0$ which implies $\theta = 90°$, since $0° \leq \theta \leq 180°$. Therefore $\overrightarrow{PQ}$ is perpendicular to $\overrightarrow{RS}$. That is, $[\overrightarrow{PQ}]$ and $[\overrightarrow{RS}]$ are orthogonal.

Further properties of the inner product will be derived in the next section after we have discussed coordinate systems.

Exercises

2.1 Prove that vector addition is well-defined. That is, suppose that $[\overrightarrow{PQ}] = [\overrightarrow{UV}]$ and $[\overrightarrow{RS}] = [\overrightarrow{EF}]$; then show that $[\overrightarrow{PQ}] + [\overrightarrow{RS}] = [\overrightarrow{UV}] + [\overrightarrow{EF}]$, where the vectors are added by the rule given in Definition 2.1.

2.2 Draw figures to illustrate the commutative law of vector addition, $[\overrightarrow{PQ}] + [\overrightarrow{RS}] = [\overrightarrow{RS}] + [\overrightarrow{PQ}]$, where $\overrightarrow{PQ}$ and $\overrightarrow{RS}$ have the same direction and where $\overrightarrow{PQ}$ and $\overrightarrow{RS}$ have opposite directions.

2.3 By 2.4, we can write $[\overrightarrow{PQ}] + [\overrightarrow{RS}] + [\overrightarrow{UV}]$ to stand for either $([\overrightarrow{PQ}] + [\overrightarrow{RS}]) + [\overrightarrow{UV}]$ or $[\overrightarrow{PQ}] + ([\overrightarrow{RS}] + [\overrightarrow{UV}])$. Let $[\overrightarrow{RS}] = [\overrightarrow{PX}]$ and $[\overrightarrow{UV}] = [\overrightarrow{PY}]$. Show that $[\overrightarrow{PQ}] + [\overrightarrow{RS}] + [\overrightarrow{UV}] = [\overrightarrow{PQ}] + [\overrightarrow{PX}] + [\overrightarrow{PY}]$ is represented by the diagonal of the parallelopiped determined by $\overrightarrow{PQ}, \overrightarrow{PX}$, and $\overrightarrow{PY}$. Note that the parallelopiped degenerates if $\overrightarrow{PQ}, \overrightarrow{PX}$, and $\overrightarrow{PY}$ are all parallel to some plane.

2.4 Prove that scalar multiplication is well-defined. That is, suppose that $[\overrightarrow{PQ}] = [\overrightarrow{RS}]$, and show that $r \cdot [\overrightarrow{PQ}] = r \cdot [\overrightarrow{RS}]$ for any real number r.

2.5 Let $[\overrightarrow{PQ}]$ be any vector. Draw figures showing the directed line segments that represent $\frac{1}{2} \cdot [\overrightarrow{PQ}]$, $5 \cdot [\overrightarrow{PQ}]$, $(-0.3) \cdot [\overrightarrow{PQ}]$, $(\sqrt{2}) \cdot [\overrightarrow{PQ}]$, $(-\sqrt{3}) \cdot [\overrightarrow{PQ}]$, and $0 \cdot [\overrightarrow{PQ}]$.

2.6 Prove Theorem 2.6.

2.7 Prove that $(-r) \cdot [\overrightarrow{PQ}] = -(r \cdot [\overrightarrow{PQ}]) = r \cdot (-[\overrightarrow{PQ}])$.

2.8 Prove that $r \cdot [\overrightarrow{PQ}] = [\overrightarrow{0}]$ implies that either $r = 0$ or $[\overrightarrow{PQ}] = [\overrightarrow{0}]$.

2.9 Prove that inner multiplication is well-defined. That is, suppose that $[\overrightarrow{PQ}] = [\overrightarrow{UV}]$ and $[\overrightarrow{RS}] = [\overrightarrow{EF}]$; then show that $[\overrightarrow{PQ}] \circ [\overrightarrow{RS}] = [\overrightarrow{UV}] \circ [\overrightarrow{EF}]$.

2.10 The point of application of a force F moves through a displacement S. Let F be a vector represented by $\overrightarrow{OP}$, and let S be a vector represented by $\overrightarrow{OQ}$. Show that the work done by the force is $[\overrightarrow{OP}] \circ [\overrightarrow{OQ}]$.

2.11 Prove that nonzero vectors $[\overrightarrow{PQ}]$ and $[\overrightarrow{RS}]$ have the same direction if and only if $[\overrightarrow{PQ}] \circ [\overrightarrow{RS}]$ is equal to the product of the lengths of the vectors.

3 Coordinate systems on a line and in a plane

A set of vectors in space is *collinear* if there is a fixed line l such that each vector in the set is represented by a directed line segment on the line l. Thus, each vector in a collinear set is either the zero vector or is represented by a directed line segment that is parallel to some fixed line. Moreover, if a line l is given, the set of all vectors represented by directed line segments on l is a collinear set, which we call the *set of vectors on the line l*. Also, if $[\overrightarrow{PQ}]$ is any vector, then the set $\{[\overrightarrow{PQ}], [\overrightarrow{0}]\}$ is collinear. That is, the zero vector is collinear with every vector.

(3.1) Theorem. Let S be a collinear set of vectors that contains a nonzero vector $[\overrightarrow{PQ}]$. Then each vector in S is $x \cdot [\overrightarrow{PQ}]$ for some real number x.

PROOF. Let $[\overrightarrow{RS}]$ be any vector in S. If $[\overrightarrow{RS}] = \overrightarrow{[0]}$, then $[\overrightarrow{RS}] = 0 \cdot [\overrightarrow{PQ}]$ by Definition 2.5. If $[\overrightarrow{RS}] \neq \overrightarrow{[0]}$, then since $[\overrightarrow{RS}]$ and $[\overrightarrow{PQ}]$ are collinear, it follows that $\overrightarrow{RS}$ and $\overrightarrow{PQ}$ are parallel. Hence $\overrightarrow{RS}$ has the same direction as $\overrightarrow{PQ}$, or $\overrightarrow{RS}$ has the direction opposite to $\overrightarrow{PQ}$. In the first case, $[\overrightarrow{RS}] = (|RS|/|PQ|) \cdot [\overrightarrow{PQ}]$, and in the second case, $[\overrightarrow{RS}] = (-|RS|/|PQ|) \cdot [\overrightarrow{PQ}]$, by Definition 2.5.

If a fixed point O is selected on a line l, then every vector on l can be represented by a unique directed line segment $\overrightarrow{OP}$ with initial point O and terminal point P on l. By Theorem 3.1, if $[\overrightarrow{OX}]$ is a fixed nonzero vector on l, then $[\overrightarrow{OP}] = x \cdot [\overrightarrow{OX}]$ for some real number x. In Figure 12, $[\overrightarrow{OP}] = (-2) \cdot [\overrightarrow{OX}]$ and $[\overrightarrow{OQ}] = \frac{3}{2} \cdot [\overrightarrow{OX}]$. The representation $[\overrightarrow{OP}] = x \cdot [\overrightarrow{OX}]$ is unique. This means that the real number x is uniquely determined by the vector $[\overrightarrow{OP}]$. To prove this, suppose that $[\overrightarrow{OP}] = x_1 \cdot [\overrightarrow{OX}]$ and $[\overrightarrow{OP}] = x_2 \cdot [\overrightarrow{OX}]$. Then, by Theorem 2.6,

$$\overrightarrow{[0]} = x_1 \cdot [\overrightarrow{OX}] - x_2 \cdot [\overrightarrow{OX}] = (x_1 - x_2) \cdot [\overrightarrow{OX}].$$

Since $[\overrightarrow{OX}] \neq \overrightarrow{[0]}$, it follows from Exercise 2.8 that $x_1 - x_2 = 0$. Thus, $x_1 = x_2$. Therefore, each vector on the line l corresponds to a unique real number x, and, conversely, for each real number x, $x \cdot [\overrightarrow{OX}]$ is a vector on l. Therefore, there is a one-to-one correspondence

$$[\overrightarrow{OP}] \leftrightarrow x$$

between the vectors on l and the set of all real numbers. Moreover, if

FIGURE 12

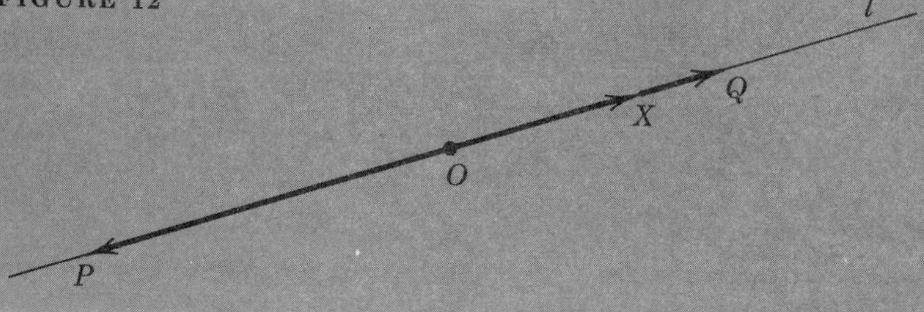

$[\overrightarrow{OP}] = x_1 \cdot [\overrightarrow{OX}]$ and $[\overrightarrow{OQ}] = x_2 \cdot [\overrightarrow{OX}]$, then, by Theorem 2.6,

$$[\overrightarrow{OP}] + [\overrightarrow{OQ}] = (x_1 + x_2) \cdot [\overrightarrow{OX}]$$
$$r \cdot [\overrightarrow{OP}] = (rx_1) \cdot [\overrightarrow{OX}]. \tag{3-1}$$

The equations (3-1) show that if $[\overrightarrow{OP}]$ corresponds to x_1 and $[\overrightarrow{OQ}]$ corresponds to x_2, then $[\overrightarrow{OP}] + [\overrightarrow{OQ}]$ corresponds to $x_1 + x_2$, and $r \cdot [\overrightarrow{OP}]$ corresponds to rx_1. Thus, the algebra of vectors on a line is just the algebra of real numbers. This was indicated in Section 1 in the example of a system of forces acting along a given line.

The fixed vector $[\overrightarrow{OX}]$ is a *coordinate system* for the vectors on the line l. Clearly, any other nonzero vector on l would serve equally well as a coordinate system. It is convenient to let the length of $[\overrightarrow{OX}]$ be the unit of length on the line l. Then each vector that has the same length as $[\overrightarrow{OX}]$ is a *unit vector*. Further, each vector $[\overrightarrow{OP}] = x \cdot [\overrightarrow{OX}]$ has length $|x|$.

A set of vectors in space is *coplanar* if there is a fixed plane π such that each vector in the set is represented by a directed line segment in the plane π. The set of all vectors represented by directed line segments in a plane π is referred to as *the set of vectors in* π. It is possible to prove a theorem about coplanar vectors that is analogous to Theorem 3.1.

(3.2) **Theorem.** Let S be a set of coplanar vectors that contains two noncollinear vectors $[\overrightarrow{PQ}]$ and $[\overrightarrow{RS}]$. Then each vector in S is $x \cdot [\overrightarrow{PQ}] + y \cdot [\overrightarrow{RS}]$ for some real numbers x and y.

PROOF. We note first that if $[\overrightarrow{PQ}]$ and $[\overrightarrow{RS}]$ are noncollinear, then neither $[\overrightarrow{PQ}]$ nor $[\overrightarrow{RS}]$ is the zero vector. Let $[\overrightarrow{UV}]$ be any vector in S. If $[\overrightarrow{UV}]$ and $[\overrightarrow{PQ}]$ are collinear, then, by Theorem 3.1, $[\overrightarrow{UV}] = x \cdot [\overrightarrow{PQ}] + 0 \cdot [\overrightarrow{RS}]$, for some x. Similarly, if $[\overrightarrow{UV}]$ and $[\overrightarrow{RS}]$ are collinear, then $[\overrightarrow{UV}] = 0 \cdot [\overrightarrow{PQ}] + y \cdot [\overrightarrow{RS}]$, for some y. Therefore, we may assume that $[\overrightarrow{UV}]$ is not collinear with either $[\overrightarrow{PQ}]$ or $[\overrightarrow{RS}]$, and, since S is a coplanar set, that all three of these vectors are represented by directed line segments in some plane π.

In the plane π, let $\overrightarrow{UT}$ and $\overrightarrow{UW}$ be directed line segments such that $[\overrightarrow{UT}] = [\overrightarrow{PQ}]$ and $[\overrightarrow{UW}] = [\overrightarrow{RS}]$. Let l, l_1, and l_2 be the lines determined by $\overrightarrow{UV}$, $\overrightarrow{UT}$, and $\overrightarrow{UW}$, respectively. Our assumptions imply that no two of these lines coincide. Let l_1', and l_2' be lines through the point V that are parallel, respectively, to l_1 and l_2 (Figure 13). Then l_1', l_2', l_1, l_2 determine a parallelogram $UAVB$, which has $\overrightarrow{UV}$ as its diagonal. Since $[\overrightarrow{UB}]$ and $[\overrightarrow{UT}]$ are collinear, it follows that $[\overrightarrow{UB}] = x \cdot [\overrightarrow{UT}]$ by Theorem 3.1. Since l_2' and

FIGURE 13

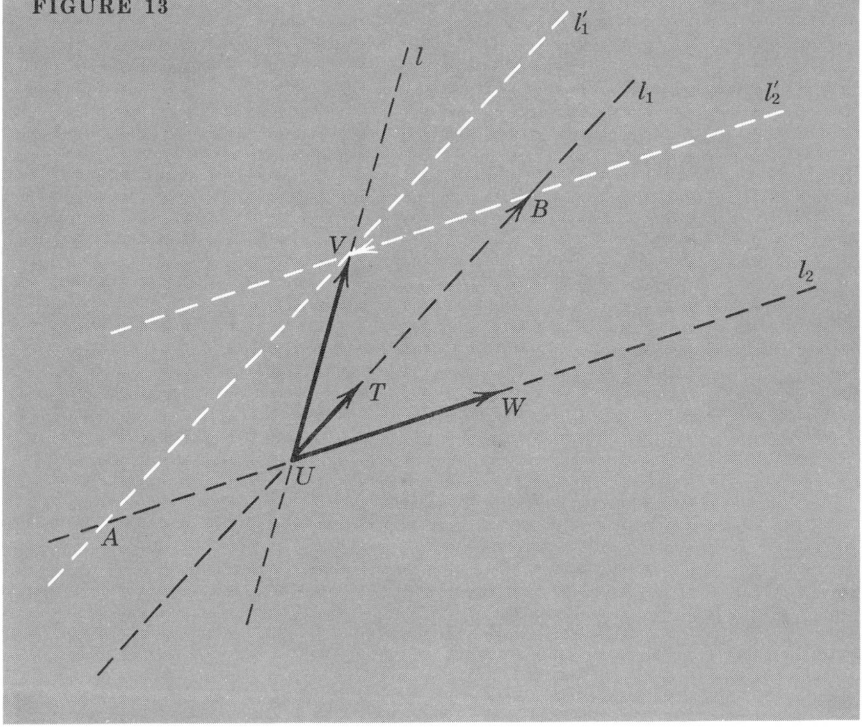

l_2 are parallel, $[\overrightarrow{BV}]$ and $[\overrightarrow{UW}]$ are collinear, and hence $[\overrightarrow{BV}] = y \cdot [\overrightarrow{UW}]$. Therefore,

$$[\overrightarrow{UV}] = [\overrightarrow{UB}] + [\overrightarrow{BV}] = x \cdot [\overrightarrow{UT}] + y \cdot [\overrightarrow{UW}] = x \cdot [\overrightarrow{PQ}] + y \cdot [\overrightarrow{RS}].$$

Now suppose that we limit our considerations to a set of coplanar vectors, that is, a set of vectors in some fixed plane π. If we choose a fixed point O in π, then every vector in π can be represented by a unique directed line segment $\overrightarrow{OP}$ in π. If $[\overrightarrow{OX}]$ and $[\overrightarrow{OY}]$ are noncollinear vectors in the plane π, then, by Theorem 3.2, $[\overrightarrow{OP}] = x \cdot [\overrightarrow{OX}] + y \cdot [\overrightarrow{OY}]$. The ordered pair of vectors $\langle [\overrightarrow{OX}], [\overrightarrow{OY}] \rangle$ provides a coordinate system for the plane just as a single nonzero vector is a coordinate system for a line. In order to show this, we must prove that the real numbers x and y are uniquely determined by $[\overrightarrow{OP}]$. Therefore, suppose that $[\overrightarrow{OP}] = x_1 \cdot [\overrightarrow{OX}] + y_1 \cdot [\overrightarrow{OY}]$ and $[\overrightarrow{OP}] = x_2 \cdot [\overrightarrow{OX}] + y_2 \cdot [\overrightarrow{OY}]$. Then

$$\begin{aligned} [\overrightarrow{0}] &= (x_1 \cdot [\overrightarrow{OX}] + y_1 \cdot [\overrightarrow{OY}]) - (x_2 \cdot [\overrightarrow{OX}] + y_2 \cdot [\overrightarrow{OY}]) \\ &= (x_1 - x_2) \cdot [\overrightarrow{OX}] + (y_1 - y_2) \cdot [\overrightarrow{OY}]. \end{aligned}$$

If either $x_1 - x_2 \neq 0$ or $y_1 - y_2 \neq 0$, this equation implies that the vectors $[\overrightarrow{OX}]$ and $[\overrightarrow{OY}]$ are collinear (see Exercise 3.1). But these vectors are noncollinear. Therefore $x_2 = x_1$ and $y_2 = y_1$. Thus, each vector $[\overrightarrow{OP}]$ corresponds to a unique ordered pair of real numbers $\langle x, y\rangle$, where $[\overrightarrow{OP}] = x \cdot [\overrightarrow{OX}] + y \cdot [\overrightarrow{OY}]$. Conversely, it is clear that each ordered pair of real numbers $\langle x, y\rangle$ determines a unique vector $x \cdot [\overrightarrow{OX}] + y \cdot [\overrightarrow{OY}]$. Hence, the correspondence

$$[\overrightarrow{OP}] \leftrightarrow \langle x, y\rangle,$$

where $[\overrightarrow{OP}] = x \cdot [\overrightarrow{OX}] + y \cdot [\overrightarrow{OY}]$, is a one-to-one correspondence between the set of vectors in the plane and the set of all ordered pairs of real numbers. The real numbers x and y are called the *coordinates* of $[\overrightarrow{OP}]$ with respect to the coordinate system $\langle[\overrightarrow{OX}], [\overrightarrow{OY}]\rangle$.

There is a natural way to define the sum of two ordered pairs of real numbers and the scalar product of a real number and an ordered pair.

(3.3) Definition. Let $\langle x_1, y_1\rangle$ and $\langle x_2, y_2\rangle$ be ordered pairs of real numbers, and let r be a real number. The *sum* of $\langle x_1, y_1\rangle$ and $\langle x_2, y_2\rangle$ is the ordered pair

$$\langle x_1, y_1\rangle + \langle x_2, y_2\rangle = \langle x_1 + x_2, y_1 + y_2\rangle.$$

The *scalar product* of r and $\langle x_1, y_1\rangle$ is the ordered pair

$$r \cdot \langle x_1, y_1\rangle = \langle rx_1, ry_1\rangle.$$

If we select a coordinate system $\langle[\overrightarrow{OX}], [\overrightarrow{OY}]\rangle$ in a plane, then Definition 3.3 enables us to replace the algebra of vectors in the plane by the algebra of ordered pairs of real numbers. Indeed, if $[\overrightarrow{OP}] = x_1 \cdot [\overrightarrow{OX}] + y_1 \cdot [\overrightarrow{OY}]$ and $[\overrightarrow{OQ}] = x_2 \cdot [\overrightarrow{OX}] + y_2 \cdot [\overrightarrow{OY}]$, then

$$[\overrightarrow{OP}] + [\overrightarrow{OQ}] \leftrightarrow \langle x_1 + x_2, y_1 + y_2\rangle = \langle x_1, y_1\rangle + \langle x_2, y_2\rangle.$$

That is, the coordinates of the sum of two vectors are the sums of the coordinates of the vectors. Also, the reader can easily verify that if the coordinates of $[\overrightarrow{OP}]$ are $\langle x, y\rangle$, then the coordinates of $r \cdot [\overrightarrow{OP}]$ are given by $\langle rx, ry\rangle = r \cdot \langle x, y\rangle$. Thus, the operations with geometric vectors in the plane can be performed algebraically.

Example 1. Let $\langle[\overrightarrow{OX}], [\overrightarrow{OY}]\rangle$ be a coordinate system in a plane. The vector $[\overrightarrow{OP}] = 2 \cdot [\overrightarrow{OX}] - 1 \cdot [\overrightarrow{OY}]$ has coordinates $\langle 2, -1\rangle$, and the vector $[\overrightarrow{OQ}] = \frac{1}{2} \cdot [\overrightarrow{OY}]$ has coordinates $\langle 0, \frac{1}{2}\rangle$. Then $[\overrightarrow{OP}] + [\overrightarrow{OQ}]$ has coordinates $\langle 2, -1\rangle + \langle 0, \frac{1}{2}\rangle = \langle 2, -\frac{1}{2}\rangle$, and $\sqrt{2} \cdot [\overrightarrow{OP}]$ has coordinates $\langle 2\sqrt{2}, -\sqrt{2}\rangle$. In Figure 14, the coordinates of a vector

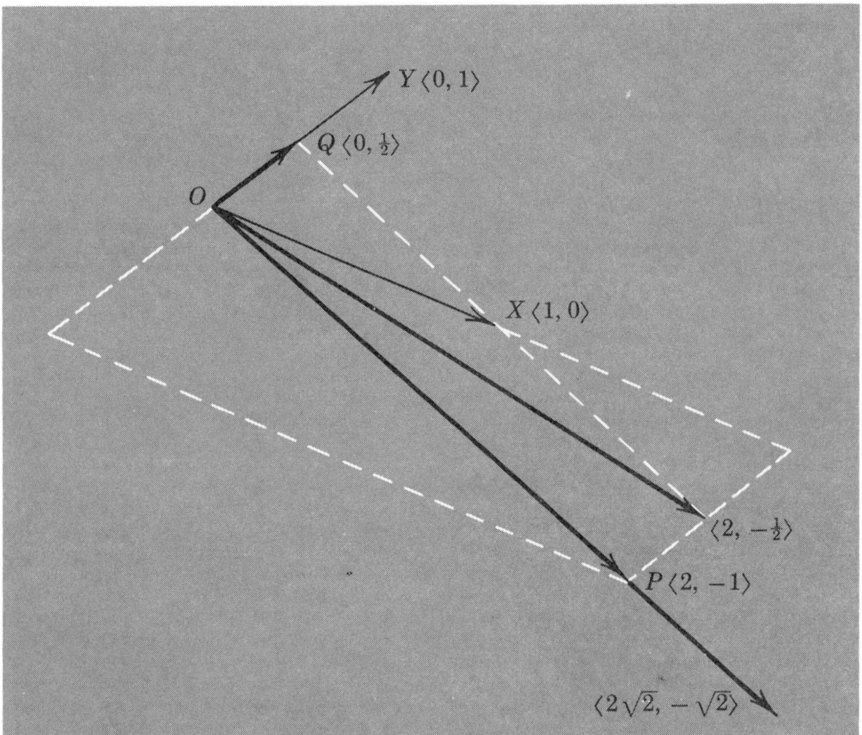

FIGURE 14

are placed at the terminal point of the directed line segment, with initial point at O, that represents the vector.

Suppose that the directed line segments $\overrightarrow{OX}$ and $\overrightarrow{OY}$, which determine a coordinate system $\langle[\overrightarrow{OX}], [\overrightarrow{OY}]\rangle$ for the vectors in a plane, are perpendicular at O and have equal lengths. Then a rectangular Cartesian coordinate system for the points in the plane is defined in the following way.

The point O is the origin and the directed lines determined by $\overrightarrow{OX}$ and $\overrightarrow{OY}$ are the X- and Y-axis, respectively. The unit of length is the length of $\overrightarrow{OX}$ (which is equal to the length of $\overrightarrow{OY}$). We assume that the reader is familiar with the properties of such a coordinate system in a plane. To distinguish the coordinates of points from the coordinates of vectors, we will write the coordinates of points in parentheses.

Let $[\overrightarrow{RS}]$ be a vector in the plane with coordinates $\langle x, y\rangle$. That is, $[\overrightarrow{RS}] = x \cdot [\overrightarrow{OX}] + y \cdot [\overrightarrow{OY}]$. Since $[\overrightarrow{OX}]$ has unit length, the vector $x \cdot [\overrightarrow{OX}]$, which has coordinates $\langle x, 0\rangle$, is represented by a directed line segment on the X-axis with initial point at the origin O and terminal point at $(x, 0)$. Simi-

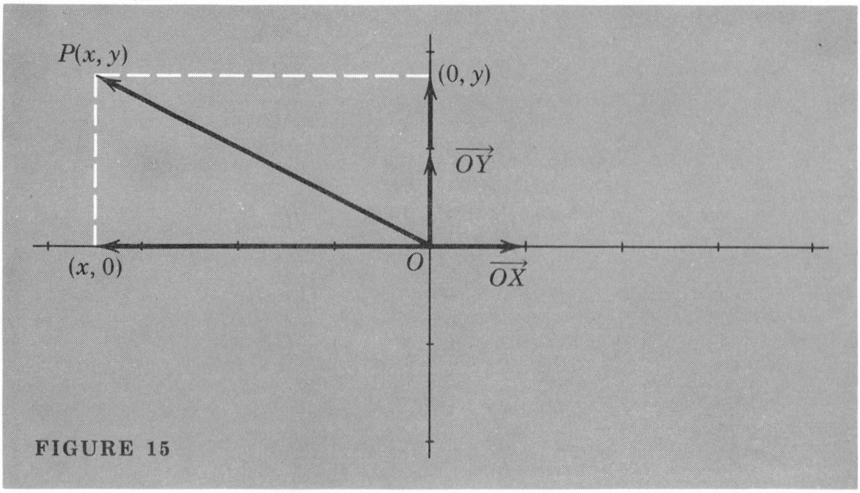

FIGURE 15

larly, $y \cdot [\overrightarrow{OY}]$ with coordinates $\langle 0, y\rangle$ is represented by a directed line segment from O to the point $(0, y)$. Thus, $[\overrightarrow{RS}] = x \cdot [\overrightarrow{OX}] + y \cdot [\overrightarrow{OY}]$ is represented by $\overrightarrow{OP}$, where the coordinates of the point P are (x, y) (Figure 15). By the theorem of Pythagoras, the length of the vector $[\overrightarrow{RS}] = [\overrightarrow{OP}]$ is $|OP| = \sqrt{x^2 + y^2}$.

Example 2. Let $\langle[\overrightarrow{OX}], [\overrightarrow{OY}]\rangle$ determine a rectangular Cartesian coordinate system in a plane. Let $[\overrightarrow{RS}]$ be a vector represented by a directed line segment in the plane from a point R with coordinates (x_R, y_R) to a point S with coordinates (x_S, y_S). The vector $[\overrightarrow{RS}]$ is represented by a directed line segment $\overrightarrow{OP}$ with initial point at O and terminal point at P, where the coordinates of P are $(x_S - x_R, y_S - y_R)$. Thus, the coordinates of the vector $[\overrightarrow{RS}] = [\overrightarrow{OP}]$ are $\langle x_S - x_R, y_S - y_R\rangle$ with respect to the given coordinate system (Figure 16). In particular, if $\overrightarrow{TU}$ is any other directed line segment that represents $[\overrightarrow{RS}]$, where the coordinates of T are (x_T, y_T) and the coordinates of U are (x_U, y_U), then $x_S - x_R = x_U - x_T$ and $y_S - y_R = y_U - y_T$.

With respect to a rectangular Cartesian coordinate system, the inner product of two vectors in a plane has a simple algebraic expression:

(3.4) **Theorem.** Let $\langle[\overrightarrow{OX}], [\overrightarrow{OY}]\rangle$ be a rectangular Cartesian coordinate system in a plane, and let $[\overrightarrow{RS}]$ and $[\overrightarrow{TU}]$ be vectors in the plane. Then

$$[\overrightarrow{RS}] \circ [\overrightarrow{TU}] = x_1x_2 + y_1y_2,$$

where the coordinates of $[\overrightarrow{RS}]$ and $[\overrightarrow{TU}]$ are $\langle x_1, y_1\rangle$ and $\langle x_2, y_2\rangle$, respectively.

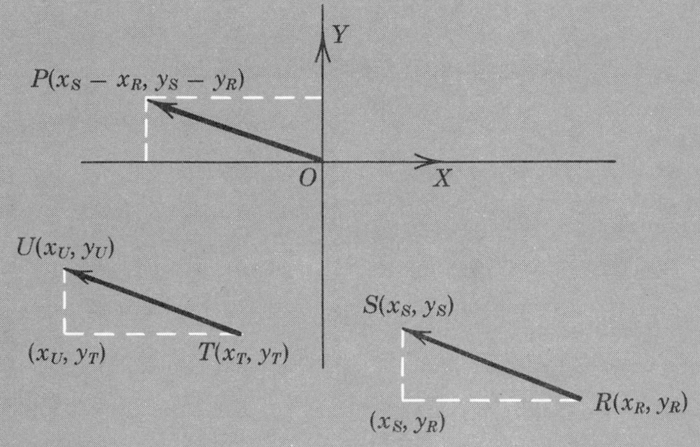

FIGURE 16

PROOF. Let $[\overrightarrow{RS}] = [\overrightarrow{OP}]$ and $[\overrightarrow{TU}] = [\overrightarrow{OQ}]$. Then P and Q have coordinates (x_1, y_1) and (x_2, y_2), respectively. By the law of cosines, we have

$$|PQ|^2 = |OP|^2 + |OQ|^2 - 2|OP|\,|OQ| \cos \theta,$$

where θ is the angle between $[\overrightarrow{OP}]$ and $[\overrightarrow{OQ}]$ (Figure 17). Therefore,

$$[\overrightarrow{OP}] \circ [\overrightarrow{OQ}] = |OP|\,|OQ| \cos \theta = \frac{|OP|^2 + |OQ|^2 - |PQ|^2}{2}.$$

FIGURE 17

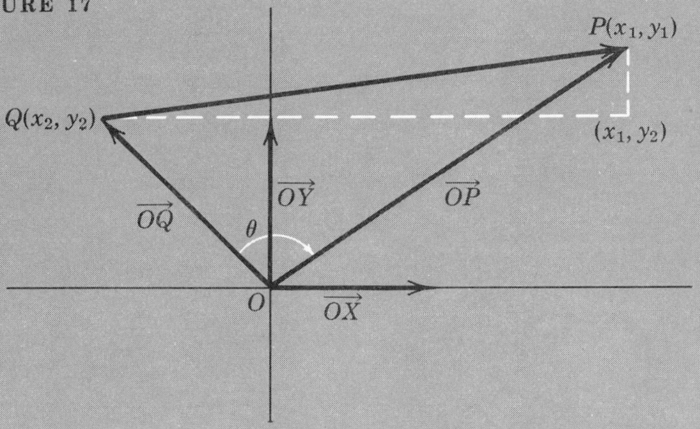

Moreover, $|OP|^2 = x_1^2 + y_1^2$, $|OQ|^2 = x_2^2 + y_2^2$, and $|PQ|^2 = (x_1 - x_2)^2 + (y_1 - y_2)^2$. Hence,

$$[\overrightarrow{RS}] \circ [\overrightarrow{TU}] = [\overrightarrow{OP}] \circ [\overrightarrow{OQ}] = \frac{x_1^2 + y_1^2 + x_2^2 + y_2^2 - (x_1 - y_2)^2 - (y_1 - y_2)^2}{2}$$

$$= x_1x_2 + y_1y_2.$$

Since any two vectors $[\overrightarrow{PQ}]$, $[\overrightarrow{RS}]$ in space are coplanar (let $[\overrightarrow{RS}] = [\overrightarrow{PT}]$), Theorem 3.4 yields the following identity connecting scalar multiplication and inner multiplication.

(3.5) Corollary. Let $[\overrightarrow{PQ}]$ and $[\overrightarrow{RS}]$ be vectors in three-dimensional space, and let r be a real number. Then

$$(r \cdot [\overrightarrow{PQ}]) \circ [\overrightarrow{RS}] = [\overrightarrow{PQ}] \circ (r \cdot [\overrightarrow{RS}]) = r([\overrightarrow{PQ}] \circ [\overrightarrow{RS}]).$$

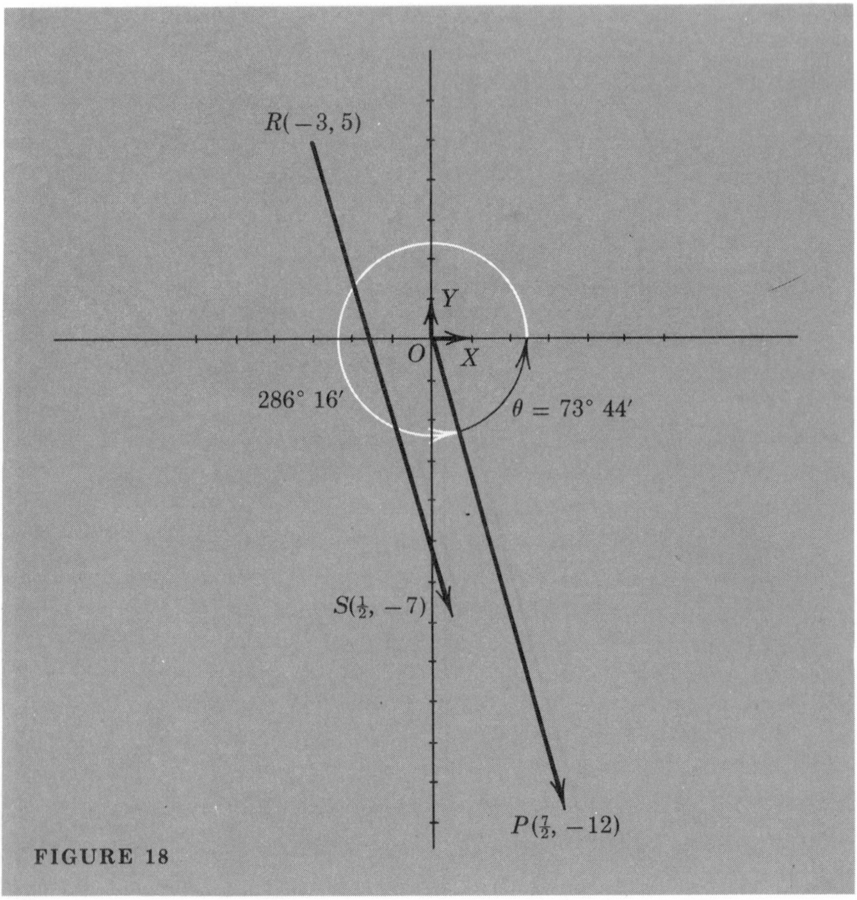

FIGURE 18

PROOF. Let $[\overrightarrow{RS}] = [\overrightarrow{PT}]$, and let π be a plane containing $\overrightarrow{PQ}$ and $\overrightarrow{PT}$. Let $[\overrightarrow{PQ}]$ have coordinates $\langle x_1, y_1\rangle$, and let $[\overrightarrow{RS}] = [\overrightarrow{PT}]$ have coordinates $\langle x_2, y_2\rangle$ with respect to a rectangular Cartesian coordinate system in π. Then the coordinates of $r \cdot [\overrightarrow{PQ}]$ are $\langle rx_1, ry_1\rangle$, and, by Theorem 3.4,

$$(r \cdot [\overrightarrow{PQ}]) \circ [\overrightarrow{RS}] = (rx_1)x_2 + (ry_1)y_2 = r(x_1x_2 + y_1y_2)$$
$$= r([\overrightarrow{PQ}] \circ [\overrightarrow{RS}]).$$

The other part of the identity is proved similarly.

Example 3. Let $\langle[\overrightarrow{OX}], [\overrightarrow{OY}]\rangle$ determine a rectangular Cartesian system in a plane. Let $[\overrightarrow{RS}]$ be a vector in the plane, where the coordinates of R are $(-3, 5)$ and the coordinates of S are $(\frac{1}{2}, -7)$. Then, by Example 2, $[\overrightarrow{RS}]$ has coordinates $\langle\frac{7}{2}, -12\rangle$. The length of $[\overrightarrow{RS}]$ is $\sqrt{\frac{49}{4} + 144} = \frac{25}{2}$. Since the coordinates of $[\overrightarrow{OX}]$ are $\langle 1, 0\rangle$, it follows from Theorem 3.4 that

$$[\overrightarrow{RS}] \circ [\overrightarrow{OX}] = 1(\tfrac{7}{2}) + 0(-12) = \tfrac{7}{2}.$$

Moreover,

$$[\overrightarrow{RS}] \circ [\overrightarrow{OX}] = |RS|\,|OX| \cos\theta = \tfrac{25}{2}\cos\theta,$$

where θ is the angle between $[\overrightarrow{RS}]$ and $[\overrightarrow{OX}]$. Hence $\cos\theta = \frac{7}{25}$ and $\theta = 73° 44'$ to the nearest minute. Since $[\overrightarrow{RS}]$ is represented by a directed line segment $\overrightarrow{OP}$ from the origin O to the point P with coordinates $(\frac{7}{2}, -12)$, the angle measured counterclockwise from the positive direction of the X-axis to $\overrightarrow{OP}$ is the fourth quadrant angle $360° - \theta = 286° 16'$ (Figure 18).

Exercises

3.1 Prove that the vectors $[\overrightarrow{PQ}]$ and $[\overrightarrow{RS}]$ are collinear if and only if there exist real numbers k_1 and k_2, not both zero, such that $k_1 \cdot [\overrightarrow{PQ}] + k_2 \cdot [\overrightarrow{RS}] = [\overrightarrow{0}]$.

3.2 Show that the vectors $[\overrightarrow{PQ}]$ and $[\overrightarrow{RS}]$ are collinear if and only if the angle θ between the vectors is $0°$ or $180°$.

3.3 Let $[\overrightarrow{OX}]$ be a coordinate system on a line l. Let $[\overrightarrow{OP}] = x \cdot [\overrightarrow{OX}]$ and $[\overrightarrow{OQ}] = y \cdot [\overrightarrow{OX}]$. Express the inner product of $[\overrightarrow{OP}]$ and $[\overrightarrow{OQ}]$ in terms of x and y.

3.4 Let $\langle[\overrightarrow{OX}], [\overrightarrow{OY}]\rangle$ be a coordinate system in a plane, and let $[\overrightarrow{OP}]$ be a vector in the plane. Prove that if the coordinates of $[\overrightarrow{OP}]$ are $\langle x, y\rangle$, then the coordinates of $r \cdot [\overrightarrow{OP}]$ are $\langle rx, ry\rangle$ and that the coordinates of $-[\overrightarrow{OP}]$ are $\langle -x, -y\rangle$.

3.5 Let $\langle[\overrightarrow{OX}], [\overrightarrow{OY}]\rangle$ be a coordinate system in a plane. Let $[\overrightarrow{OX}]$ have length 2, $[\overrightarrow{OY}]$ have length 3, and let the angle between $[\overrightarrow{OX}]$ and $[\overrightarrow{OY}]$ be 30°. Sketch the directed line segments, with initial point at O, that represent the vectors having the following coordinates: $\langle -1, 3\rangle$; $\langle 0, \frac{1}{3}\rangle$; $\langle 4, 6\rangle$; $\langle 1, 0\rangle$; $\langle -\frac{1}{2}, -\frac{1}{3}\rangle$.

3.6 Let $\langle[\overrightarrow{OX}], [\overrightarrow{OY}]\rangle$ be a rectangular Cartesian coordinate system in a plane, and let $[\overrightarrow{PQ}]$ and $[\overrightarrow{RS}]$ be defined by the points $P = (-2, 3)$, $Q = (7, 8)$, $R = (5, 0)$, and $S = (1/5, 1/10)$. Find the coordinates of the following vectors:

$$(-3) \cdot [\overrightarrow{PQ}] + 4 \cdot [\overrightarrow{RS}], \qquad [\overrightarrow{PQ}] - [\overrightarrow{RS}], \qquad 5 \cdot [\overrightarrow{PQ}] + 10 \cdot [\overrightarrow{RS}].$$

Sketch the directed line segments, with initial point at O, that represent these vectors.

3.7 Find the lengths of the vectors given in Exercise 3.6. Find the angles measured counterclockwise from the positive direction of the X-axis to the directed line segments from the origin that represent these vectors.

3.8 The coordinates of the following pairs of vectors are given with respect to a rectangular Cartesian coordinate system $\langle[\overrightarrow{OX}], [\overrightarrow{OY}]\rangle$ in a plane. Find the inner product of each pair of vectors. Find the cosine of the angle between each pair of vectors. (a) $\langle 1, 1\rangle$, $\langle\sqrt{2}, \sqrt{2}\rangle$; (b) $\langle -3, 0\rangle$, $\langle 0, 4\rangle$; (c) $\langle 3/2, 1\rangle$, $\langle 1/2, \sqrt{3}\rangle$; (d) $\langle\sqrt{5}, 7\rangle$, $\langle 7, \sqrt{5}\rangle$; (e) $\langle 6, -1\rangle$, $\langle -6, 1\rangle$.

***3.9** Let $[\overrightarrow{PQ}]$ and $[\overrightarrow{RS}]$ be vectors in space, and let r and s be real numbers. Prove that

$$(r \cdot [\overrightarrow{PQ}]) \circ (s \cdot [\overrightarrow{RS}]) = rs([\overrightarrow{PQ}] \circ [\overrightarrow{RS}]).$$

3.10 Let $[\overrightarrow{PQ}]$, $[\overrightarrow{RS}]$, and $[\overrightarrow{TU}]$ be coplanar vectors. Prove that

$$[\overrightarrow{PQ}] \circ ([\overrightarrow{RS}] + [\overrightarrow{TU}]) = [\overrightarrow{PQ}] \circ [\overrightarrow{RS}] + [\overrightarrow{PQ}] \circ [\overrightarrow{TU}].$$

3.11 Prove that the vectors $[\overrightarrow{PQ}]$, $[\overrightarrow{RS}]$, and $[\overrightarrow{TU}]$ are coplanar if and only if there are real numbers k_1, k_2, and k_3, not all zero, such that, $k_1 \cdot [\overrightarrow{PQ}] + k_2 \cdot [\overrightarrow{RS}] + k_3 \cdot [\overrightarrow{TU}] = \overline{[0]}$.

4 Coordinate systems in three-dimensional space

The construction of coordinate systems for geometrical vectors in three-dimensional space is based on the following theorem.

(4.1) Theorem. Let S be a set of vectors that contains the noncoplanar vectors $[\overrightarrow{PQ}]$, $[\overrightarrow{RS}]$, and $[\overrightarrow{TU}]$. Then every vector in S is $x \cdot [\overrightarrow{PQ}] + y \cdot [\overrightarrow{RS}] + z \cdot [\overrightarrow{TU}]$ for some real numbers x, y, and z.

PROOF. Let $[\overrightarrow{VW}]$ be any vector in S. Let the three given noncoplanar vectors in S be represented by directed line segments with initial point at V. That is, $[\overrightarrow{PQ}] = [\overrightarrow{VL}]$, $[\overrightarrow{RS}] = [\overrightarrow{VM}]$, and $[\overrightarrow{TU}] = [\overrightarrow{VN}]$. Since these given vectors are noncoplanar, in particular, $[\overrightarrow{PQ}]$ and $[\overrightarrow{RS}]$ are not collinear, so

FIGURE 19

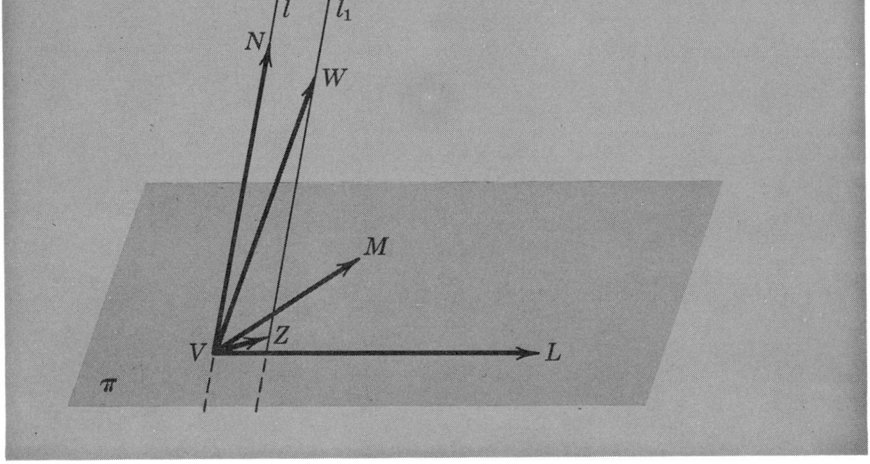

that $\overrightarrow{VL}$ and $\overrightarrow{VM}$ determine a plane π. If $\overrightarrow{VW}$ is in the plane π, then, by Theorem 3.2,

$$[\overrightarrow{VW}] = x \cdot [\overrightarrow{VL}] + y \cdot [\overrightarrow{VM}] = x \cdot [\overrightarrow{PQ}] + y \cdot [\overrightarrow{RS}] + 0 \cdot [\overrightarrow{TU}].$$

If $\overrightarrow{VW}$ is not in the plane π, let l_1 be a line through the point W parallel to the line l determined by $\overrightarrow{VN}$ (Figure 19). Then l_1 intersects π in a point Z. If l_1 and l coincide, then

$$[\overrightarrow{VW}] = z \cdot [\overrightarrow{VN}] = 0 \cdot [\overrightarrow{PQ}] + 0 \cdot [\overrightarrow{RS}] + z \cdot [\overrightarrow{TU}].$$

If l_1 does not coincide with l, then Z does not coincide with V, and $\overrightarrow{VZ}$ is a nonzero directed line segment that lies both in the plane π and the plane determined by the parallel lines l_1 and l. By Theorem 3.2,

$$[\overrightarrow{VZ}] = m \cdot [\overrightarrow{VL}] + n \cdot [\overrightarrow{VM}] \quad \text{and} \quad [\overrightarrow{VW}] = u \cdot [\overrightarrow{VZ}] + v \cdot [\overrightarrow{VN}].$$

Therefore,

$$\begin{aligned} [\overrightarrow{VW}] &= u \cdot (m \cdot [\overrightarrow{VL}] + n \cdot [\overrightarrow{VM}]) + v \cdot [\overrightarrow{VN}] \\ &= (um) \cdot [\overrightarrow{VL}] + (un) \cdot [\overrightarrow{VM}] + v \cdot [\overrightarrow{VN}] \\ &= x \cdot [\overrightarrow{PQ}] + y \cdot [\overrightarrow{RS}] + z \cdot [\overrightarrow{TU}], \end{aligned}$$

where $x = um$, $y = un$, and $z = v$.

Let O by any point in space, and let $[\overrightarrow{OX}]$, $[\overrightarrow{OY}]$, and $[\overrightarrow{OZ}]$ be noncoplanar vectors. Then every vector in space can be represented by a unique directed

FIGURE 20

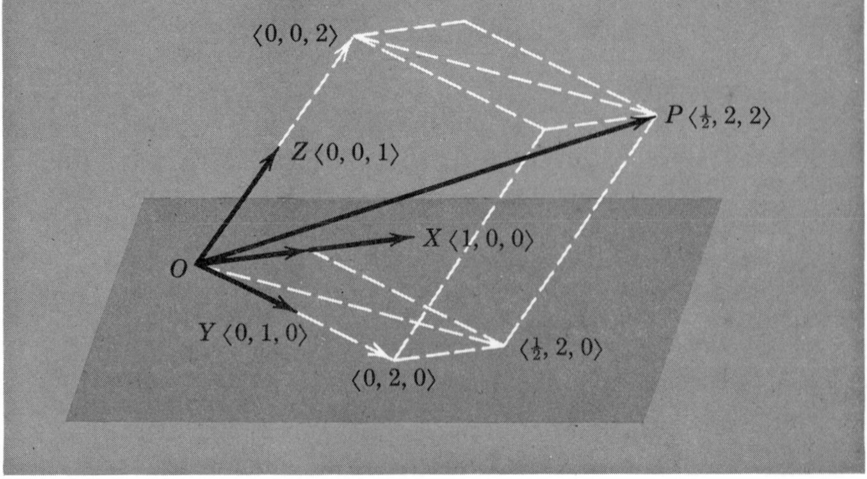

line segment $\overrightarrow{OP}$, and it follows from Theorem 4.1 that

$$[\overrightarrow{OP}] = x \cdot [\overrightarrow{OX}] + y \cdot [\overrightarrow{OY}] + z \cdot [\overrightarrow{OZ}]. \tag{4-1}$$

The ordered triple of vectors $\langle[\overrightarrow{OX}], [\overrightarrow{OY}], [\overrightarrow{OZ}]\rangle$ is a coordinate system for the geometrical vectors in three-dimensional space, since it can be shown that the expression for a vector given by equation (4-1) is unique. That is, the real numbers x, y, and z are uniquely determined by the vector $[\overrightarrow{OP}]$ (see Exercise 4.1). Therefore, each vector $[\overrightarrow{OP}]$ corresponds to a unique ordered triple of real numbers $\langle x, y, z\rangle$, where $[\overrightarrow{OP}]$ is given by (4-1). The correspondence

$$[\overrightarrow{OP}] \leftrightarrow \langle x, y, z\rangle$$

is a one-to-one correspondence between the set of all vectors in space and the set of all ordered triples of real numbers. The real numbers x, y, and z are the coordinates of $[\overrightarrow{OP}]$ with respect to the coordinate system $\langle[\overrightarrow{OX}], [\overrightarrow{OY}], [\overrightarrow{OZ}]\rangle$. In Figure 20, the coordinates of a vector are placed at the terminal point of the directed line segment, with initial point at O, that represents the vectors.

The reader has certainly observed that our treatment of coordinate systems for vectors in space closely parallels the corresponding discussion in Section 3 for vectors on a line or in a plane. The similarity of these situations is continued by the following definition.

(4.2) Definition. Let $\langle x_1, y_1, z_1\rangle$ and $\langle x_2, y_2, z_2\rangle$ be ordered triples of real numbers, and let r be a real number. The *sum* of $\langle x_1, y_1, z_1\rangle$ and $\langle x_2, y_2, z_2\rangle$ is the ordered triple

$$\langle x_1, y_1, z_1\rangle + \langle x_2, y_2, z_2\rangle = \langle x_1 + x_2, y_1 + y_2, z_1 + z_2\rangle.$$

The *scalar product* of r and $\langle x_1, y_1, z_1\rangle$ is the ordered triple

$$r \cdot \langle x_1, y_1, z_1\rangle = \langle rx_1, ry_1, rz_1\rangle.$$

Let $\langle[\overrightarrow{OX}], [\overrightarrow{OY}], [\overrightarrow{OZ}]\rangle$ be a given coordinate system in space. It follows from Definition 4.2 that if $[\overrightarrow{OP}]$ has coordinates $\langle x_1, y_1, z_1\rangle$ and $[\overrightarrow{OQ}]$ has coordinates $\langle x_2, y_2, z_2\rangle$, then $[\overrightarrow{OP}] + [\overrightarrow{OQ}]$ has coordinates

$$\langle x_1 + x_2, y_1 + y_2, z_1 + z_2\rangle = \langle x_1, y_1, z_1\rangle + \langle x_2, y_2, z_2\rangle.$$

Similarly $r \cdot [\overrightarrow{OP}]$ has coordinates

$$\langle rx_1, ry_1, rz_1\rangle = r \cdot \langle x_1, y_1, z_1\rangle.$$

Thus, the introduction of a coordinate system allows us to describe in algebraic language the geometrically defined vector operations of addition and scalar multiplication.

If the directed line segments $\overrightarrow{OX}$, $\overrightarrow{OY}$, and $\overrightarrow{OZ}$ are mutually perpendicular and if each has the same length (which is selected as the unit of length), then they determine a rectangular Cartesian coordinate system for the points in three space with origin O and with the X-, Y-, and Z-axis having the direction of $\overrightarrow{OX}$, $\overrightarrow{OY}$, and $\overrightarrow{OZ}$, respectively. In this case, the coordinate system $\langle[\overrightarrow{OX}], [\overrightarrow{OY}], [\overrightarrow{OZ}]\rangle$ for the vectors in three-dimensional space is also referred to as a rectangular Cartesian coordinate system.

Suppose that a vector $[\overrightarrow{RS}]$ has coordinates $\langle x, y, z\rangle$. Then, similar to the situation for vectors in a plane, $[\overrightarrow{RS}]$ is represented by a directed line segment $\overrightarrow{OP}$ from the origin O to the point P with coordinates (x, y, z). The details of the proof (Figure 21) of this result are left as an exercise (Exercise 4.5). If the coordinates of R are (x_R, x_R, z_R) and the coordinates of S are (x_S, y_S, z_S), then

$$x = x_S - x_R, \qquad y = y_S - y_R, \quad \text{and} \quad z = z_S - z_R.$$

That is, the coordinates of the vector $[\overrightarrow{RS}]$ are $\langle x_S - x_R, y_S - y_R, z_S - z_R\rangle$.

It follows from the discussion above that if a vector $[\overrightarrow{RS}]$ has coordinates $\langle x, y, z\rangle$ with respect to a rectangular Cartesian coordinate system $\langle[\overrightarrow{OX}], [\overrightarrow{OY}], [\overrightarrow{OZ}]\rangle$, then the length of $[\overrightarrow{RS}]$ is $\sqrt{x^2 + y^2 + z^2}$. Moreover, the law of cosines can be used exactly as in the proof of Theorem 3.4 to derive the expression for the inner product of two vectors in terms of the coordinates of the vectors.

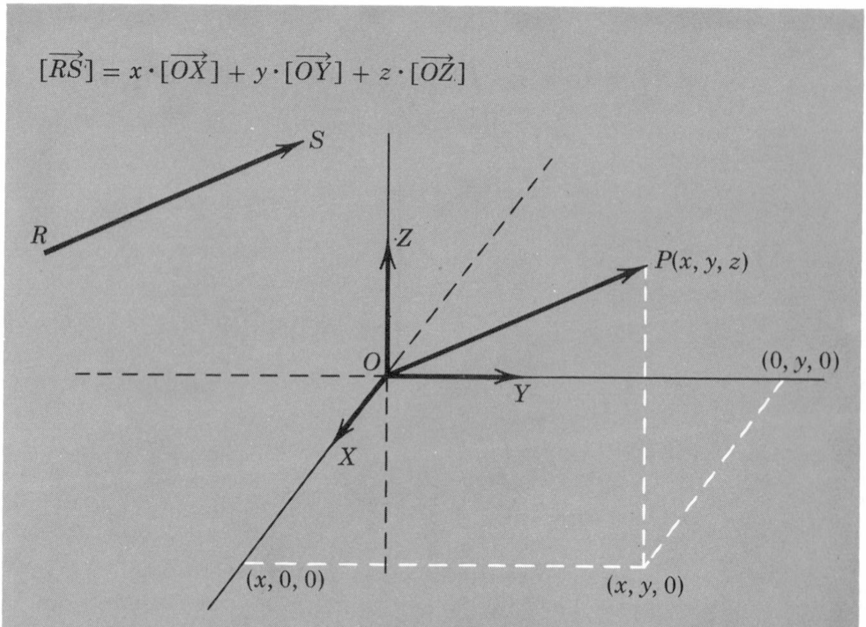

FIGURE 21

(4.3) Theorem. Let $\langle[\overrightarrow{OX}], [\overrightarrow{OY}], [\overrightarrow{OZ}]\rangle$ be a rectangular Cartesian coordinate system in space. Let $[\overrightarrow{RS}]$ and $[\overrightarrow{TU}]$ be vectors with coordinates $\langle x_1, y_1, z_1\rangle$ and $\langle x_2, y_2, z_2\rangle$, respectively. Then

$$[\overrightarrow{RS}] \circ [\overrightarrow{TU}] = x_1x_2 + y_1y_2 + z_1z_2.$$

Theorem 4.3 can be used to show that inner multiplication is distributive with respect to vector addition.

(4.4) Corollary. Let $[\overrightarrow{PQ}]$, $[\overrightarrow{RS}]$, and $[\overrightarrow{TU}]$ be any three vectors. Then

$$[\overrightarrow{PQ}] \circ ([\overrightarrow{RS}] + [\overrightarrow{TU}]) = [\overrightarrow{PQ}] \circ [\overrightarrow{RS}] + [\overrightarrow{PQ}] \circ [\overrightarrow{TU}].$$

PROOF. Let $[\overrightarrow{PQ}]$ have coordinates $\langle x_1, y_1, z_1\rangle$, $[\overrightarrow{RS}]$ have coordinates $\langle x_2, y_2, z_2\rangle$, and $[\overrightarrow{TU}]$ have coordinates $\langle x_3, y_3, z_3\rangle$ with respect to a rectangular Cartesian coordinate system. Then the coordinates of $[\overrightarrow{RS}] + [\overrightarrow{TU}]$ are $\langle x_2 + x_3, y_2 + y_3, z_2 + z_3\rangle$. By Theorem 4.3,

$$\begin{aligned}[\overrightarrow{PQ}] \circ ([\overrightarrow{RS}] + [\overrightarrow{TU}]) &= x_1(x_2 + x_3) + y_1(y_2 + y_3) + z_1(z_2 + z_3)\\ &= (x_1x_2 + y_1y_2 + z_1z_2) + (x_1x_3 + y_1y_3 + z_1z_3)\\ &= [\overrightarrow{PQ}] \circ [\overrightarrow{RS}] + [\overrightarrow{PQ}] \circ [\overrightarrow{TU}].\end{aligned}$$

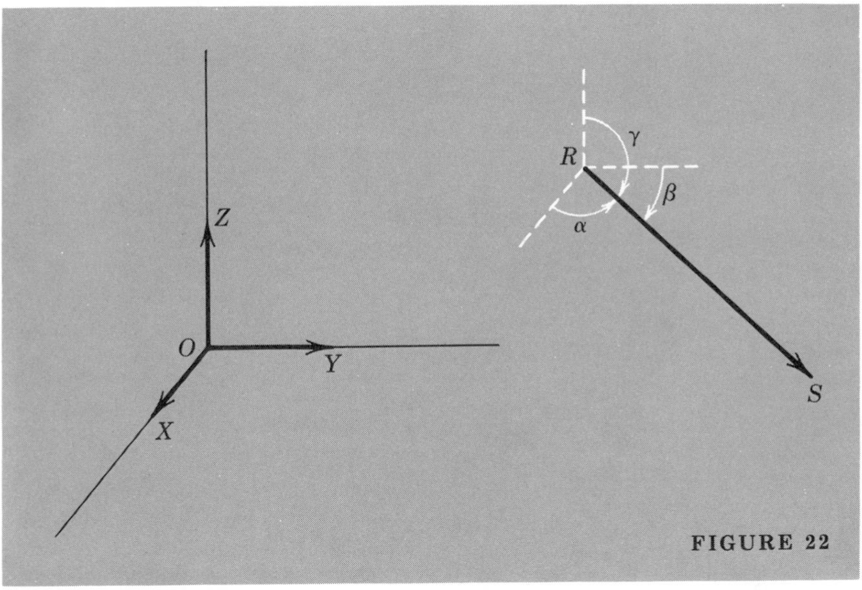

FIGURE 22

Example 1. Let $\langle[\overrightarrow{OX}], [\overrightarrow{OY}], [\overrightarrow{OZ}]\rangle$ be a rectangular Cartesian coordinate system. Let $[\overrightarrow{RS}]$ be a vector, where R has coordinates $(-2, 0, 3)$ and S has coordinates $(5, -2, -6)$. Let $[\overrightarrow{TU}]$ be a vector, where T has coordinates $(0, \frac{1}{2}, \frac{1}{3})$ and U has coordinates $(1, 1, 1)$. Then $[\overrightarrow{RS}]$ has coordinates $\langle 7, -2, -9\rangle$ and $[\overrightarrow{TU}]$ has coordinates $\langle 1, \frac{1}{2}, \frac{2}{3}\rangle$. The length of $[\overrightarrow{RS}]$ is $\sqrt{49 + 4 + 81} = \sqrt{134}$ and the length of $[\overrightarrow{TU}]$ is $\sqrt{1 + \frac{1}{4} + \frac{4}{9}} = (\frac{1}{6})\sqrt{61}$. The inner product of $[\overrightarrow{RS}]$ and $[\overrightarrow{TU}]$ is $(7)1 + (-2)\frac{1}{2} + (-9)\frac{2}{3} = 0$. Hence, the vectors $[\overrightarrow{RS}]$ and $[\overrightarrow{TU}]$ are orthogonal.

Example 2. Let $\langle[\overrightarrow{OX}], [\overrightarrow{OY}], [\overrightarrow{OZ}]\rangle$ be a rectangular Cartesian coordinate system. The *direction angles* of a nonzero directed line segment $\overrightarrow{RS}$ are the angles α, β, γ, where α is the angle measured from the direction of the X-axis to the direction of $\overrightarrow{RS}$ and $0° \leq \alpha \leq 180°$, β is the angle from the direction of the Y-axis to the direction of $\overrightarrow{RS}$ and $0° \leq \beta \leq 180°$, and γ is the angle from the direction of the Z-axis to the direction of $\overrightarrow{RS}$ and $0° \leq \gamma \leq 180°$ (Figure 22). Therefore,

$$[\overrightarrow{RS}] \circ [\overrightarrow{OX}] = |RS| \cos \alpha, \qquad [\overrightarrow{RS}] \circ [\overrightarrow{OY}] = |RS| \cos \beta,$$

and

$$[\overrightarrow{RS}] \circ [\overrightarrow{OZ}] = |RS| \cos \gamma.$$

Suppose that R has coordinates (x_R, y_R, z_R) and S has coordinates (x_S, y_S, z_S). Then the coordinates of the vector $[\overrightarrow{RS}]$ are $\langle x_S - x_R, y_S - y_R, z_S - z_R\rangle$, the length of $[\overrightarrow{RS}]$ is $\sqrt{(x_S - x_R)^2 + (y_S - y_R)^2 + (z_S - z_R)^2}$, and

$$[\overrightarrow{RS}] \circ [\overrightarrow{OX}] = (x_S - x_R)1 + (y_S - y_R)0 + (z_S - z_R)0 = x_S - x_R.$$

Therefore,

$$\cos\alpha = \frac{x_S - x_R}{\sqrt{(x_S - x_R)^2 + (y_S - y_R)^2 + (z_S - z_R)^2}}.$$

Similarly,

$$\cos\beta = \frac{y_S - y_R}{\sqrt{(x_S - x_R)^2 + (y_S - y_R)^2 + (z_S - z_R)^2}},$$

$$\cos\gamma = \frac{z_S - z_R}{\sqrt{(x_S - x_R)^2 + (y_S - y_R)^2 + (z_S - z_R)^2}}.$$

The numbers $\cos\alpha$, $\cos\beta$, and $\cos\gamma$, where α, β, γ are the direction angles of a directed line segment, are called the *direction cosines* of the segment. It follows immediately from these formulas for the direction cosines of a directed line segment that

$$\cos^2\alpha + \cos^2\beta + \cos^2\gamma = 1.$$

Exercises

4.1 Let $[\overrightarrow{OX}]$, $[\overrightarrow{OY}]$, and $[\overrightarrow{OZ}]$ be noncoplanar vectors. Prove that the expression

$$[\overrightarrow{OP}] = x \cdot [\overrightarrow{OX}] + y \cdot [\overrightarrow{OY}] + z \cdot [\overrightarrow{OZ}]$$

for a vector $[\overrightarrow{OP}]$ is unique.

4.2 Let $\langle[\overrightarrow{OX}], [\overrightarrow{OY}], [\overrightarrow{OZ}]\rangle$ be a coordinate system. Let $[\overrightarrow{OP}]$ have coordinates $\langle x_1, y_1, z_1\rangle$ and $[\overrightarrow{OQ}]$ have coordinates $\langle x_2, y_2, z_2\rangle$. Prove that the coordinates of $[\overrightarrow{OP}] + [\overrightarrow{OQ}]$ are $\langle x_1, y_1, z_1\rangle + \langle x_2, y_2, z_2\rangle$ and that the coordinates of $r \cdot [\overrightarrow{OP}]$ are $r \cdot \langle x_1, y_1, z_1\rangle$.

4.3 Let $[\overrightarrow{PQ}]$, $[\overrightarrow{RS}]$, and $[\overrightarrow{TU}]$ have coordinates $\langle -1, 0, 3\rangle$, $\langle \sqrt{2}, \frac{1}{2}, -5\rangle$, and $\langle 0, -7, \sqrt{3}\rangle$ with respect to a given coordinate system. Compute the coordinates of the following vectors:

$$5 \cdot [\overrightarrow{PQ}] - \sqrt{2} \cdot [\overrightarrow{RS}], \qquad [\overrightarrow{PQ}] + [\overrightarrow{RS}] + [\overrightarrow{TU}],$$

$$3 \cdot (2 \cdot [\overrightarrow{PQ}] + 6 \cdot [\overrightarrow{TU}]), \qquad \tfrac{1}{2} \cdot (-[\overrightarrow{PQ}] + [\overrightarrow{TU}]) + 7 \cdot [\overrightarrow{RS}].$$

4.4 Let $\langle[\overrightarrow{OX}], [\overrightarrow{OY}], [\overrightarrow{OZ}]\rangle$ be a coordinate system. Let

$$[\overrightarrow{AB}] = [\overrightarrow{OX}] + [\overrightarrow{OY}] + [\overrightarrow{OZ}], \qquad [\overrightarrow{CD}] = 2 \cdot [\overrightarrow{OX}] + 3 \cdot [\overrightarrow{OY}],$$

$$[\overrightarrow{EF}] = 3 \cdot [\overrightarrow{OX}] + 5 \cdot [\overrightarrow{OY}] - 2 \cdot [\overrightarrow{OZ}], \quad \text{and} \quad [\overrightarrow{GH}] = -[\overrightarrow{OY}] + [\overrightarrow{OZ}].$$

Prove that the vectors $[\overrightarrow{AB}] - [\overrightarrow{CD}]$ and $[\overrightarrow{EF}] - [\overrightarrow{GH}]$ are collinear. Prove that $[\overrightarrow{OX}] - [\overrightarrow{OY}]$, $[\overrightarrow{OY}] - [\overrightarrow{OZ}]$, and $[\overrightarrow{OZ}] - [\overrightarrow{OX}]$ are coplanar.

4.5 Prove that if $[\overrightarrow{RS}]$ has coordinates $\langle x, y, z\rangle$ with respect to a rectangular Cartesian coordinate system $\langle[\overrightarrow{OX}], [\overrightarrow{OY}], [\overrightarrow{OZ}]\rangle$, then $[\overrightarrow{RS}]$ is represented by a directed line segment $\overrightarrow{OP}$, where P has coordinates (x, y, z).

4.6 Let $\langle[\overrightarrow{OX}], [\overrightarrow{OY}], [\overrightarrow{OZ}]\rangle$ be a rectangular Cartesian coordinate system, and let $[\overrightarrow{PQ}]$, and $[\overrightarrow{RS}]$ be defined by the points $P(1, 0, 3)$, $Q(-5, \frac{1}{2}, -2)$, $R(1 - \sqrt{5}, 3\sqrt{2}, -3)$, and $S(\sqrt{5}, 2\sqrt{2}, 4)$. Find the coordinates of the following vectors:

$$[\overrightarrow{PQ}] + [\overrightarrow{RS}], \qquad [\overrightarrow{PQ}] - [\overrightarrow{RS}], \qquad 2 \cdot [\overrightarrow{PQ}] + 4 \cdot [\overrightarrow{RS}].$$

Sketch the directed line segments, with initial point at O, that represent these vectors.

4.7 Find the lengths of the vectors given in Exercise 4.6. Find the direction cosines of the directed line segments that represent these vectors.

4.8 The coordinates of the following pairs of vectors are given with respect to a rectangular Cartesian coordinate system. Find the inner product of each pair of vectors. Find the cosine of the angle between each pair of vectors. (a) $\langle 2, -1, 3\rangle$, $\langle 6, -5, 11\rangle$; (b) $\langle 1, 0, 1\rangle$, $\langle 0, 16, 0\rangle$; (c) $\langle \frac{1}{2}, -\frac{1}{3}, \frac{1}{5}\rangle$, $\langle 4, -12, 25\rangle$; (d) $\langle 1, -4, 3\rangle$, $\langle -3, 12, -9\rangle$.

4.9 Prove Theorem 4.3.

4.10 Check the identity of Corollary 4.4 for the vectors $[\overrightarrow{PQ}]$, $[\overrightarrow{RS}]$, and $[\overrightarrow{TU}]$ given in Exercise 4.3.

4.11 Let $[\overrightarrow{PQ}]$ and $[\overrightarrow{RS}]$ be vectors such that $[\overrightarrow{PQ}] \circ [\overrightarrow{RS}] = t$ and $|RS| = r \neq 0$. Prove that $[\overrightarrow{PQ}] - (t/r^2) \cdot [\overrightarrow{RS}]$ and $[\overrightarrow{RS}]$ are orthogonal. Express $[\overrightarrow{PQ}]$ as the sum of two orthogonal vectors.

4.12 Give an example which shows that Theorem 4.3 is not true for an arbitrary coordinate system $\langle[\overrightarrow{OX}], [\overrightarrow{OY}], [\overrightarrow{OZ}]\rangle$.

5 Applications to geometry

As an application of the results of the preceding sections, we will express in vector language the solution of some elementary linear problems in a plane and in three-dimensional space. In this section, whenever we refer to a coordinate system in a plane or in space, we will mean a rectangular Cartesian coordinate system. Moreover, to simplify our notation, the unit vectors that determine the directions of the coordinate axes in a plane will be written $[\overrightarrow{OX}] = \mathbf{I}$ and $[\overrightarrow{OY}] = \mathbf{J}$. Similarly, in space we will write $[\overrightarrow{OX}] = \mathbf{I}$, $[\overrightarrow{OY}] = \mathbf{J}$, and $[\overrightarrow{OZ}] = \mathbf{K}$.

The fact that the length of $r \cdot [\overrightarrow{PQ}]$ is $|r|\,|PQ|$ (see Definition 2.5) can be used in geometric problems that involve the division of a line segment in a given ratio.

Example 1. Let P and Q be points in a plane with a coordinate system, and let (x_P, y_P) and (x_Q, y_Q) be the coordinates of P and Q, respectively. Let R be a point on

FIGURE 23

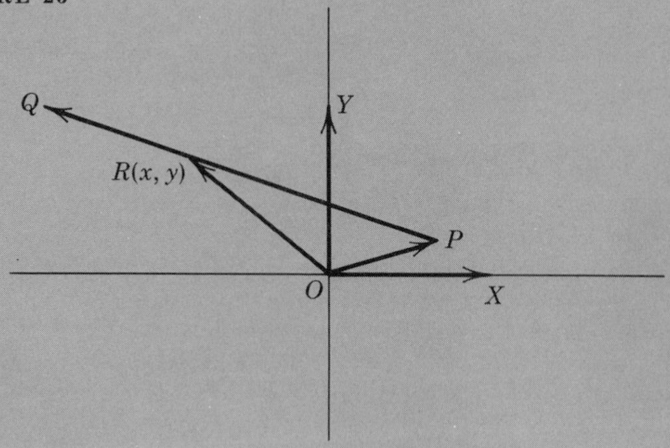

the line segment joining P and Q such that $|PR|/|PQ| = r$. Then r is a real number such that $0 \leq r \leq 1$. We wish to find the coordinates of R in terms of the coordinates of P and Q (Figure 23). By the definitions of vector addition and scalar multiplication,

$$[\overrightarrow{OR}] = [\overrightarrow{OP}] + [\overrightarrow{PR}] = [\overrightarrow{OP}] + r \cdot [\overrightarrow{PQ}].$$

Denote the coordinates of R by (x, y). Then the coordinates of $[\overrightarrow{OR}]$, $[\overrightarrow{OP}]$, and $[\overrightarrow{PQ}]$ are $\langle x, y\rangle$, $\langle x_P, y_P\rangle$, and $\langle x_Q - x_P, y_P - y_Q\rangle$, respectively. Hence,

$$\begin{aligned}\langle x, y\rangle &= \langle x_P, y_P\rangle + r \cdot \langle x_Q - x_P, y_Q - y_P\rangle \\ &= \langle (1 - r)x_P + rx_Q, (1 - r)y_P + ry_Q\rangle.\end{aligned}$$

Therefore, the coordinates of the point R are $x = (1 - r)x_P + rx_Q$ and $y = (1 - r)y_P + ry_Q$. In particular, if R bisects PQ, then $r = \frac{1}{2}$, and $x = \frac{1}{2}(x_P + x_Q)$, $y = \frac{1}{2}(y_P + y_Q)$.

If P and Q are points with coordinates (x_P, y_P, z_P) and (x_Q, y_Q, z_Q) with respect to a coordinate system in three-dimensional space, and if R is a point on $\overrightarrow{PQ}$ such that $|PR|/|PQ| = r$, then essentially the same derivation as given above shows that R has coordinates $x = (1 - r)x_P + rx_Q$, $y = (1 - r)y_P + ry_Q$, $z = (1 - r)z_P + rz_Q$. (See Exercise 5.2.)

Example 2. Prove that the diagonals of a parallelogram bisect each other. Let $ABCD$ be a parallelogram with diagonals AC and BD intersecting at P (Figure 24). Then $[\overrightarrow{AB}] = [\overrightarrow{DC}]$ and $[\overrightarrow{AD}] = [\overrightarrow{BC}]$. (Here we assume the more elementary theorem from geometry that the opposite sides of a parallelogram are equal. In fact, this was assumed in the proof of the commutative law of vector addition.) We have

$$[\overrightarrow{AP}] = r \cdot [\overrightarrow{AC}] = r \cdot ([\overrightarrow{AB}] + [\overrightarrow{BC}]) = r \cdot [\overrightarrow{AB}] + r \cdot [\overrightarrow{BC}],$$

FIGURE 24

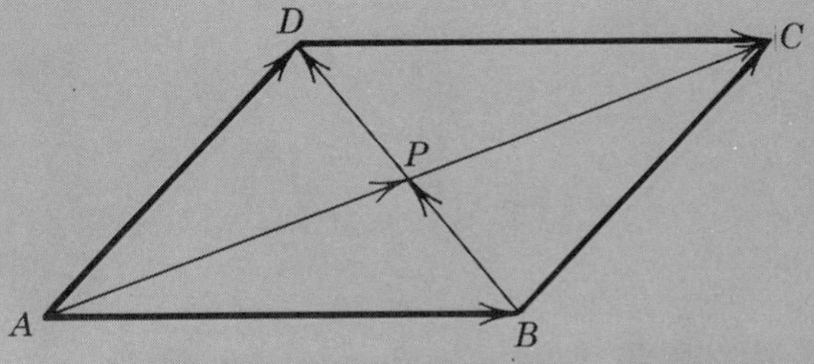

and

$$[\overrightarrow{AP}] = [\overrightarrow{AB}] + [\overrightarrow{BP}] = [\overrightarrow{AB}] + s \cdot [\overrightarrow{BD}]$$
$$= [\overrightarrow{AB}] + s \cdot ([\overrightarrow{AD}] - [\overrightarrow{AB}]) = [\overrightarrow{AB}] + s \cdot ([\overrightarrow{BC}] - [\overrightarrow{AB}])$$
$$= (1 - s) \cdot [\overrightarrow{AB}] + s \cdot [\overrightarrow{BC}].$$

Therefore,

$$r \cdot [\overrightarrow{AB}] + r \cdot [\overrightarrow{BC}] = (1 - s) \cdot [\overrightarrow{AB}] + s \cdot [\overrightarrow{BC}],$$

or

$$(r + s - 1) \cdot [\overrightarrow{AB}] + (r - s) \cdot [\overrightarrow{BC}] = [\overrightarrow{0}].$$

However, $[\overrightarrow{AB}]$ and $[\overrightarrow{BC}]$ are noncollinear. Hence, by Exercise 3.1, $r + s - 1 = 0$ and $r - s = 0$. Solving these equations, we find $r = s = ½$. Therefore $[\overrightarrow{AP}] = ½ \cdot [\overrightarrow{AC}]$ and $[\overrightarrow{BP}] = ½ \cdot [\overrightarrow{BD}]$, which means that the diagonals bisect each other.

Example 3. Let $\overrightarrow{PQ}$ be a directed line segment in a plane with a coordinate system. Suppose that $|PQ| = 5$ and that the angle θ from the X-axis to the direction of $\overrightarrow{PQ}$ is 60°. Find the coordinates of the vector $[\overrightarrow{PQ}]$.

Let $[\overrightarrow{PQ}]$ have coordinates $\langle x, y\rangle$. Then by Theorem 3.4, $\mathbf{I} \circ [\overrightarrow{PQ}] = 1x + 0y = x$ and $\mathbf{J} \circ [\overrightarrow{PQ}] = 0x + 1y = y$. The angle between $\mathbf{I}$ and $[\overrightarrow{PQ}]$ is 60°, and the angle between $\mathbf{J}$ and $[\overrightarrow{PQ}]$ is 30°. Therefore,

$$x = \mathbf{I} \circ [\overrightarrow{PQ}] = |PQ| \cos 60° = 5\left(\frac{1}{2}\right) = \frac{5}{2},$$

$$y = \mathbf{J} \circ [\overrightarrow{PQ}] = |PQ| \cos 30° = 5\left(\frac{\sqrt{3}}{2}\right) = \frac{5\sqrt{3}}{2}.$$

Hence, $[\overrightarrow{PQ}]$ has coordinates $\langle 5/2, 5\sqrt{3}/2\rangle$. That is, $[\overrightarrow{PQ}] = (5/2) \cdot \mathbf{I} + (5\sqrt{3}/2) \cdot \mathbf{J}$.

Example 4. In a plane with a coordinate system, $[\overrightarrow{PQ}] = 5 \cdot \mathbf{I} - 7 \cdot \mathbf{J}$. Find the unit vector in the plane that has the same direction as $[\overrightarrow{PQ}]$. The coordinates of $[\overrightarrow{PQ}]$ are $\langle 5, -7\rangle$. The length of $[\overrightarrow{PQ}]$ is $\sqrt{25 + 49} = \sqrt{74}$. The unit vector with the same direction as $[\overrightarrow{PQ}]$ is the vector $(1/|PQ|) \cdot [\overrightarrow{PQ}]$. Therefore, the desired vector is

$$\left(\frac{1}{\sqrt{74}}\right) \cdot (5 \cdot \mathbf{I} - 7 \cdot \mathbf{J}) = \left(\frac{5}{\sqrt{74}}\right) \cdot \mathbf{I} - \left(\frac{7}{\sqrt{74}}\right) \cdot \mathbf{J}.$$

Example 5. Let l_1 be a line in three-dimensional space that passes through the points with coordinates (1, 1, 1) and (2, −3, 4), and let l_2 be a line through (1, 1, 1) and (−1, 6, 2). Find the acute angle between the lines l_1 and l_2. The vector $[\overrightarrow{PQ}]$ represented by the directed line segment from (1, 1, 1) to (2, −3, 4) has coordinates $\langle 2 - 1, -3 - 1, 4 - 1 \rangle = \langle 1, -4, 3 \rangle$. The vector $[\overrightarrow{RS}]$ represented by the segment from (1, 1, 1) to (−1, 6, 2) has coordinates $\langle -1 - 1, 6 - 1, 2 - 1 \rangle = \langle -2, 5, 1 \rangle$. Therefore

$$|PQ| = \sqrt{1 + 16 + 9} = \sqrt{26}, \qquad |RS| = \sqrt{4 + 25 + 1} = \sqrt{30},$$

$$[\overrightarrow{PQ}] \circ [\overrightarrow{RS}] = 1(-2) + (-4)5 + 3(1) = -19,$$

and

$$\cos \theta = \frac{-19}{\sqrt{26}\,\sqrt{30}},$$

where θ is the angle between $[\overrightarrow{PQ}]$ and $[\overrightarrow{RS}]$. Thus, the acute angle between the lines l_1 and l_2 is the acute angle whose cosine is $19/\sqrt{26}\,\sqrt{30}$.

Example 6. Let l be a line in a plane, and let O be any point in the plane. We will derive the vector equation of l relative to the selected point O.

Let A and B be distinct points on l, and let P be any other point on l. Then we have $[\overrightarrow{OP}] = [\overrightarrow{OA}] + [\overrightarrow{AP}]$, and $[\overrightarrow{AP}] = k \cdot [\overrightarrow{AB}]$ (Figure 25). Therefore,

$$[\overrightarrow{OP}] = [\overrightarrow{OA}] + k \cdot [\overrightarrow{AB}]. \tag{5-1}$$

Of course, the value of k in equation (5-1) depends on the position of the point P on l. If P is on the same side of A as B, then $k = |AP|/|AB|$; and if P is on the opposite side of A from B, then $k = -|AP|/|AB|$. Thus, any vector represented by a

FIGURE 25

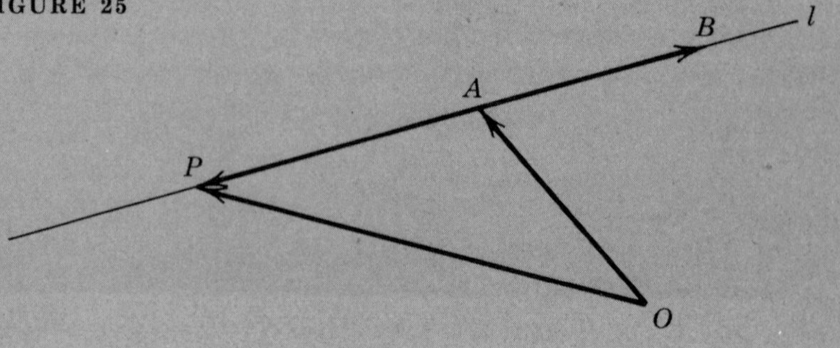

directed line segment $\overrightarrow{OP}$ with terminal point on the line l satisfies the vector equation (5-1), where A and B are distinct points on l.

Conversely, suppose that $[\overrightarrow{RS}]$ is any vector that satisfies (5-1), that is, $[\overrightarrow{RS}] = [\overrightarrow{OA}] + k \cdot [\overrightarrow{AB}]$ for some value of k. Let $\overrightarrow{OQ}$ be a directed line segment such that $[\overrightarrow{RS}] = [\overrightarrow{OQ}]$. Since $k \cdot [\overrightarrow{AB}]$ is represented by a directed line segment $\overrightarrow{AC}$ with terminal point on l, it follows that $[\overrightarrow{OA}] + k \cdot [\overrightarrow{AB}]$ is represented by $\overrightarrow{OC}$ with terminal point on l. Thus, $[\overrightarrow{OQ}] = [\overrightarrow{OC}]$, which implies that $Q = C$. Therefore, the vector $[\overrightarrow{RS}]$ that satisfies equation (5-1) is represented by a directed line segment $\overrightarrow{OQ}$ with terminal point Q on l.

Note that the derivation above could be used equally well in three-dimensional space. Thus, (5-1) is the vector equation of a line in three-dimensional space relative to some fixed point O.

Example 7. Let l be a line in three-dimensional space, and let O be the origin of a coordinate system; let A and B be distinct points on l. In equation (5-1), the coordinates of the vectors $[\overrightarrow{OP}]$, $[\overrightarrow{OA}]$, and $[\overrightarrow{AB}]$ are $\langle x_P, y_P, z_P\rangle$, $\langle x_A, y_A, z_A\rangle$, and $\langle x_B - x_A, y_B - y_A, z_B - z_A\rangle$, respectively. Thus, by (5-1)

$$\begin{aligned}\langle x_P, y_P, z_P\rangle &= \langle x_A, y_A, z_A\rangle + k \cdot \langle x_B - x_A, y_B - y_A, z_B - z_A\rangle \\ &= \langle x_A + k(x_B - x_A), y_A + k(y_B - y_A), z_A + k(z_B - z_A)\rangle.\end{aligned}$$

We obtain

$$x_P = x_A + k(x_B - x_A), \qquad y_P = y_A + k(y_B - y_A), \qquad z_P = z_A + k(z_B - z_A),$$

which are the so-called *parametric equations* of a line through two given points A and B in three-dimensional space.

Example 8. Let π be a plane, and let A, B, and C be points on π, which do not lie in a line on π. Let O be any point in space, and let P be any point on π. By Theorem 3.2,

$$[\overrightarrow{AP}] = k_1 \cdot [\overrightarrow{AB}] + k_2 \cdot [\overrightarrow{AC}].$$

Moreover, $[\overrightarrow{OA}] + [\overrightarrow{AP}] = [\overrightarrow{OP}]$. Thus,

$$[\overrightarrow{OP}] = [\overrightarrow{OA}] + k_1 \cdot [\overrightarrow{AB}] + k_2 \cdot [\overrightarrow{AC}]. \tag{5-2}$$

We have shown that any vector that is represented by a directed line segment $\overrightarrow{OP}$ with terminal point on the plane π satisfies (5-2) for some real numbers k_1 and k_2, where A, B, and C are three noncollinear points on π. The proof of the converse, that if $[\overrightarrow{RS}]$ is any vector that satisfies (5-2), then $[\overrightarrow{RS}]$ is represented by a directed line segment $\overrightarrow{OQ}$ with terminal point Q on π, is left as an exercise (Exercise 5.10).

Example 9. Show that the points A (0, 0, 1), B (2, 1, 0), C (−5, 2, 17), and P (1, 1, 2) lie on a plane. The coordinates of $[\overrightarrow{OA}]$, $[\overrightarrow{AB}]$, $[\overrightarrow{AC}]$, and $[\overrightarrow{OP}]$ are $\langle 0, 0, 1\rangle$, $\langle 2, 1, -1\rangle$, $\langle -5, 2, 16\rangle$, and $\langle 1, 1, 2\rangle$, respectively. By (5-2), P lies on the plane determined by A, B, and C if and only if real numbers k_1 and k_2 exist such that

$$\begin{aligned}\langle 1, 1, 2\rangle &= \langle 0, 0, 1\rangle + k_1 \cdot \langle 2, 1, -1\rangle + k_2 \cdot \langle -5, 2, 16\rangle \\ &= \langle 0 + 2k_1 - 5k_2, 0 + k_1 + 2k_2, 1 - k_1 + 16k_2\rangle.\end{aligned}$$

This equation is satisfied if and only if

$$2k_1 - 5k_2 = 1, \qquad k_1 + 2k_2 = 1, \qquad 1 - k_1 + 16k_2 = 2.$$

Solving the first and second equations simultaneously, we find $k_1 = 7/9$, $k_2 = 1/9$. Substituting these values in the third equation, $1 - 7/9 + 16/9 = 18/9 = 2$. Thus, $k_1 = 7/9$, $k_2 = 1/9$ satisfy the three equations, so that the four given points lie on a plane.

Exercises

5.1 Let P $(1/2, 1/3)$ and Q $(-4, 6)$ be points in the plane. Find the coordinates of the point R on the line segment PQ such that (a) $|PR|/|PQ| = 1/2$; (b) $|PR|/|PQ| = 4/5$; (c) $|PR|/|PQ| = 1/\sqrt{2}$.

5.2 Let P (x_P, y_P, z_P) and Q (x_Q, y_Q, z_Q) be points in three-dimensional space. Derive the formula for the coordinates of the point R (x, y, z) on the line segment PQ such that $|PR|/|PQ| = r$.

5.3 Find the coordinates of the point that is one-third of the way from P $(1, 1, 1)$ to Q $(-1, -1, -1)$.

5.4 Use vector methods to prove that the diagonals of a rhombus are perpendicular.

5.5 Use vector methods to prove that any two medians of a triangle intersect at a point two-thirds of the way along either median from the vertex through which it passes to the opposite side.

5.6 The vectors $[\overrightarrow{PQ}]$ and $[\overrightarrow{RS}]$ in a plane have coordinates $\langle 1, 3\rangle$ and $\langle -4, 2\rangle$, respectively. Find the real numbers k_1 and k_2 such that each of the following vectors is expressed in the form $k_1 \cdot [\overrightarrow{PQ}] + k_2 \cdot [\overrightarrow{RS}]$: (a) the vector represented by a directed line segment from the point $(3, 5)$ to the point $(-1, 2)$; (b) the vector $2 \cdot \mathbf{I} - 5 \cdot \mathbf{J}$; (c) the vector $\mathbf{I}$; (d) the vector $\mathbf{J}$.

5.7 Let $\overrightarrow{PQ}$ be a directed line segment such that $|PQ| = 12$ and the direction angles of $\overrightarrow{PQ}$ are $\alpha = 60°$, $\beta = 45°$, $\gamma = 30°$ with respect to a coordinate system in three-dimensional space. Find the coordinates of the vector $[\overrightarrow{PQ}]$.

5.8 Let O and A be fixed points in space. (a) Show that the set of all points P such that $([\overrightarrow{OP}] - [\overrightarrow{OA}]) \circ [\overrightarrow{OP}] = 0$ is a sphere. (b) Show that the set of all points P such that $([\overrightarrow{OP}] - [\overrightarrow{OA}]) \circ [\overrightarrow{OA}] = 0$ is a plane.

5.9 Derive the parametric equations of the line through the points $(1, -5, 6)$ and $(2, 7, -10)$. Show that the point $(3/2, 1, -2)$ is on the line.

5.10 Complete the derivation of the vector equation of a plane given in Example 8. That is, prove that if $[\overrightarrow{RS}]$ is any vector that satisfies

$$[\overrightarrow{RS}] = [\overrightarrow{OA}] + k_1 \cdot [\overrightarrow{AB}] + k_2 \cdot [\overrightarrow{AC}],$$

then $[\overrightarrow{RS}]$ is represented by a directed line segment $\overrightarrow{OQ}$ with terminal point on the plane π determined by the three points A, B, and C.

The set $\{\mathbf{V}_1, \mathbf{V}_2\}$ is linearly dependent if and only if there exist real numbers k_1, k_2, not both zero, such that $k_1 \cdot \mathbf{V}_1 + k_2 \cdot \mathbf{V}_2 = \mathbf{0}$. This is equivalent to

$$\begin{aligned}\mathbf{0} &= k_1 \cdot (r_1 \cdot \mathbf{U} + r_2 \cdot \mathbf{W}) + k_2 \cdot (s_1 \cdot \mathbf{U} + s_2 \cdot \mathbf{W}) \\ &= (k_1 r_1 + k_2 s_1) \cdot \mathbf{U} + (k_1 r_2 + k_2 s_2) \cdot \mathbf{W}.\end{aligned}$$

Since $\langle \mathbf{U}, \mathbf{W} \rangle$ is a coordinate system (and therefore $\mathbf{U}$ and $\mathbf{W}$ are noncollinear), it follows that this condition is satisfied if and only if $k_1 r_1 + k_2 s_1 = 0$ and $k_1 r_2 + k_2 s_2 = 0$. Therefore, $\{\mathbf{V}_1, \mathbf{V}_2\}$ is a linearly dependent set if and only if the equations

$$\begin{aligned} r_1 x + s_1 y &= 0 \\ r_2 x + s_2 y &= 0 \end{aligned} \tag{6-1}$$

have a simultaneous solution $x = k_1$, $y = k_2$, where not both k_1 and k_2 are zero. Since equations (6-1) always have at least one solution $x = 0$, $y = 0$, we have shown that $\{\mathbf{V}_1, \mathbf{V}_2\}$ is a linearly dependent set if and only if the equations (6-1) do not have a unique solution. Thus, our original problem is reduced to one concerning the solutions of systems of equations.

Example 1. Let $\langle \mathbf{I}, \mathbf{J} \rangle$ be a rectangular Cartesian coordinate system in a plane. Let the coordinates of $\mathbf{V}_1$ and $\mathbf{V}_2$ be $\langle 2, -6 \rangle$ and $\langle 1/5, -3/5 \rangle$, respectively. Then $\{\mathbf{V}_1, \mathbf{V}_2\}$ is a linearly dependent set if and only if the equations

$$\begin{aligned} 2x + \tfrac{1}{5}y &= 0 \\ -6x - \tfrac{3}{5}y &= 0 \end{aligned}$$

have a solution other than $x = 0$, $y = 0$. Multiplying the first equation by -3 yields a system

$$\begin{aligned} -6x - \tfrac{3}{5}y &= 0 \\ -6x - \tfrac{3}{5}y &= 0 \end{aligned}$$

with the same solutions as the original system. It is now clear that the system has solutions other than $x = 0$, $y = 0$. In fact, if k is any nonzero real number, then $x = k$, $y = -10k$ is such a solution. Hence $\{\mathbf{V}_1, \mathbf{V}_2\}$ is a linearly dependent set.

Let $\langle \mathbf{U}, \mathbf{W}, \mathbf{T} \rangle$ be a coordinate system in $\mathcal{E}_3$, and let

$$\begin{aligned} \mathbf{V}_1 &= q_1 \cdot \mathbf{U} + q_2 \cdot \mathbf{W} + q_3 \cdot \mathbf{T} \\ \mathbf{V}_2 &= r_1 \cdot \mathbf{U} + r_2 \cdot \mathbf{W} + r_3 \cdot \mathbf{T} \\ \mathbf{V}_3 &= s_1 \cdot \mathbf{U} + s_2 \cdot \mathbf{W} + s_3 \cdot \mathbf{T} \end{aligned}$$

Then $\{\mathbf{V}_1, \mathbf{V}_2, \mathbf{V}_3\}$ is a linearly independent set in $\mathcal{E}_3$ if and only if

$$\begin{aligned}\mathbf{0} &= k_1 \cdot (q_1 \cdot \mathbf{U} + q_2 \cdot \mathbf{W} + q_3 \cdot \mathbf{T}) + k_2 \cdot (r_1 \cdot \mathbf{U} + r_2 \cdot \mathbf{W} + r_3 \cdot \mathbf{T}) \\ &\quad + k_3 \cdot (s_1 \cdot \mathbf{U} + s_2 \cdot \mathbf{W} + s_3 \cdot \mathbf{T}) \\ &= (k_1 q_1 + k_2 r_1 + k_3 s_1) \cdot \mathbf{U} + (k_1 q_2 + k_2 r_2 + k_3 s_2) \cdot \mathbf{W} \\ &\quad + (k_1 q_3 + k_2 r_3 + k_3 s_3) \cdot \mathbf{T},\end{aligned}$$

for some k_1, k_2, k_3, not all zero. This condition is equivalent to the statement that the equations

$$\begin{aligned} q_1x + r_1y + s_1z &= 0 \\ q_2x + r_2y + s_2z &= 0 \\ q_3x + r_3y + s_3z &= 0 \end{aligned} \tag{6-2}$$

have a solution other than $x = 0, y = 0, z = 0$. As in our previous discussion, the problem of deciding whether $\{\mathbf{V}_1, \mathbf{V}_2, \mathbf{V}_3\}$ is a linearly dependent set leads to the analysis of a system of equations. Such systems will be completely discussed in Chapter Three.

Exercises

6.1 Let **U**, **W**, and **T** have coordinates $\langle 1, 1, 1\rangle$, $\langle 2, -3, 1\rangle$, and $\langle -5, 3, -2\rangle$, respectively, with respect to a Cartesian coordinate system $\langle \mathbf{I}, \mathbf{J}, \mathbf{K}\rangle$ in three-dimensional space. Prove that **U**, **W**, and **T** are noncoplanar. Find the coordinates of the unit vectors **I**, **J**, and **K** with respect to the coordinate system $\langle \mathbf{U}, \mathbf{W}, \mathbf{T}\rangle$.

***6.2** Let S be a set of vectors in $\mathcal{E}_3$. (a) Prove that if $\mathbf{0} \in S$, then S is a linearly dependent set. (b) Prove that if some subset of S is a linearly dependent set, then S is a linearly dependent set.

6.3 Which of the following sets of vectors in $\mathcal{E}_3$ are linearly dependent sets?

(a) $\{\mathbf{I}, \mathbf{J}, \mathbf{K}\}$;

(b) $\{\mathbf{I} - 3 \cdot \mathbf{J} + 4 \cdot \mathbf{K}, -3 \cdot \mathbf{I} + 5 \cdot \mathbf{J} + 6 \cdot \mathbf{K}, -2 \cdot \mathbf{I} + 2 \cdot \mathbf{J} + 10 \cdot \mathbf{K}\}$;

(c) $\{\mathbf{I} + \mathbf{J} + \mathbf{K}, 2 \cdot \mathbf{I}, \mathbf{J} - \mathbf{K}, \mathbf{I} + \mathbf{J}\}$;

(d) $\{5 \cdot \mathbf{I} - 3 \cdot \mathbf{J} + \mathbf{K}, \mathbf{I} + 2 \cdot \mathbf{J} + \mathbf{K}, 2 \cdot \mathbf{I} - 3 \cdot \mathbf{J} + 5 \cdot \mathbf{K}\}$.

7 Real vector spaces

In Chapter One, rules for addition and scalar multiplication were given for vectors in $\mathcal{E}_3$. If **U** and **V** are any two vectors in $\mathcal{E}_3$, then $\mathbf{U} + \mathbf{V}$ is a unique vector in $\mathcal{E}_3$. Also, if r is any real number and **U** is any vector in $\mathcal{E}_3$, then $r \cdot \mathbf{U}$ is a unique vector in $\mathcal{E}_3$. It was shown that the operations of addition and scalar multiplication of vectors satisfy certain algebraic identities. These results are summarized in the following theorem.

(7.1) **Theorem.** The vectors in $\mathcal{E}_3$ satisfy the following conditions:

(a) If **U** and **V** are in $\mathcal{E}_3$, then $\mathbf{U} + \mathbf{V}$ is a unique vector in $\mathcal{E}_3$.

(b) $(\mathbf{U} + \mathbf{V}) + \mathbf{W} = \mathbf{U} + (\mathbf{V} + \mathbf{W})$ for all **U**, **V**, **W** in $\mathcal{E}_3$.

(c) $\mathbf{U} + \mathbf{V} = \mathbf{V} + \mathbf{U}$ for all **U**, **V** in $\mathcal{E}_3$.

(d) There is a vector **0** in $\mathcal{E}_3$ such that $\mathbf{U} + \mathbf{0} = \mathbf{0} + \mathbf{U} = \mathbf{U}$ for every **U** in $\mathcal{E}_3$.

(e) If $\mathbf{U}$ is in $\mathcal{E}_3$, then there is a vector $-\mathbf{U}$ in $\mathcal{E}_3$ such that $\mathbf{U} + (-\mathbf{U}) = (-\mathbf{U}) + \mathbf{U} = \mathbf{0}$.

(f) If $\mathbf{U}$ is in $\mathcal{E}_3$ and r is any real number, then $r \cdot \mathbf{U}$ is a unique vector in $\mathcal{E}_3$.

(g) $c \cdot (d \cdot \mathbf{U}) = d \cdot (c \cdot \mathbf{U}) = (cd) \cdot \mathbf{U}$ for all real numbers c, d and vectors $\mathbf{U}$ in $\mathcal{E}_3$.

(h) $(c + d) \cdot \mathbf{U} = c \cdot \mathbf{U} + d \cdot \mathbf{U}$ for all real numbers c, d and vectors $\mathbf{U}$ in $\mathcal{E}_3$.

(i) $c \cdot (\mathbf{U} + \mathbf{V}) = c \cdot \mathbf{U} + c \cdot \mathbf{V}$ for all real numbers c and vectors $\mathbf{U}$, $\mathbf{V}$ in $\mathcal{E}_3$.

(j) $1 \cdot \mathbf{U} = \mathbf{U}$ for every vector $\mathbf{U}$ in $\mathcal{E}_3$.

The algebraic properties of $\mathcal{E}_3$ given in Theorem 7.1 admit a generalization that is one of the basic notions of modern mathematics.

(7.2) Definition. Let $\mathcal{V}$ be a set of elements for which operations of addition (+) and scalar multiplication by a real number (·) are defined that satisfy the conditions (a) through (j) of Theorem 7.1 (with $\mathcal{E}_3$ replaced by $\mathcal{V}$). Then $\mathcal{V}$ is called a *real vector space.*

It should be understood that the concept of a real vector space $\mathcal{V}$ is *abstract* in the following sense. The elements of $\mathcal{V}$ can be any objects whatsoever and the rules of addition and scalar multiplication can be any rules of combination as long as $\mathcal{V}$ together with these operations satisfy the conditions (a) through (j) of Theorem 7.1. Nothing else is assumed about the elements of $\mathcal{V}$ or the operations. Of course, in specific examples of real vector spaces, such as $\mathcal{E}_3$, the elements and the operations may have additional properties.

The elements of any real vector space are called *vectors*. The vector $\mathbf{0}$, whose existence is asserted in 7.1(d) is called the *zero vector*. By 7.1(e), for every $\mathbf{U}$ in $\mathcal{V}$, there is a vector $-\mathbf{U}$ such that $\mathbf{U} + (-\mathbf{U}) = \mathbf{0}$. The vector $-\mathbf{U}$ is called the *negative* of $\mathbf{U}$. *Subtraction* is defined in $\mathcal{V}$ by $\mathbf{U} - \mathbf{V} = \mathbf{U} + (-\mathbf{V})$.

Example 1. The set of all polynomials in a variable x with real coefficients together with ordinary polynomial addition and multiplication by a real number, is a real vector space. Denote this set of polynomials by $R[x]$. Let

$$f(x) = a_nx^n + a_{n-1}x^{n-1} + \cdots + a_1x + a_0$$

and

$$g(x) = b_mx^m + b_{m-1}x^{m-1} + \cdots + b_1x + b_0$$

be in $R[x]$. Suppose that $n \geq m$. Then

$$f(x) + g(x) = a_nx^n + \cdots + a_{m+1}x^{m+1} + (a_m + b_m)x^m + \cdots + (a_1 + b_1)x + (a_0 + b_0)$$

is in $R[x]$. If r is any real number, then

$$r \cdot f(x) = (ra_n)x^n + (ra_{n-1})x^{n-1} + \cdots + (ra_1)x + ra_0 \text{ is in } R[x].$$

The zero polynomial is the constant polynomial a_0, where $a_0 = 0$. The negative of the polynomial $f(x)$ is

$$(-1) \cdot f(x) = (-a_n)x^n + (-a_{n-1})x^{n-1} + \cdots + (-a_1)x + (-a_0).$$

Thus $R[x]$ satisfies (a), (f), (d), and (e) of Theorem 7.1 (with $\mathcal{E}_3$ replaced by $R[x]$). The fact that $R[x]$ has the rest of the properties listed in 7.1 should be well-known to the reader from elementary algebra.

Example 2. Let $\mathfrak{F} = \{f, g, \ldots\}$ be the set of all real-valued functions defined at every point of the closed interval $[a, b]$, with addition and scalar multiplication defined by

$$(f + g)(x) = f(x) + g(x), \qquad (c \cdot f)(x) = cf(x)$$

for all x in $[a, b]$. Then $\mathfrak{F}$ is a real vector space. The subset $\mathcal{G}$ of $\mathfrak{F}$, consisting of the continuous functions, is also a real vector space with respect to the same operations of addition and scalar multiplication.

Example 3. Let C be the set of all complex numbers. Then if $a + bi$ and $c + di$ are in C and r is any real number, it follows that

$$(a + bi) + (c + di) = (a + c) + (b + d)i, \quad \text{and} \quad r \cdot (a + bi) = (ra) + (rb)i.$$

The reader can verify that C is a real vector space.

Example 4. Let $\mathcal{V}_n$, for any positive integer n, be the set of all ordered n-tuples $\langle a_1, a_2, \ldots, a_n\rangle$ of real numbers. Define

$$\langle a_1, a_2, \ldots, a_n\rangle = \langle b_1, b_2, \ldots, b_n\rangle$$

if and only if $a_i = b_i$ for $i = 1, 2, \ldots, n$;

$$\langle a_1, a_2, \ldots, a_n\rangle + \langle b_1, b_2, \ldots, b_n\rangle = \langle a_1 + b_1, a_2 + b_2, \ldots, a_n + b_n\rangle;$$

$$r \cdot \langle a_1, a_2, \ldots, a_n\rangle = \langle ra_1, ra_2, \ldots, ra_n\rangle,$$

where r is any real number. Note that the definitions of addition and scalar multiplication in $\mathcal{V}_n$ are analogous to the descriptions of these operations in $\mathcal{E}_3$ when the vectors in $\mathcal{E}_3$ are given by coordinates. It is easy to verify that $\mathcal{V}_n$ satisfies (a) through (j) of Theorem 7.1.

The real vector spaces $\mathcal{V}_n$ for each positive integer n, which are described in Example 4, are of considerable importance, because we will discover that they serve as models for an important class of real vector spaces. For any vector $\langle a_1, a_2, \ldots, a_n\rangle$ in $\mathcal{V}_n$, the real numbers $a_1, a_2, \ldots, a_n$ are called the *components* of the vector; a_i is called the ith *component*.

Henceforth, we will refer to a real vector space simply as a *vector space*. The following theorem lists some useful properties of addition and scalar multiplication in a vector space that follow from the basic assumptions.

(7.3) Theorem. Let $\mathcal{V}$ be a vector space. Let $\mathbf{U}$ and $\mathbf{V}$ be any vectors in $\mathcal{V}$, and let r be any real number.

(a) There is one and only one vector $\mathbf{X}$ in $\mathcal{V}$ such that $\mathbf{U} + \mathbf{X} = \mathbf{V}$.
(b) $r \cdot \mathbf{0} = \mathbf{0}$ and $0 \cdot \mathbf{U} = \mathbf{0}$.
(c) $r \cdot (-\mathbf{U}) = (-r) \cdot \mathbf{U} = -(r \cdot \mathbf{U})$.
(d) If $r \cdot \mathbf{U} = \mathbf{0}$, then either $r = 0$ or $\mathbf{U} = \mathbf{0}$.

PROOF. (a) If $\mathbf{X}$ is a vector such that $\mathbf{U} + \mathbf{X} = \mathbf{V}$, then, by 7.1(d), (e), and (b),

$$\mathbf{X} = \mathbf{0} + \mathbf{X} = (-\mathbf{U} + \mathbf{U}) + \mathbf{X} = -\mathbf{U} + (\mathbf{U} + \mathbf{X}) = -\mathbf{U} + \mathbf{V}.$$

Moreover, by direct substitution, $\mathbf{U} + (-\mathbf{U} + \mathbf{V}) = \mathbf{V}$. Thus, $\mathbf{X} = -\mathbf{U} + \mathbf{V}$ is the unique solution of the equation $\mathbf{U} + \mathbf{X} = \mathbf{V}$.

(b) By 7.1(d) and (i), $r \cdot \mathbf{0} = r \cdot (\mathbf{0} + \mathbf{0}) = r \cdot \mathbf{0} + r \cdot \mathbf{0}$. Also, $r \cdot \mathbf{0} = r \cdot \mathbf{0} + \mathbf{0}$. By part (a), the equation $r \cdot \mathbf{0} = r \cdot \mathbf{0} + \mathbf{X}$ has a unique solution. Hence $r \cdot \mathbf{0} = \mathbf{0}$. By 7.1(h),

$$0 \cdot \mathbf{U} = (0 + 0) \cdot \mathbf{U} = 0 \cdot \mathbf{U} + 0 \cdot \mathbf{U}.$$

Again using part (a), $0 \cdot \mathbf{U} = \mathbf{0}$.

(c) $r \cdot \mathbf{U} + r \cdot (-\mathbf{U}) = r \cdot [\mathbf{U} + (-\mathbf{U})] = r \cdot \mathbf{0} = \mathbf{0}$ by 7.1(e) and (i) and part (b) above. Moreover, $r \cdot \mathbf{U} + [-(r \cdot \mathbf{U})] = \mathbf{0}$. Therefore, $r \cdot (-\mathbf{U}) = -(r \cdot \mathbf{U})$ by (a). A similar argument shows that $(-r) \cdot \mathbf{U} = -(r \cdot \mathbf{U})$.

(d) Suppose that $r \cdot \mathbf{U} = \mathbf{0}$ and $r \neq 0$. Then

$$\mathbf{U} = 1 \cdot \mathbf{U} = \frac{1}{r} \cdot (r \cdot \mathbf{U}) = \frac{1}{r} \cdot \mathbf{0} = \mathbf{0}$$

by 7.1(j) and (g) and by part (b).

If $\mathcal{V}$ is a vector space, there are, in general, many subsets of $\mathcal{V}$ that are vector spaces with respect to the operations of addition and scalar multiplication defined in $\mathcal{V}$. We have already remarked in Example 2 that the set $\mathcal{S}$ of real-valued continuous functions defined on a closed interval $[a, b]$ is a vector space with respect to the operations given for the set $\mathcal{F}$ of all real-valued functions defined on $[a, b]$. As another example, consider the set $\mathcal{S}$ of vectors in $\mathcal{V}_5$ such that the third component is the sum of the first and fifth components. That is, $\mathbf{A} = \langle a_1, a_2, a_3, a_4, a_5 \rangle$ is in $\mathcal{S}$ if and only if $a_3 = a_1 + a_5$. Suppose that $\mathbf{A}$ and $\mathbf{B} = \langle b_1, b_2, b_3, b_4, b_5 \rangle$ are in $\mathcal{S}$. Then

$$\mathbf{A} + \mathbf{B} = \langle a_1 + b_1, a_2 + b_2, a_3 + b_3, a_4 + b_4, a_5 + b_5 \rangle,$$

and

$$a_3 + b_3 = (a_1 + a_5) + (b_1 + b_5) = (a_1 + b_1) + (a_5 + b_5).$$

Hence $\mathbf{A} + \mathbf{B}$ is in $\mathcal{S}$, and $\mathcal{S}$ satisfies (a) of Theorem 7.1. If r is any real number, then

$$r \cdot \mathbf{A} = \langle ra_1, ra_2, ra_3, ra_4, ra_5 \rangle$$

and

$$ra_3 = r(a_1 + a_5) = ra_1 + ra_5.$$

Thus, $r \cdot \mathbf{A}$ is in $\mathcal{S}$, so that $\mathcal{S}$ satisfies 7.1(f). Taking $r = 0$ and $r = -1$, we find that $\mathbf{0} = \langle 0, 0, 0, 0, 0\rangle$ is in $\mathcal{S}$ and $-\mathbf{A} = \langle -a_1, -a_2, -a_3, -a_4, -a_5\rangle$ is in $\mathcal{S}$. Hence, (d) and (e) of Theorem 7.1 are satisfied. The other parts of Theorem 7.1 are automatically satisfied by the vectors in $\mathcal{S}$, since they hold for all vectors in $\mathcal{V}_5$ and $\mathcal{S}$ is a subset of $\mathcal{V}_5$. Thus $\mathcal{S}$ is a vector space. These examples suggest the following definition.

(7.4) **Definition.** A nonempty subset $\mathcal{S}$ of a vector space $\mathcal{V}$ that is a vector space with respect to the operations of addition and scalar multiplication defined in $\mathcal{V}$ is called a *subspace* of $\mathcal{V}$.

(7.5) **Theorem.** Let $\mathcal{S}$ be a nonempty subset of a vector space $\mathcal{V}$ such that: (a) if $\mathbf{A}$ and $\mathbf{B}$ are in $\mathcal{S}$, then $\mathbf{A} + \mathbf{B}$ is in $\mathcal{S}$; and (b) if $\mathbf{A}$ is in $\mathcal{S}$ and r is any real number, then $r \cdot \mathbf{A}$ is in $\mathcal{S}$. Then $\mathcal{S}$ is a subspace of $\mathcal{V}$.

PROOF. Conditions (a) and (b) of the theorem are just the properties (a) and (f) of Theorem 7.1. As in the example of the subspace of $\mathcal{V}_5$ discussed above, the laws (b), (c), (g), (h), (i), and (j) of Theorem 7.1 are satisfied by the vectors in $\mathcal{S}$, since they are satisfied by all vectors in $\mathcal{V}$ and the operations in $\mathcal{S}$ are those of $\mathcal{V}$. Since $\mathcal{S}$ is nonempty, there is a vector $\mathbf{U}$ in $\mathcal{S}$. Hence $0 \cdot \mathbf{U}$ is in $\mathcal{S}$. By Theorem 7.3(b), $0 \cdot \mathbf{U} = \mathbf{0}$. Thus, the zero vector of $\mathcal{V}$ is in $\mathcal{S}$, so that 7.1(d) is satisfied. Moreover, for every vector $\mathbf{U}$ in $\mathcal{S}$, $(-1) \cdot \mathbf{U}$ is in $\mathcal{S}$. It follows from Theorem 7.3(c) that $(-1) \cdot \mathbf{U} = -(1 \cdot \mathbf{U}) = -\mathbf{U}$ is in $\mathcal{S}$. Therefore $\mathcal{S}$ satisfies 7.1(e), which completes the proof of the theorem.

We observe that the set containing only the vector $\mathbf{0}$ is a subspace of $\mathcal{V}$. This subspace is called the *zero subspace* and is denoted by $\{\mathbf{0}\}$. By Definition 7.4, a vector space $\mathcal{V}$ is a subspace of itself. If $\mathcal{S}$ is a subspace of $\mathcal{V}$ that does not contain every vector in $\mathcal{V}$, then $\mathcal{S}$ is called a *proper subspace*.

Example 5. Consider the vector space $R[x]$ of Example 1. Let $\mathcal{S}$ be the set of polynomials in $R[x]$ of degree at most k, where $k \geq 0$, including the zero polynomial (the zero polynomial has no degree and a polynomial has degree zero if and only if it is a constant polynomial $a_0 \neq 0$). Clearly, $\mathcal{S}$ is nonempty. Since the sum of two polynomials of degree at most k is either the zero polynomial or is a polynomial of degree at most k, condition (a) of Theorem 7.5 is satisfied. Also $r \cdot f(x)$, where r is a real number, is either 0 or is a polynomial with the same degree as $f(x)$. Hence, condition (b) of Theorem 7.5 is also satisfied. Therefore $\mathcal{S}$ is a subspace of $R[x]$.

Example 6. Let $\mathbf{U}$ be any nonzero vector in $\mathcal{E}_3$. Let $\mathcal{S}$ be the set of all vectors in $\mathcal{E}_3$ that are collinear with $\mathbf{U}$. Since $\mathbf{U}$ is in $\mathcal{S}$, $\mathcal{S}$ is nonempty. If $\mathbf{V}$ is any vector in $\mathcal{E}_3$ that is collinear with $\mathbf{U}$, then by Theorem 3.1, $\mathbf{V} = r \cdot \mathbf{U}$ for some real number r. Let $\mathbf{V}$ and $\mathbf{W}$ be vectors in $\mathcal{S}$. Then $\mathbf{U}$ and $\mathbf{V}$ are collinear and $\mathbf{U}$ and $\mathbf{W}$ are collinear. Thus, $\mathbf{V} = r \cdot \mathbf{U}$ and $\mathbf{W} = s \cdot \mathbf{U}$ for real numbers r and s. Hence,

$$\mathbf{V} + \mathbf{W} = r \cdot \mathbf{U} + s \cdot \mathbf{U} = (r + s) \cdot \mathbf{U}.$$

Therefore, $\mathbf{V} + \mathbf{W}$ and $\mathbf{U}$ are collinear. That is, $\mathbf{V} + \mathbf{W}$ is in $\mathcal{S}$, and Theorem 7.5(a) is satisfied. If t is any real number, then $t \cdot \mathbf{V} = t \cdot (r \cdot \mathbf{U}) = (tr) \cdot \mathbf{U}$. Thus $t \cdot \mathbf{V}$ and $\mathbf{U}$ are collinear, so that $t \cdot \mathbf{V}$ is in $\mathcal{S}$. Therefore, Theorem 7.5 (b) is satisfied, and $\mathcal{S}$ is a subspace of $\mathcal{E}_3$.

Example 7. Let π be a plane in three-dimensional space. Denote by $\mathcal{E}_\pi$ the set of all vectors in $\mathcal{E}_3$ that are in the plane π. That is, $\mathcal{E}_\pi$ consists of all geometrical vectors that are represented by directed line segments in π. If $\mathbf{U}$ and $\mathbf{W}$ are in $\mathcal{E}_\pi$, then it follows from the definitions of addition and scalar multiplication of geometrical vectors that $\mathbf{U} + \mathbf{W}$ and $r \cdot \mathbf{U}$, where r is a real number, are in $\mathcal{E}_\pi$. Therefore, by Theorem 7.5, $\mathcal{E}_\pi$ is a subspace of $\mathcal{E}_3$.

Suppose that $\langle \mathbf{I}, \mathbf{J}, \mathbf{K} \rangle$ is a rectangular Cartesian coordinate system for $\mathcal{E}_3$ such that $\mathbf{I}$ and $\mathbf{J}$ are in the plane π. Then $\langle \mathbf{I}, \mathbf{J} \rangle$ is a rectangular Cartesian coordinate system for $\mathcal{E}_\pi$. A vector $\mathbf{U} \in \mathcal{E}_\pi$ with coordinates $\langle x, y \rangle$ with respect to $\langle \mathbf{I}, \mathbf{J} \rangle$ has coordinates $\langle x, y, 0 \rangle$ with respect to $\langle \mathbf{I}, \mathbf{J}, \mathbf{K} \rangle$. Thus, $\mathcal{E}_\pi$ is the set of all vectors in $\mathcal{E}_3$ with third coordinate zero. When there is no reason to distinguish the particular plane π, we will denote the set of all vectors in a plane by $\mathcal{E}_2$.

Let S be any nonempty set of vectors contained in a vector space $\mathcal{V}$. If $\{\mathbf{U}_1, \mathbf{U}_2, \ldots, \mathbf{U}_k\}$ is a finite subset of S, then any subspace of $\mathcal{V}$ that contains the set S contains every linear combination $r_1 \cdot \mathbf{U}_1 + r_2 \cdot \mathbf{U}_2 + \cdots + r_k \cdot \mathbf{U}_k$ of the vectors $\mathbf{U}_1, \mathbf{U}_2, \ldots, \mathbf{U}_k$. On the other hand, it follows readily from Theorem 7.5, that the set of all such linear combinations of elements in S is a subspace $\mathcal{S}$ of $\mathcal{V}$ (see Exercise 7.8). Therefore, $\mathcal{S}$ is the "smallest" subspace of $\mathcal{V}$ that contains the set $\mathcal{S}$. This subspace is called the subspace of $\mathcal{V}$ *spanned* by S. In particular, the whole space $\mathcal{V}$ is spanned by a set S if every element of $\mathcal{V}$ is a linear combination of elements in S. We will be mainly interested in the situation where $S = \{\mathbf{U}_1, \mathbf{U}_2, \ldots, \mathbf{U}_n\}$ is finite. In this case, the subspace spanned by S is just the set of all linear combinations $r_1 \cdot \mathbf{U}_1 + r_2 \cdot \mathbf{U}_2 + \cdots + r_n \cdot \mathbf{U}_n$. For example, the subspace of Example 6 is spanned by the single vector $\mathbf{U}$. By Theorem 4.1, $\mathcal{E}_3$ is spanned by any three noncoplanar vectors.

Example 8. Let $\mathcal{V}$ be the vector space $R[x]$ of Example 1. Let $S = \{1, x^2, x^4, \ldots, x^{2n}, \ldots\}$ be the infinite set containing 1 and the even powers of x. The subspace $\mathcal{S}$ of $R[x]$ spanned by S is not spanned by any finite subset of S.

(7.6) Theorem. Let $\mathcal{S}$ be the subspace of a vector space spanned by $S = \{\mathbf{U}_1, \mathbf{U}_2, \ldots, \mathbf{U}_n\}$. If some $\mathbf{U}_i$ is a linear combination of the remaining vectors in S, then $\mathcal{S}$ is spanned by $\{\mathbf{U}_1, \mathbf{U}_2, \ldots, \mathbf{U}_{i-1}, \mathbf{U}_{i+1}, \ldots, \mathbf{U}_n\}$.

PROOF. Each vector $\mathbf{V}$ in $\mathcal{S}$ has the form

$$\mathbf{V} = r_1 \cdot \mathbf{U}_1 + r_2 \cdot \mathbf{U}_2 + \cdots + r_n \cdot \mathbf{U}_n.$$

Further,

$$\mathbf{U}_i = s_1 \cdot \mathbf{U}_1 + s_2 \cdot \mathbf{U}_2 + \cdots + s_{i-1} \cdot \mathbf{U}_{i-1} + s_{i+1} \cdot \mathbf{U}_{i+1} + \cdots + s_n \cdot \mathbf{U}_n.$$

Therefore,

$$\mathbf{V} = (r_1 + r_is_1) \cdot \mathbf{U}_1 + \cdots + (r_{i-1} + r_is_{i-1}) \cdot \mathbf{U}_{i-1} + (r_{i+1} + r_is_{i+1}) \cdot \mathbf{U}_{i+1} + \cdots + (r_n + r_is_n) \cdot \mathbf{U}_n.$$

Hence, $\mathcal{S}$ is spanned by $\{\mathbf{U}_1, \mathbf{U}_2, \ldots, \mathbf{U}_{i-1}, \mathbf{U}_{i+1}, \ldots, \mathbf{U}_n\}$.

(7.7) **Theorem.** Let $S = \{\mathbf{U}_1, \ldots, \mathbf{U}_m\}$ and $T = \{\mathbf{V}_1, \ldots, \mathbf{V}_n\}$ be subsets of a vector space $\mathcal{V}$. If each $\mathbf{U}_i$, $i = 1, 2, \ldots, m$, is a linear combination of the vectors in T and each $\mathbf{V}_j$, $j = 1, 2, \ldots, n$, is a linear combination of the vectors in S, then S and T span the same subspace of $\mathcal{V}$.

PROOF. Let $\mathcal{S}$ and $\mathcal{T}$ be the subspaces of $\mathcal{V}$ spanned by S and T, respectively. Every element of $\mathcal{S}$ is a linear combination of the $\mathbf{U}_i$, $i = 1, 2, \ldots, m$, and each $\mathbf{U}_i$ is a linear combination of the $\mathbf{V}_j$, $j = 1, 2, \ldots, n$. Hence, every element of $\mathcal{S}$ is a linear combination of the $\mathbf{V}_j$. Thus, $\mathcal{S} \subseteq \mathcal{T}$. A similar argument shows that $\mathcal{T} \subseteq \mathcal{S}$. Therefore, $\mathcal{S} = \mathcal{T}$.

Let $\mathcal{S}$ and $\mathcal{T}$ be subspaces of a vector space $\mathcal{V}$. Other subspaces of $\mathcal{V}$ can be obtained from these given subspaces. The ordinary set intersection, $\mathcal{S} \cap \mathcal{T}$, of $\mathcal{S}$ and $\mathcal{T}$ contains the vectors that are in both $\mathcal{S}$ and $\mathcal{T}$. The reader can easily show that $\mathcal{S} \cap \mathcal{T}$ is a subspace of $\mathcal{V}$. The subset of $\mathcal{V}$ consisting of all vectors $\mathbf{U} + \mathbf{V}$, where $\mathbf{U} \in \mathcal{S}$, $\mathbf{V} \in \mathcal{T}$, is called the *sum* of $\mathcal{S}$ and $\mathcal{T}$ and is denoted by $\mathcal{S} + \mathcal{T}$. [It is left as an exercise (Exercise 7.10) to prove that $\mathcal{S} + \mathcal{T}$ is a subspace of $\mathcal{V}$.]

If $\mathcal{V} = \mathcal{S} + \mathcal{T}$, then $\mathcal{V}$ is said to be the *sum of its subspaces* $\mathcal{S}$ *and* $\mathcal{T}$. In the particular case where $\mathcal{V} = \mathcal{S} + \mathcal{T}$ and $\mathcal{S} \cap \mathcal{T} = \{\mathbf{0}\}$, the zero subspace, $\mathcal{V}$ is called the *direct sum* of $\mathcal{S}$ *and* $\mathcal{T}$.

For example, if $\mathbf{U}$, $\mathbf{V}$, and $\mathbf{W}$ are noncoplaner vectors in $\mathcal{E}_3$, then $\mathcal{E}_3$ is the sum of the subspace $\mathcal{S}$ spanned by $\mathbf{U}$ and $\mathbf{V}$ and the subspace $\mathcal{T}$ spanned by $\mathbf{U}$ and $\mathbf{W}$, but $\mathcal{E}_3$ is not the direct sum of $\mathcal{S}$ and $\mathcal{T}$. However, $\mathcal{E}_3$ is the direct sum of the subspace $\mathcal{S}$ spanned by $\mathbf{U}$ and $\mathbf{V}$ and the subspace $\mathcal{W}$ spanned by $\mathbf{W}$.

Exercises

7.1 Show that the set $\mathcal{F}$ of functions described in Example 2 is a real vector space. Show that the subset of continuous functions is also a real vector space.

7.2 Verify that the set of all complex numbers C is a real vector space with respect to the operations of ordinary addition and multiplication of complex numbers (see Example 3). Show that the set of all real numbers R is a real vector space with respect to ordinary addition and multiplication.

7.3 Let $\mathbf{U} = \langle -3, 0, \frac{1}{2}, \sqrt{2} \rangle$. $\mathbf{V} = \langle 0, \sqrt{3}, -\frac{2}{9}, 1 \rangle$, and $\mathbf{W} = \langle 1, 1, -1, -1 \rangle$ be vectors in $\mathcal{V}_4$ (see Example 4). Compute the following vectors: (a) $2 \cdot \mathbf{U} - 3 \cdot (\mathbf{V} - \frac{1}{2} \cdot \mathbf{W})$; (b) $\sqrt{3} \cdot \mathbf{U} + \sqrt{2} \cdot \mathbf{V} + \sqrt{6} \cdot \mathbf{W}$; (c) $\mathbf{U} - \mathbf{V} - \mathbf{W}$.

7.4 For any positive integer n, show that the set of all vectors in $\mathcal{V}_n$ with first component 0 is a subspace of $\mathcal{V}_n$.

7.5 Which of the following are subspaces of $\mathcal{V}_3$: (a) all vectors with $a_2 = 6a_3$; (b) all vectors with $a_1^2 = a_1a_2a_3$; (c) all vectors with $a_2 - a_3 = a_1$; (d) all vectors with $a_1 + a_2 + a_3 = 1$.

7.6 Prove that $\mathcal{S}$ is a subspace of a vector space $\mathcal{V}$ if and only if $\mathcal{S}$ is nonempty and $r \cdot \mathbf{A} + s \cdot \mathbf{B}$ is in $\mathcal{S}$ for all $\mathbf{A}$, $\mathbf{B}$ in $\mathcal{S}$ and all real numbers r, s.

7.7 Let $\mathbf{U}$ and $\mathbf{W}$ be noncollinear vectors in $\mathcal{E}_3$. Prove that the set of all vectors in $\mathcal{E}_3$ that are coplanar with $\mathbf{U}$ and $\mathbf{W}$ form a subspace of $\mathcal{E}_3$.

***7.8** Let S be any nonempty set of vectors in a vector space $\mathcal{V}$. Prove that the set of all linear combinations of vectors in S is a subspace $\mathcal{S}$ of $\mathcal{V}$. Prove that $\mathcal{S}$ is contained in every subspace of $\mathcal{V}$ that contains the set S.

7.9 Prove the converse of Theorem 7.7.

7.10 Let $\mathcal{S}$ and $\mathcal{J}$ be subspaces of a vector space $\mathcal{V}$. Prove that $\mathcal{S} \cap \mathcal{J}$ and $\mathcal{S} + \mathcal{J}$ are subspaces of $\mathcal{V}$.

***7.11** Let $\mathcal{S}_1, \mathcal{S}_2, \ldots, \mathcal{S}_k$ be subspaces of a vector space $\mathcal{V}$. Prove that the set of all vectors $\mathbf{U}_1 + \mathbf{U}_2 + \cdots + \mathbf{U}_k$, where $\mathbf{U}_i \in \mathcal{S}_i$ for $i = 1, 2, \ldots, k$, is a subspace of $\mathcal{V}$. This subspace is denoted by $\mathcal{S}_1 + \mathcal{S}_2 + \cdots + \mathcal{S}_k$ and is called the *sum of the subspaces* $\mathcal{S}_1, \mathcal{S}_2, \ldots, \mathcal{S}_k$. If

$$\mathcal{S}_i \cap (\mathcal{S}_1 + \mathcal{S}_2 + \cdots + \mathcal{S}_{i-1} + \mathcal{S}_{i+1} + \cdots + \mathcal{S}_k) = \{\mathbf{0}\},$$

for $i = 1, 2, \ldots, k$, then $\mathcal{S}_1 + \mathcal{S}_2 + \cdots + \mathcal{S}_k$ is the *direct sum of the subspaces* $\mathcal{S}_1, \mathcal{S}_2, \ldots, \mathcal{S}_k$.

7.12 Express $\mathcal{V}_4$ as a direct sum: (a) of four nonzero subspaces; (b) of two nonzero subspaces.

7.13 Prove that the set of all vectors in $\mathcal{E}_3$ that are orthogonal to a fixed vector $\mathbf{U} \in \mathcal{E}_3$ is a subspace $\mathcal{S}$ of $\mathcal{E}_3$. Prove that $\mathcal{E}_3$ is the direct sum of $\mathcal{S}$ and the subspace spanned by $\mathbf{U}$.

8 Dimension of a vector space

In Section 6, we defined a linearly dependent set of vectors in $\mathcal{E}_3$. We now adopt essentially this same definition (6.1) for any vector space $\mathcal{V}$.

(8.1) Definition. Let S be a subset of a vector space $\mathcal{V}$. The subset S is called a *linearly dependent set* if there is a finite subset $\{\mathbf{U}_1, \mathbf{U}_2, \ldots, \mathbf{U}_k\}$ of S such that $r_1 \cdot \mathbf{U}_1 + r_2 \cdot \mathbf{U}_2 + \cdots + r_k \cdot \mathbf{U}_k = \mathbf{0}$, where at least one of the real numbers $r_1, r_2, \ldots, r_k$ is not zero.

It follows from Definition 8.1 that any subset S of $\mathcal{V}$ that contains the zero vector is a linearly dependent set. Further, if $T \supseteq S$ and S is a linearly dependent set, then T is a linearly dependent set. As in $\mathcal{E}_3$, a *linearly independent set* of vectors in $\mathcal{V}$ is defined to be a set that is not linearly dependent. Thus, S is a linearly independent set in $\mathcal{V}$ if, for every finite subset $\{\mathbf{U}_1, \mathbf{U}_2, \ldots, \mathbf{U}_k\}$ of S, $r_1 \cdot \mathbf{U}_1 + r_2 \cdot \mathbf{U}_2 + \cdots + r_k \cdot \mathbf{U}_k = \mathbf{0}$ implies that

$r_1 = r_2 = \cdots = r_k = 0$. It is clear that every subset of a linearly independent set is linearly independent.

Example 1. Let $\mathcal{V}$ be the vector space of Example 1, Section 7. Let S be the set $\{2x, x + 5, 3x - 4\}$ in $\mathcal{V} = R[x]$. Then S is linearly dependent, since

$$19(2x) + (-8)(x + 5) + (-10)(3x - 4) = 0.$$

Let T be the set $\{1, x, x^2, \ldots, x^n, \ldots\}$ consisting of all powers of x. Let $\{x^{n_1}, x^{n_2}, \ldots, x^{n_k}\}$ be any finite subset of T (where $0 \leq n_1 < n_2 < \cdots < n_k$). If

$$a_{n_k}x^{n_k} + a_{n_{k-1}}x^{n_{k-1}} + \cdots + a_{n_2}x^{n_2} + a_{n_1}x^{n_1}$$

is the zero polynomial for real numbers $a_{n_1}, a_{n_2}, \ldots, a_{n_k}$, then $a_{n_1} = a_{n_2} = \cdots = a_{n_k} = 0$. Hence T is a linearly independent set.

Example 2. In $\mathcal{V}_n$, denote the vector whose ith component is equal to 1 and all other components 0 by $\mathbf{E}_i^{(n)}$. That is, $\mathbf{E}_1^{(n)} = \langle 1, 0, 0, \ldots, 0\rangle$, $\mathbf{E}_2^{(n)} = \langle 0, 1, 0, \ldots, 0\rangle$, and so forth. Let $E^{(n)} = \{\mathbf{E}_1^{(n)}, \mathbf{E}_2^{(n)}, \ldots, \mathbf{E}_n^{(n)}\}$. If $r_1, r_2, \ldots, r_n$ are real numbers such that

$$r_1 \cdot \mathbf{E}_1^{(n)} + r_2 \cdot \mathbf{E}_2^{(n)} + \cdots + r_n \cdot \mathbf{E}_n^{(n)} = \mathbf{0},$$

then

$$\begin{aligned}\langle r_1, r_2, \ldots, r_n\rangle &= \langle r_1, 0, 0, \ldots, 0\rangle + \langle 0, r_2, 0, \ldots, 0\rangle + \cdots + \langle 0, 0, \ldots, 0, r_n\rangle \\ &= \langle 0, 0, \ldots, 0\rangle.\end{aligned}$$

This implies that $r_1 = r_2 = \cdots = r_n = 0$. Hence $E^{(n)}$ is a linearly independent set. We also note that the set $E^{(n)}$ spans $\mathcal{V}_n$. Indeed, if $\mathbf{U} = \langle a_1, a_2, \ldots, a_n\rangle$ is any vector in $\mathcal{V}_n$, then

$$\mathbf{U} = a_1 \cdot \mathbf{E}_1^{(n)} + a_2 \cdot \mathbf{E}_2^{(n)} + \cdots + a_n \cdot \mathbf{E}_n^{(n)}.$$

The following theorem gives a useful characterization of linear dependence for finite sets.

(8.2) Theorem. Let $S = \{\mathbf{U}_1, \mathbf{U}_2, \ldots, \mathbf{U}_k\}$ be a subset of a vector space $\mathcal{V}$. Then S is a linearly dependent set if and only if either $\mathbf{U}_1 = \mathbf{0}$ or some $\mathbf{U}_j$ for $j \geq 2$ is contained in the subspace of $\mathcal{V}$ spanned by $\{\mathbf{U}_1, \mathbf{U}_2, \ldots, \mathbf{U}_{j-1}\}$.

PROOF. Suppose first that S is a linearly dependent set. Assume $\mathbf{U}_1 \neq \mathbf{0}$. Then $\{\mathbf{U}_1\}$ is a linearly independent set by Theorem 7.3(d). Let j be the least positive integer such that $\{\mathbf{U}_1, \mathbf{U}_2, \ldots, \mathbf{U}_j\}$ is linearly dependent. Then $2 \leq j \leq k$. By Definition 8.1, there are real numbers $r_1, r_2, \ldots, r_j$, not all zero, such that $r_1 \cdot \mathbf{U}_1 + r_2 \cdot \mathbf{U}_2 + \cdots + r_j \cdot \mathbf{U}_j = \mathbf{0}$. Moreover, $r_j \neq 0$, since otherwise $\{\mathbf{U}_1, \mathbf{U}_2, \ldots, \mathbf{U}_{j-1}\}$ is a linearly dependent set, contrary to the choice of j. Therefore,

$$\mathbf{U}_j = \left(\frac{-r_1}{r_j}\right) \cdot \mathbf{U}_1 + \left(\frac{-r_2}{r_j}\right) \cdot \mathbf{U}_2 + \cdots + \left(\frac{-r_{j-1}}{r_j}\right) \cdot \mathbf{U}_{j-1}$$

is in the subspace spanned by $\{\mathbf{U}_1, \mathbf{U}_2, \ldots, \mathbf{U}_{j-1}\}$.

Conversely, suppose that $\mathbf{U}_1 = \mathbf{0}$, or $\mathbf{U}_j$ for some $j \geq 2$, is in the subspace spanned by $\{\mathbf{U}_1, \mathbf{U}_2, \ldots, \mathbf{U}_{j-1}\}$. If $\mathbf{U}_1 = \mathbf{0}$, then S contains the zero vector and is a linearly dependent set. If

$$\mathbf{U}_j = r_1 \cdot \mathbf{U}_1 + r_2 \cdot \mathbf{U}_2 + \cdots + r_{j-1} \cdot \mathbf{U}_{j-1},$$

then

$$r_1 \cdot \mathbf{U}_1 + r_2 \cdot \mathbf{U}_2 + \cdots + r_{j-1} \cdot \mathbf{U}_{j-1} + r_j \cdot \mathbf{U}_j = \mathbf{0},$$

with $r_j = -1 \neq 0$. Hence, $\{\mathbf{U}_1, \mathbf{U}_2, \ldots, \mathbf{U}_j\}$ is a linearly dependent set. Since $S \supseteq \{\mathbf{U}_1, \mathbf{U}_2, \ldots, \mathbf{U}_j\}$, it follows that S is linearly dependent.

By Theorem 3.2, the vector space $\mathcal{E}_2$ consisting of all vectors in a plane (see Example 7, Section 7) is spanned by any two noncollinear vectors in $\mathcal{E}_2$. Also by Theorem 6.2(c), any three vectors in $\mathcal{E}_2$ are linearly dependent. Similarly, by Theorem 4.1, $\mathcal{E}_3$ is spanned by any three noncoplanar vectors, and, by Theorem 6.2(d), any four vectors in $\mathcal{E}_3$ are linearly dependent. We will be concerned with vector spaces that are spanned by a finite number of vectors. The following theorem, which is a generalization of the results in $\mathcal{E}_2$ and $\mathcal{E}_3$ that we have just mentioned, is fundamental in the study of such vector spaces.

(8.3) Theorem. Let $\mathcal{V}$ be a vector space that is spanned by a finite set $\{\mathbf{U}_1, \mathbf{U}_2, \ldots, \mathbf{U}_k\}$ of k vectors that is linearly independent. Then any set of $k+1$ vectors in $\mathcal{V}$ is linearly dependent.

PROOF. Assume that there is some set of $k+1$ vectors $\{\mathbf{V}_1, \mathbf{V}_2, \ldots, \mathbf{V}_k, \mathbf{V}_{k+1}\}$ in $\mathcal{V}$ that is linearly independent. Since $\{\mathbf{U}_1, \mathbf{U}_2, \ldots, \mathbf{U}_k\}$ spans $\mathcal{V}$, it follows that

$$\mathbf{V}_1 = r_1 \cdot \mathbf{U}_1 + r_2 \cdot \mathbf{U}_2 + \cdots + r_k \cdot \mathbf{U}_k.$$

Hence, $\{\mathbf{V}_1, \mathbf{U}_1, \mathbf{U}_2, \ldots, \mathbf{U}_k\}$ is a linearly dependent set. Moreover, $\mathbf{V}_1 \neq \mathbf{0}$ since $\mathbf{V}_1$ is an element of a linearly independent set. By Theorem 8.2, there is some i such that $\mathbf{U}_i$ is in the subspace spanned by $\{\mathbf{V}_1, \mathbf{U}_1, \ldots, \mathbf{U}_{i-1}\}$ (here i may be equal to 1, in which case $\mathbf{U}_1$ is in the subspace spanned by $\mathbf{V}_1$). Clearly, $\{\mathbf{V}_1, \mathbf{U}_1, \ldots, \mathbf{U}_{i-1}, \mathbf{U}_i, \mathbf{U}_{i+1}, \ldots, \mathbf{U}_k\}$ spans $\mathcal{V}$. Therefore, by Theorem 7.6, $\{\mathbf{V}_1, \mathbf{U}_1, \ldots, \mathbf{U}_{i-1}, \mathbf{U}_{i+1}, \ldots, \mathbf{U}_k\}$ spans $\mathcal{V}$. Now repeating the argument above, the set $\{\mathbf{V}_1, \mathbf{V}_2, \mathbf{U}_1, \ldots, \mathbf{U}_{i-1}, \mathbf{U}_{i+1}, \ldots, \mathbf{U}_k\}$ spans $\mathcal{V}$ and is linearly dependent. Since $\{\mathbf{V}_1, \mathbf{V}_2\}$ is linearly independent, again by Theorem 8.2, it follows that some $\mathbf{U}_j$ is a linear combination of preceding vectors. By Theorem 7.6, $\{\mathbf{V}_1, \mathbf{V}_2, \mathbf{U}_1, \ldots, \mathbf{U}_{j-1}, \mathbf{U}_{j+1}, \ldots, \mathbf{U}_{i-1}, \mathbf{U}_{i+1}, \ldots, \mathbf{U}_k\}$ spans $\mathcal{V}$.

This replacement process can be continued. Each time a $\mathbf{V}$ is added, a $\mathbf{U}$ can be deleted so that the new set spans $\mathcal{V}$. After k steps, all of the $\mathbf{U}$'s have been deleted and $\{\mathbf{V}_1, \mathbf{V}_2, \ldots, \mathbf{V}_k\}$ spans $\mathcal{V}$. Then

$$\mathbf{V}_{k+1} = s_1 \cdot \mathbf{V}_1 + s_2 \cdot \mathbf{V}_2 + \cdots + s_k \cdot \mathbf{V}_k,$$

so that $\{\mathbf{V}_1, \mathbf{V}_2, \ldots, \mathbf{V}_k, \mathbf{V}_{k+1}\}$ is a linearly dependent set. But this is a contradiction, since it was assumed that this set was linearly independent. Therefore, there is no set of $k + 1$ vectors in $\mathcal{V}$ that is linearly independent. That is, every set of $k + 1$ vectors is linearly dependent.

In Section 6, we observed that any three noncoplanar vectors in $\mathcal{E}_3$ could be used for a coordinate system. The vectors in a coordinate system are linearly independent and span $\mathcal{E}_3$. Similarly, in Example 2 of this section, it was remarked that the set $\{\mathbf{E}_1^{(n)}, \mathbf{E}_2^{(n)}, \ldots, \mathbf{E}_n^{(n)}\}$ is linearly independent and spans $\mathcal{V}_n$. These are examples of the following concept.

(8.4) Definition. A linearly independent set that spans a vector space $\mathcal{V}$ is called a *basis* of $\mathcal{V}$.

Although we will not prove it here, every real vector space (except the space consisting of the zero vector alone) possesses a basis. The discussion preceding Definition 8.4 shows that each $\mathcal{V}_n$ has a basis. A basis of a vector space is the analogue of a coordinate system in $\mathcal{E}_3$, and this is the content of the following theorem.

(8.5) Theorem. The subset S of a vector space $\mathcal{V}$ is a basis of $\mathcal{V}$ if and only if each vector $\mathbf{V}$ in $\mathcal{V}$ has a unique expression as a linear combination of elements of S.

PROOF. To say that a vector $\mathbf{V}$ has a unique expression as a linear combination of elements of S amounts to two statements. First,

$$\mathbf{V} = r_1 \cdot \mathbf{U}_{i_1} + r_2 \cdot \mathbf{U}_{i_2} + \cdots + r_k \cdot \mathbf{U}_{i_k}, \tag{8-1}$$

where $\mathbf{U}_{i_1}, \mathbf{U}_{i_2}, \ldots, \mathbf{U}_{i_k}$ are distinct vectors in S. Second, if

$$\mathbf{V} = s_1 \cdot \mathbf{U}_{i_1} + s_2 \cdot \mathbf{U}_{i_2} + \cdots + s_k \cdot \mathbf{U}_{i_k} + t_1 \cdot \mathbf{U}_{i_{k+1}} + \cdots + t_l \cdot \mathbf{U}_{i_{k+l}}$$

is any other expression for $\mathbf{V}$ as a linear combination of elements of S, then $s_j = r_j$ for $j = 1, 2, \ldots, k$, and $t_i = 0$ for $i = 1, 2, \ldots, l$.

If S is a basis of $\mathcal{V}$, then S spans $\mathcal{V}$. Hence, if $\mathbf{V}$ is any vector in $\mathcal{V}$, $\mathbf{V}$ can be expressed as in (8-1). Assume that $\mathbf{V}$ has a different expression as a linear combination of elements in S. Then

$$\mathbf{V} = s_1 \cdot \mathbf{U}_{i_1} + s_2 \cdot \mathbf{U}_{i_2} + \cdots + s_k \cdot \mathbf{U}_{i_k} + t_1 \cdot \mathbf{U}_{i_{k+1}} + \cdots + t_l \cdot \mathbf{U}_{i_{k+l}}, \tag{8-2}$$

where either some $s_j \neq r_j$ or some $t_j \neq 0$. Here the vectors $\mathbf{U}_{i_{k+1}}, \ldots, \mathbf{U}_{i_{k+l}}$ are distinct vectors in S and none of them is in the set $\{\mathbf{U}_{i_1}, \mathbf{U}_{i_2}, \ldots, \mathbf{U}_{i_k}\}$. Combining equations (8-1) and (8-2), we obtain

$$(s_1 - r_1) \cdot \mathbf{U}_{i_1} + (s_2 - r_2) \cdot \mathbf{U}_{i_2} + \cdots + (s_k - r_k) \cdot \mathbf{U}_{i_k} + t_1 \cdot \mathbf{U}_{i_{k+1}} + \cdots + t_l \cdot \mathbf{U}_{i_{k+l}} = \mathbf{0}.$$

Since S is a basis of $\mathcal{V}$, S is a linearly independent set. Hence the set $\{\mathbf{U}_{i_1}, \mathbf{U}_{i_2}, \ldots, \mathbf{U}_{i_k}, \mathbf{U}_{i_{k+1}}, \ldots, \mathbf{U}_{i_{k+l}}\}$ is linearly independent. Therefore $s_j - r_j = 0$ for $j = 1, 2, \ldots, k$ and $t_j = 0$ for $j = 1, 2, \ldots, l$. This contradicts our assumption concerning the expression (8-2). Thus (8-1) is the unique expression for $\mathbf{V}$.

Conversely, if each vector in $\mathcal{V}$ has a unique expression as a linear combination of elements in S, then S spans $\mathcal{V}$. We complete the proof by showing that S is a linearly independent set. Let $\{\mathbf{U}_{i_1}, \mathbf{U}_{i_2}, \ldots, \mathbf{U}_{i_k}\}$ be any finite subset of S. Assume that

$$r_1 \cdot \mathbf{U}_{i_1} + r_2 \cdot \mathbf{U}_{i_2} + \cdots + r_k \cdot \mathbf{U}_{i_k} = \mathbf{0}.$$

In particular, the vector $\mathbf{0}$ has a unique expression as a linear combination of elements in S, and, certainly,

$$0 \cdot \mathbf{U}_{i_1} + 0 \cdot \mathbf{U}_{i_2} + \cdots + 0 \cdot \mathbf{U}_{i_k} = \mathbf{0}.$$

Therefore, $r_1 = r_2 = \cdots = r_k = 0$. This proves that S is a linearly independent set (see the discussion following Definition 8.1).

It follows from Theorem 8.3 that if a vector space $\mathcal{V}$ has a finite basis, then any basis of $\mathcal{V}$ is finite and any two bases have the same number of elements. Suppose that $\{\mathbf{U}_1, \mathbf{U}_2, \ldots, \mathbf{U}_k\}$ is a basis of $\mathcal{V}$. Then, by Theorem 8.3, any set of $k + 1$ vectors in $\mathcal{V}$ is linearly dependent. Hence, any other basis of $\mathcal{V}$ has h elements, where $h \leq k$. However, if $h < k$, then again by Theorem 8.3, any set of $(h + 1) \leq k$ vectors is linearly dependent. This is a contradiction, since $\{\mathbf{U}_1, \mathbf{U}_2, \ldots, \mathbf{U}_k\}$ is a linearly independent set. Therefore, $h = k$. In particular, every basis of $\mathcal{V}$ is finite. We are now prepared to make the following definition.

(8.6) Definition. A vector space $\mathcal{V} \neq \{\mathbf{0}\}$ is *finite dimensional* if $\mathcal{V}$ has a finite basis. The *dimension* of a finite dimensional vector space is the number of elements in a basis. The vector space $\mathcal{V} = \{\mathbf{0}\}$ is finite dimensional with dimension 0.

In Example 1 of this section, we showed that the infinite set $T = \{1, x, x^2, \ldots, x^n, \ldots\}$ in $R[x]$ is linearly independent. It is clear that each polynomial in $R[x]$ can be expressed as a linear combination of elements in T. Hence T spans $R[x]$. Therefore, T is a basis of $R[x]$. By the remarks preceding Definition 8.6, $R[x]$ cannot have a finite basis, so $R[x]$ is not a finite dimensional vector space. Since $\{\mathbf{E}_1^{(n)}, \mathbf{E}_2^{(n)}, \ldots, \mathbf{E}_n^{(n)}\}$ is a basis of $\mathcal{V}_n$, each $\mathcal{V}_n$ is finite dimensional with dimension n.

(8.7) Theorem. Let $\mathcal{V} \neq \{\mathbf{0}\}$ be a vector space spanned by a set $T = \{\mathbf{U}_1, \mathbf{U}_2, \ldots, \mathbf{U}_m\}$. Then T contains a subset that is a basis of $\mathcal{V}$. In particular, $\mathcal{V}$ is finite dimensional and has dimension $k \leq m$.

PROOF. Since T is finite and $\mathcal{V} \neq \{\mathbf{0}\}$, there exists a maximal independent set $S = \{\mathbf{U}_{i_1}, \mathbf{U}_{i_2}, \ldots, \mathbf{U}_{i_k}\}$, with $k \geq 1$, contained in T. That is, S is linearly independent, and any subset of T properly containing S is linearly dependent. If some element $\mathbf{U}_j$ of T is not in S, then $\{\mathbf{U}_j, \mathbf{U}_{i_1}, \ldots, U_{i_k}\}$ is a linearly dependent set. Thus, there are real numbers $r, r_1, r_2, \ldots, r_k$, not all zero, such that

$$r \cdot \mathbf{U}_j + r_1 \cdot \mathbf{U}_{i_1} + r_2 \cdot \mathbf{U}_{i_2} + \cdots + r_k \cdot \mathbf{U}_{i_k} = \mathbf{0}.$$

The number r is not zero, for otherwise the linear independence of $\{\mathbf{U}_{i_1}, \mathbf{U}_{i_2}, \ldots, \mathbf{U}_{i_k}\}$ is contradicted. Therefore,

$$\mathbf{U}_j = \left(\frac{-r_1}{r}\right) \cdot \mathbf{U}_{i_1} + \left(\frac{-r_2}{r}\right) \cdot \mathbf{U}_{i_2} + \cdots + \left(\frac{-r_k}{r}\right) \cdot \mathbf{U}_{i_k}.$$

Hence, every element of T can be written as a linear combination of elements of S. Since T spans $\mathcal{V}$, every element of $\mathcal{V}$ can be written as a linear combination of elements in T. Thus, every element of $\mathcal{V}$ has an expression as a linear combination of elements in S. That is, S spans $\mathcal{V}$. Since S is linearly independent, S is a basis of $\mathcal{V}$. The last statement in the theorem follows from Definition 8.6 and the fact that S is a subset of T.

(8.8) Corollary. Let $\mathcal{V}$ be a finite dimensional vector space of dimension k.
(a) Any set of k linearly independent vectors is a basis.
(b) Any set of k vectors that spans $\mathcal{V}$ is a basis.

PROOF. (a) Let $\{\mathbf{U}_1, \mathbf{U}_2, \ldots, \mathbf{U}_k\}$ be linearly independent. Since $\mathcal{V}$ has dimension k, it follows from Definition 8.6 and Theorem 8.3, that $\{\mathbf{U}, \mathbf{U}_1, \mathbf{U}_2, \ldots, \mathbf{U}_k\}$ is a linearly dependent set, where $\mathbf{U}$ is any vector in $\mathcal{V}$. By the argument used in the proof of Theorem 8.7, $\mathbf{U}$ can be expressed as a linear combination of $\mathbf{U}_1, \mathbf{U}_2, \ldots, \mathbf{U}_k$. Hence $\{\mathbf{U}_1, \mathbf{U}_2, \ldots, \mathbf{U}_k\}$ spans $\mathcal{V}$, and is therefore a basis of $\mathcal{V}$.

(b) Let $\{\mathbf{U}_1, \mathbf{U}_2, \ldots, \mathbf{U}_k\}$ span $\mathcal{V}$. By Theorem 8.7, this set contains a subset S that is a basis of $\mathcal{V}$. If S were a proper subset, then $\mathcal{V}$ would have dimension less than k. Hence $S = \{\mathbf{U}_1, \mathbf{U}_2, \ldots, \mathbf{U}_k\}$.

(8.9) Corollary. A subspace $\mathcal{S}$ is a proper subspace of a finite dimensional vector space $\mathcal{V}$ if and only if the dimension of $\mathcal{S}$ is less than that of $\mathcal{V}$.

[The proof of Corollary 8.9 is left as an exercise (Exercise 8.7).]

If $\{\mathbf{U}_1, \mathbf{U}_2, \ldots, \mathbf{U}_n\}$ is a basis of a vector space $\mathcal{V}$, then, by Theorem 8.5, every vector $\mathbf{V}$ in $\mathcal{V}$ has a unique expression

$$\mathbf{V} = r_1 \cdot \mathbf{U}_1 + r_2 \cdot \mathbf{U}_2 + \cdots + r_n \cdot \mathbf{U}_n.$$

The coefficients $r_1, r_2, \ldots, r_n$ are called the *coordinates* of $\mathbf{V}$ with respect to the basis $\{\mathbf{U}_1, \mathbf{U}_2, \ldots, \mathbf{U}_n\}$. For example, the coordinates of a vector $\mathbf{V} \in \mathcal{V}_n$ with respect to the basis $\{\mathbf{E}_1^{(n)}, \mathbf{E}_2^{(n)}, \ldots, \mathbf{E}_n^{(n)}\}$ are just the components of $\mathbf{V}$.

Exercises

8.1 Let $\mathfrak{F}$ be the vector space of all real-valued functions defined on the closed interval [0, 1]. Note that the zero vector in $\mathfrak{F}$ is the function f defined by $f(x) = 0$ for all $0 \leq x \leq 1$. Which of the following sets of functions are linearly dependent?

(a) $\{f_1(x) = 2\sin^2 x, f_2(x) = -\cos^2 x, f_3(x) = 5\}$;

(b) $\{f_1(x) = e^x, f_2(x) = xe^x, f_3(x) = x^2e^x\}$;

(c) $\{f_1(x) = \sin x, f_2(x) = \cos x\}$;

(d) $\{f_1(x) = x + 3x^2, f_2(x) = x^2, f_3(x) = 1 + x^2, f_4(x) = 2x - 3x^2\}$.

8.2 Prove that every set of $n + 1$ vectors in $\mathcal{V}_n$ is a linearly dependent set.

8.3 (a) Prove that $\{\langle 2, -\frac{1}{2}, 1\rangle, \langle 3, 2, 1\rangle, \langle 0, 1, 1\rangle\}$ is a basis of $\mathcal{V}_3$. (b) Prove that $\{\langle 1, 1, 1, 1, 1\rangle, \langle 0, 1, 1, 1, 1\rangle, \langle 0, 0, 1, 1, 1\rangle, \langle 0, 0, 0, 1, 1\rangle, \langle 0, 0, 0, 0, 1\rangle\}$ is a basis of $\mathcal{V}_5$.

8.4 Let $\mathcal{S}$ be the subspace of $R[x]$ consisting of those polynomials of degree at most k (see Example 5, Section 7). Find a basis for $\mathcal{S}$.

***8.5** Let $\mathcal{V}$ be a finite dimensional vector space of dimension n. Prove that any set of k linearly independent vectors in $\mathcal{V}$ $(k \leq n)$ is contained in a basis of $\mathcal{V}$.

***8.6** Let $\mathcal{S}$ and $\mathfrak{T}$ be subspaces of a finite dimensional space $\mathcal{V}$. (a) Prove the following relation between the dimensions of $\mathcal{S}$, $\mathfrak{T}$, $\mathcal{S} + \mathfrak{T}$, and $\mathcal{S} \cap \mathfrak{T}$:

$$\dim(\mathcal{S} + \mathfrak{T}) = \dim \mathcal{S} + \dim \mathfrak{T} - \dim(\mathcal{S} \cap \mathfrak{T}).$$

(b) Prove that $\dim(\mathcal{S} \oplus \mathfrak{T}) = \dim \mathcal{S} + \dim \mathfrak{T}$.

8.7 Prove Corollary 8.9.

9 Euclidean vector spaces

The definition of a real vector space (Definition 7.2) was obtained by abstracting the properties of addition and scalar multiplication of vectors in $\mathcal{E}_3$. The operation of inner multiplication in $\mathcal{E}_3$ can also be generalized. The first step is to list the characteristic properties of inner multiplication in $\mathcal{E}_3$.

(9.1) **Theorem.** Inner multiplication in $\mathcal{E}_3$ is a mapping from ordered pairs of vectors in $\mathcal{E}_3$ to the real numbers which satisfies the following conditions for vectors $\mathbf{U}_1, \mathbf{U}_2\ \mathbf{W}_1, \mathbf{W}_2 \in \mathcal{E}_3$ and real numbers r_1, r_2, s_1, s_2:

(a) $(r_1 \cdot \mathbf{U}_1 + r_2 \cdot \mathbf{U}_2) \circ (s_1 \cdot \mathbf{W}_1 + s_2 \cdot \mathbf{W}_2)$
$= r_1s_1(\mathbf{U}_1 \circ \mathbf{W}_1) + r_1s_2(\mathbf{U}_1 \circ \mathbf{W}_2) + r_2s_1(\mathbf{U}_2 \circ \mathbf{W}_1) + r_2s_2(\mathbf{U}_2 \circ \mathbf{W}_2)$;

(b) $\mathbf{U}_1 \circ \mathbf{U}_2 = \mathbf{U}_2 \circ \mathbf{U}_1$;

(c) $\mathbf{U}_1 \circ \mathbf{U}_1 > 0$ if $\mathbf{U}_1 \neq \mathbf{0}$, and $\mathbf{0} \circ \mathbf{0} = 0$.

Conditions (a), (b), and (c) of Theorem 9.1 follow from the discussion of the properties of inner multiplication in Chapter One. The identity (a) is called a *bilinearity condition*, that is, the inner product $\mathbf{U}_1 \circ \mathbf{U}_2$ is linear in each argument. By (b), inner multiplication is *symmetric*, and, by (c), it is *positive definite.*

(9.2) Definition. Let $\mathcal{V}$ be a finite dimensional vector space. Let $\mathcal{G}$ be a mapping from ordered pairs of vectors in $\mathcal{V}$ to the real numbers which satisfies the following conditions for vectors $\mathbf{U}_1, \mathbf{U}_2, \mathbf{W}_1, \mathbf{W}_2 \in \mathcal{V}$ and real numbers r_1, r_2, s_1, s_2:

(a) $\mathcal{G}(r_1 \cdot \mathbf{U}_1 + r_2 \cdot \mathbf{U}_2, s_1 \cdot \mathbf{W}_1 + s_2 \cdot \mathbf{W}_2)$
$= r_1s_1\mathcal{G}(\mathbf{U}_1, \mathbf{W}_1) + r_1s_2\mathcal{G}(\mathbf{U}_1, \mathbf{W}_2) + r_2s_1\mathcal{G}(\mathbf{U}_2, \mathbf{W}_1) + r_2s_2\mathcal{G}(\mathbf{U}_2, \mathbf{W}_2)$;

(b) $\mathcal{G}(\mathbf{U}_1, \mathbf{U}_2) = \mathcal{G}(\mathbf{U}_2, \mathbf{U}_1)$;

(c) $\mathcal{G}(\mathbf{U}_1, \mathbf{U}_1) > 0$ if $\mathbf{U}_1 \neq \mathbf{0}$, $\mathcal{G}(\mathbf{0}, \mathbf{0}) = 0$.

Then $\mathcal{G}(\mathbf{U}_1, \mathbf{U}_2)$ is called an *inner product* of $\mathbf{U}_1$ and $\mathbf{U}_2$, and the space $\mathcal{V}$ equipped with such an inner product is called a *Euclidean vector space.*

Thus, for vectors $\mathbf{U}_1, \mathbf{U}_2 \in \mathcal{V}$, $\mathcal{G}(\mathbf{U}_1, \mathbf{U}_2)$ is a real number, and the mapping $\mathcal{G}$ is bilinear, symmetric, and positive definite. It follows from condition (a) that

$$\mathcal{G}(\mathbf{U}_1 + \mathbf{U}_2, \mathbf{W}_1) = \mathcal{G}(\mathbf{U}_1, \mathbf{W}_1) + \mathcal{G}(\mathbf{U}_2, \mathbf{W}_1),$$

$$\mathcal{G}(\mathbf{U}_1, \mathbf{W}_1 + \mathbf{W}_2) = \mathcal{G}(\mathbf{U}_1, \mathbf{W}_1) + \mathcal{G}(\mathbf{U}_1, \mathbf{W}_2),$$

and

$$\mathcal{G}(r_1 \cdot \mathbf{U}_1, s_1 \cdot \mathbf{W}_1) = r_1s_1\mathcal{G}(\mathbf{U}_1, \mathbf{W}_1).$$

Example 1. An inner product can be defined for any finite dimensional vector space $\mathcal{V}$. Let $B = \{\mathbf{U}_1, \mathbf{U}_2, \ldots, \mathbf{U}_n\}$ be a basis of $\mathcal{V}$, and let

$$\mathbf{U} = r_1 \cdot \mathbf{U}_1 + r_2 \cdot \mathbf{U}_2 + \cdots + r_n \cdot \mathbf{U}_n$$

$$\mathbf{W} = s_1 \cdot \mathbf{U}_1 + s_2 \cdot \mathbf{U}_2 + \cdots + s_n \cdot \mathbf{U}_n$$

be any vectors in $\mathcal{V}$. Define

$$\mathcal{G}(\mathbf{U}, \mathbf{W}) = r_1s_1 + r_2s_2 + \cdots + r_ns_n.$$

Then conditions (a), (b), and (c) of Definition 9.2 can easily be verified (see Exercise 9.1). We call this inner product the B-inner product of $\mathcal{V}$. In particular, if $\mathcal{V} = \mathcal{V}_n$ and $\mathbf{U} = \langle a_1, a_2, \ldots, a_n\rangle$, $\mathbf{W} = \langle b_1, b_2, \ldots, b_n\rangle$ are vectors in $\mathcal{V}_n$, then $\mathcal{G}(\mathbf{U}, \mathbf{W}) = a_1b_1 + a_2b_2 + \cdots + a_nb_n$ is the $E^{(n)}$-inner product in $\mathcal{V}_n$.

In Example 1, the value of the B-inner product of two vectors in $\mathcal{V}$ depends upon the choice of the basis B. Thus, it is evident that different inner products can be defined on the same space $\mathcal{V}$. When we refer to a Euclidean vector space, we will assume that a particular mapping $\mathcal{G}$ satisfying Definition 9.2 is given and is fixed throughout the discussion.

The result 2.9 suggests that, in a Euclidean vector space $\mathcal{V}$, we define the *length* of a vector $\mathbf{U}$ to be $|\mathbf{U}| = [\mathcal{G}(\mathbf{U}, \mathbf{U})]^{1/2}$. A vector $\mathbf{U}$ is a *unit vector* if $|\mathbf{U}| = 1$. We note that

$$|r \cdot \mathbf{U}| = [\mathcal{G}(r \cdot \mathbf{U}, r \cdot \mathbf{U})]^{1/2} = [r^2\mathcal{G}(\mathbf{U}, \mathbf{U})]^{1/2} = |r|[\mathcal{G}(\mathbf{U}, \mathbf{U})]^{1/2} = |r|\,|\mathbf{U}|.$$

Thus if $\mathbf{U}$ is any nonzero vector in $\mathcal{V}$, then $(1/|\mathbf{U}|) \cdot \mathbf{U}$ is a unit vector.

Following 2.10, the vectors $\mathbf{U}_1$ and $\mathbf{U}_2$ in $\mathcal{V}$ are defined to be *orthogonal* if $\mathcal{g}(\mathbf{U}_1, \mathbf{U}_2) = 0$. Since

$$\mathcal{g}(\mathbf{0}, \mathbf{U}) = \mathcal{g}(\mathbf{0} + \mathbf{0}, \mathbf{U}) = \mathcal{g}(\mathbf{0}, \mathbf{U}) + \mathcal{g}(\mathbf{0}, \mathbf{U}),$$

it follows that $\mathbf{0}$ and any vector $\mathbf{U}$ are orthogonal. Further, $\mathcal{g}(r \cdot \mathbf{U}, s \cdot \mathbf{W}) = rs\mathcal{g}(\mathbf{U}, \mathbf{W})$ implies that if $r \neq 0$, $s \neq 0$ then $\mathbf{U}$ and $\mathbf{W}$ are orthogonal if and only if $r \cdot \mathbf{U}$ and $s \cdot \mathbf{W}$ are orthogonal.

In Example 1, the basis $B = \{\mathbf{U}_1, \mathbf{U}_2, \ldots, \mathbf{U}_n\}$ has the property that $|\mathbf{U}_i| = 1$ for $i = 1, 2, \ldots, n$ and $\mathcal{g}(\mathbf{U}_i, \mathbf{U}_j) = 0$ for all i, j with $i \neq j$. This suggests the following definition.

(**9.3**) **Definition.** Let $\mathcal{V}$ be a Euclidean vector space with inner product $\mathcal{g}$. A basis $\{\mathbf{U}_1, \mathbf{U}_2, \ldots, \mathbf{U}_n\}$ of $\mathcal{V}$ such that $|\mathbf{U}_i| = 1$ for $i = 1, 2, \ldots, n$ and $\mathcal{g}(\mathbf{U}_i, \mathbf{U}_j) = 0$ for all i, j with $i \neq j$ is called an *orthonormal basis* of $\mathcal{V}$.

In order to prove that each subspace of a Euclidean vector space has an orthonormal basis, we need the following preliminary results.

(**9.4**) **Theorem.** If the nonzero vectors $\mathbf{U}_1, \mathbf{U}_2, \ldots, \mathbf{U}_k$ in a Euclidean vector space $\mathcal{V}$ are mutually orthogonal, then they are linearly independent.

PROOF. Assume there is a relation

$$r_1 \cdot \mathbf{U}_1 + r_2 \cdot \mathbf{U}_2 + \cdots + r_k \cdot \mathbf{U}_k = \mathbf{0}.$$

Then for each $i = 1, 2, \ldots, k$,

$$\begin{aligned} 0 = \mathcal{g}(\mathbf{U}_i, \mathbf{0}) &= \mathcal{g}(\mathbf{U}_i, r_1 \cdot \mathbf{U}_1 + r_2 \cdot \mathbf{U}_2 + \cdots + r_k \cdot \mathbf{U}_k) \\ &= r_1\mathcal{g}(\mathbf{U}_i, \mathbf{U}_1) + r_2\mathcal{g}(\mathbf{U}_i, \mathbf{U}_2) + \cdots + r_k\mathcal{g}(\mathbf{U}_i, \mathbf{U}_k) \\ &= r_i\mathcal{g}(\mathbf{U}_i, \mathbf{U}_i), \end{aligned}$$

since $\mathcal{g}(\mathbf{U}_i, \mathbf{U}_j) = 0$ if $i \neq j$. By (c) of Definition 9.2, $\mathcal{g}(\mathbf{U}_i, \mathbf{U}_i) \neq 0$. Hence $r_i = 0$ for $i = 1, 2, \ldots, k$. Therefore $\{\mathbf{U}_1, \mathbf{U}_2, \ldots, \mathbf{U}_k\}$ is a linearly independent set.

(**9.5**) **Theorem.** If $\{\mathbf{U}_1, \mathbf{U}_2, \ldots, \mathbf{U}_k\}$ is a linearly independent set of vectors in a Euclidean vector space $\mathcal{V}$, then the subspace $\mathcal{S}$ of $\mathcal{V}$ spanned by $\{\mathbf{U}_1, \mathbf{U}_2, \ldots, \mathbf{U}_k\}$ has an orthonormal basis.

PROOF. If $k = 1$, let $\mathbf{V}_1 = (1/|\mathbf{U}_1|) \cdot \mathbf{U}_1$. Then $\mathbf{V}_1$ is an orthonormal basis of the subspace spanned by $\{\mathbf{U}_1\}$. Assume that the statement of the theorem is true for any linearly independent set of $k - 1$ vectors ($k > 1$). Let $\{\mathbf{V}_1, \mathbf{V}_2, \ldots, \mathbf{V}_{k-1}\}$ be an orthonormal basis of the subspace of $\mathcal{V}$ spanned by $\{\mathbf{U}_1, \mathbf{U}_2, \ldots, \mathbf{U}_{k-1}\}$. Define

$$\mathbf{V}_k^* = \mathbf{U}_k - \mathcal{g}(\mathbf{U}_k, \mathbf{V}_1) \cdot \mathbf{V}_1 - \mathcal{g}(\mathbf{U}_k, \mathbf{V}_2) \cdot \mathbf{V}_2 - \cdots - \mathcal{g}(\mathbf{U}_k, \mathbf{V}_{k-1}) \cdot \mathbf{V}_{k-1}.$$

Then $\mathbf{V}_k^* \neq \mathbf{0}$, for otherwise $\mathbf{U}_k$ is in the subspace spanned by $\{\mathbf{U}_1, \mathbf{U}_2, \ldots, \mathbf{U}_{k-1}\}$, contradicting the linear independence of $\{\mathbf{U}_1, \mathbf{U}_2, \ldots, \mathbf{U}_{k-1}, \mathbf{U}_k\}$. Moreover,

$$\begin{aligned}
&\mathcal{G}(\mathbf{V}_k^*, \mathbf{V}_i) \\
&= \mathcal{G}(\mathbf{U}_k - \mathcal{G}(\mathbf{U}_k, \mathbf{V}_1)\cdot \mathbf{V}_1 - \mathcal{G}(\mathbf{U}_k, \mathbf{V}_2)\cdot \mathbf{V}_2 - \cdots - \mathcal{G}(\mathbf{U}_k, \mathbf{V}_{k-1})\cdot \mathbf{V}_{k-1}, \mathbf{V}_i) \\
&= \mathcal{G}(\mathbf{U}_k, \mathbf{V}_i) - \mathcal{G}(\mathbf{U}_k, \mathbf{V}_i)\mathcal{G}(\mathbf{V}_i, \mathbf{V}_i) \\
&= \mathcal{G}(\mathbf{U}_k, \mathbf{V}_i) - \mathcal{G}(\mathbf{U}_k, \mathbf{V}_i) = 0,
\end{aligned}$$

for $i = 1, 2, \ldots, k-1$, since $\{\mathbf{V}_1, \mathbf{V}_2, \ldots, \mathbf{V}_{k-1}\}$ is an orthonormal basis. Therefore, $\mathbf{V}_k^*$ is orthogonal to $\mathbf{V}_i$ for $i = 1, 2, \ldots, k-1$, and the vectors $\mathbf{V}_1, \mathbf{V}_2, \ldots, \mathbf{V}_{k-1}, \mathbf{V}_k^*$ are mutually orthogonal.

By Theorem 9.4, $\{\mathbf{V}_1, \mathbf{V}_2, \ldots, \mathbf{V}_{k-1}, \mathbf{V}_k^*\}$ is a linearly independent set contained in the subspace $\mathcal{S}$ of $\mathcal{V}$ spanned by $\{\mathbf{U}_1, \mathbf{U}_2, \ldots, \mathbf{U}_k\}$. By Corollary 8.8, $\{\mathbf{V}_1, \mathbf{V}_2, \ldots, \mathbf{V}_{k-1}, \mathbf{V}_k^*\}$ is a basis of $\mathcal{S}$. Replacing $\mathbf{V}_k^*$ by the unit vector $\mathbf{V}_k = (1/|\mathbf{V}_k^*|)\cdot \mathbf{V}_k^*$, the set $\{\mathbf{V}_1, \mathbf{V}_2, \ldots, \mathbf{V}_{k-1}, \mathbf{V}_k\}$ is an orthonormal basis of $\mathcal{S}$. This completes the induction and the proof of the theorem.

(9.6) Theorem. Each subspace $\mathcal{S} \neq \{\mathbf{0}\}$ of a Euclidean vector space $\mathcal{V}$ has an orthonormal basis. If $\{\mathbf{V}_1, \mathbf{V}_2, \ldots, \mathbf{V}_k\}$ is an orthonormal basis of $\mathcal{S}$ and

$$\mathbf{U} = a_1\cdot \mathbf{V}_1 + a_2\cdot \mathbf{V}_2 + \cdots + a_k\cdot \mathbf{V}_k$$

$$\mathbf{W} = b_1\cdot \mathbf{V}_1 + b_2\cdot \mathbf{V}_2 + \cdots + b_k\cdot \mathbf{V}_k,$$

then $\mathcal{G}(\mathbf{U}, \mathbf{W}) = a_1b_1 + a_2b_2 + \cdots + a_kb_k$.

PROOF. If $\mathcal{V}$ has dimension n, then by Theorem 8.7, $\mathcal{S}$ has a basis of k vectors for some $k \leq n$. By Theorem 9.5, $\mathcal{S}$ has an orthonormal basis $\{\mathbf{V}_1, \mathbf{V}_2, \ldots, \mathbf{V}_k\}$. Suppose

$$\mathbf{U} = a_1\cdot \mathbf{V}_1 + a_2\cdot \mathbf{V}_2 + \cdots + a_k\cdot \mathbf{V}_k$$

and

$$\mathbf{W} = b_1\cdot \mathbf{V}_1 + b_2\cdot \mathbf{V}_2 + \cdots + b_k\cdot \mathbf{V}_k.$$

Then by Definition 9.2(a),

$$\begin{aligned}
\mathcal{G}(\mathbf{U}, \mathbf{W}) &= a_1b_1\mathcal{G}(\mathbf{V}_1, \mathbf{V}_1) + a_1b_2\mathcal{G}(\mathbf{V}_1, \mathbf{V}_2) + \cdots + a_1b_k\mathcal{G}(\mathbf{V}_1, \mathbf{V}_k) \\
&\quad + a_2b_1\mathcal{G}(\mathbf{V}_2, \mathbf{V}_1) + a_2b_2\mathcal{G}(\mathbf{V}_2, \mathbf{V}_2) + \cdots + a_2b_k\mathcal{G}(\mathbf{V}_2, \mathbf{V}_k) \\
&\quad + \cdots + a_kb_1\mathcal{G}(\mathbf{V}_k, \mathbf{V}_1) + a_kb_2\mathcal{G}(\mathbf{V}_k, \mathbf{V}_2) \\
&\quad + \cdots + a_kb_k\mathcal{G}(\mathbf{V}_k, \mathbf{V}_k) \\
&= a_1b_1 + a_2b_2 + \cdots + a_kb_k.
\end{aligned}$$

The method of the proof of Theorem 9.5, which is called the Gram-Schmidt orthogonalization process, gives a procedure for constructing an orthonormal basis of a subspace of a Euclidean vector space. In practice, it is convenient to modify the method by first obtaining a basis of mutually orthogonal vectors, and then replacing these vectors by unit vectors.

Example 2. Let $\mathcal{S}$ be the subspace of $\mathcal{V}_5$ spanned by $\mathbf{U}_1 = \langle 0, 1, 3, 0, 4\rangle$, $\mathbf{U}_2 = \langle 1, -2, 0, 1, 6\rangle$, and $\mathbf{U}_3 = \langle 0, 0, 0, 1, 1\rangle$. These vectors are linearly independent, so that $\{\mathbf{U}_1, \mathbf{U}_2, \mathbf{U}_3\}$ is a basis of $\mathcal{S}$. The inner product in $\mathcal{V}_5$ is the one defined in Example 1. Let $\mathbf{V}_1^* = \mathbf{U}_1$. Define

$$\begin{aligned}\mathbf{V}_2^* &= \mathbf{U}_2 - \left(\frac{\mathcal{I}(\mathbf{U}_2, \mathbf{V}_1^*)}{\mathcal{I}(\mathbf{V}_1^*, \mathbf{V}_1^*)}\right)\cdot \mathbf{V}_1^*\\ &= \langle 1, -2, 0, 1, 6\rangle - \left(\frac{11}{13}\right)\cdot\langle 0, 1, 3, 0, 4\rangle\\ &= \left\langle 1, -\frac{37}{13}, -\frac{33}{13}, 1, \frac{34}{13}\right\rangle.\end{aligned}$$

Then $\mathcal{I}(\mathbf{V}_1^*, \mathbf{V}_2^*) = 0$. Define

$$\begin{aligned}\mathbf{V}_3^* &= \mathbf{U}_3 - \left(\frac{\mathcal{I}(\mathbf{U}_3, \mathbf{V}_1^*)}{\mathcal{I}(\mathbf{V}_1^*, \mathbf{V}_1^*)}\right)\cdot \mathbf{V}_1^* - \left(\frac{\mathcal{I}(\mathbf{U}_3, \mathbf{V}_2^*)}{\mathcal{I}(\mathbf{V}_2^*, \mathbf{V}_2^*)}\right)\cdot \mathbf{V}_2^*\\ &= \langle 0, 0, 0, 1, 1\rangle - \left(\frac{2}{13}\right)\cdot\langle 0, 1, 3, 0, 4\rangle - \left(\frac{47}{304}\right)\cdot\left\langle 1, -\frac{37}{13}, -\frac{33}{13}, 1, \frac{34}{13}\right\rangle\\ &= \left(\frac{1}{3952}\right)\cdot\langle -611, 1131, -273, 3341, -78\rangle.\end{aligned}$$

The vectors $\mathbf{V}_1^*, \mathbf{V}_2^*, \mathbf{V}_3^*$ are mutually orthogonal. Therefore,

$$\left(\frac{1}{|\mathbf{V}_1^*|}\right)\cdot \mathbf{V}_1^* = \left(\frac{1}{\sqrt{26}}\right)\cdot\langle 0, 1, 3, 0, 4\rangle,$$

$$\left(\frac{1}{|\mathbf{V}_2^*|}\right)\cdot \mathbf{V}_2^* = \left(\frac{1}{4\sqrt{247}}\right)\cdot\langle 13, -37, -33, 13, 34\rangle,$$

and

$$\left(\frac{1}{|\mathbf{V}_3^*|}\right)\cdot \mathbf{V}_3^* = \left(\frac{1}{52\sqrt{4769}}\right)\cdot\langle -611, 1131, -273, 3341, -78\rangle$$

is an orthonormal basis of $\mathcal{S}$.

Exercises

9.1 Prove that the B-inner product in $\mathcal{V}$, defined in Example 1, satisfies conditions (a), (b), and (c) of Definition 9.2.

***9.2** Let $S = \{\mathbf{U}_1, \mathbf{U}_2, \ldots, \mathbf{U}_k\}$ be any set of vectors in a Euclidean vector space $\mathcal{V}$. Prove that the set of all vectors in $\mathcal{V}$ that are orthogonal to every vector in S is a subspace $\mathfrak{J}$ of $\mathcal{V}$. Prove that every vector in $\mathfrak{J}$ is orthogonal to every vector in the subspace $\mathcal{S}$ of $\mathcal{V}$ that is spanned by S.

***9.3** Let $\mathcal{S}$ be a subspace of a Euclidean vector space $\mathcal{V}$. Let $\mathfrak{J}$ be the subspace of all vectors in $\mathcal{V}$ that are orthogonal to every vector in $\mathcal{S}$ (see Exercise 9.2). Prove that $\mathbf{V} = \mathcal{S} \oplus \mathfrak{J}$. $\mathfrak{J}$ is called the *orthogonal complement* of $\mathcal{S}$.

***9.4** Prove that the following inequalities hold in a Euclidean vector space:

(a) $[\mathcal{I}(\mathbf{U}, \mathbf{V})]^2 \leq |\mathbf{U}|^2 |\mathbf{V}|^2$ (the Schwarz inequality);

(b) $|\mathbf{U} + \mathbf{V}| \leq |\mathbf{U}| + |\mathbf{V}|$ (the triangle inequality).

9.5 Construct an orthonormal basis for the subspace of $\mathcal{V}_4$ spanned by each of the following sets of vectors:

(a) $\{\langle 3, -5, 2, 1\rangle\}$;

(b) $\{\langle \frac{1}{2}, 3, 0, 2\rangle, \langle 1, -\frac{1}{2}, 3, 1\rangle\}$;

(c) $\{\langle 1, 0, 1, 1\rangle, \langle 0, 2, 1, -1\rangle, \langle 2, 1, -1, 0\rangle\}$.

CHAPTER THREE

Systems of Linear Equations

10 Elementary transformations

We observed in Section 6 that the problem of deciding when sets of vectors in $\mathcal{E}_3$ are linearly dependent leads to the consideration of systems of linear equations. Similarly, in $\mathcal{V}_n$, the vectors

$$\mathbf{U}_1 = \langle a_{1,1}, a_{2,1}, \ldots, a_{n,1}\rangle, \qquad \mathbf{U}_2 = \langle a_{1,2}, a_{2,2}, \ldots, a_{n,2}\rangle, \quad \ldots, \quad \mathbf{U}_m = \langle a_{1,m}, a_{2,m}, \ldots, a_{n,m}\rangle$$

form a linearly dependent set if and only if there exist real numbers x_1, x_2, $\ldots$, x_m, not all zero, such that

$$x_1 \cdot \langle a_{1,1}, a_{2,1}, \ldots, a_{n,1}\rangle + x_2 \cdot \langle a_{1,2}, a_{2,2}, \ldots, a_{n,2}\rangle + \cdots + x_m \cdot \langle a_{1,m}, a_{2,m}, \ldots, a_{n,m}\rangle = \langle 0, 0, \ldots, 0\rangle.$$

That is, $\{\mathbf{U}_1, \mathbf{U}_2, \ldots, \mathbf{U}_m\}$ is a linearly dependent set if and only if the system of linear equations

$$\begin{aligned} a_{1,1}x_1 + a_{1,2}x_2 + \cdots + a_{1,m}x_m &= 0 \\ a_{2,1}x_1 + a_{2,2}x_2 + \cdots + a_{2,m}x_m &= 0 \\ &\cdots \\ a_{n,1}x_1 + a_{n,2}x_2 + \cdots + a_{n,m}x_m &= 0 \end{aligned}$$

has a solution other than $x_1 = x_2 = \cdots = x_m = 0$.

Let $\mathbf{V} = \langle b_1, b_2, \ldots, b_n\rangle$ be a given vector in $\mathcal{V}_n$. Then $\mathbf{V}$ is in the subspace of $\mathcal{V}_n$ spanned by $\{\mathbf{U}_1, \mathbf{U}_2, \ldots, \mathbf{U}_m\}$ if and only if there exist real numbers $x_1, x_2, \ldots, x_m$ such that

$$x_1 \cdot \langle a_{1,1}, a_{2,1}, \ldots, a_{n,1}\rangle + x_2 \cdot \langle a_{1,2}, a_{2,2}, \ldots, a_{n,2}\rangle + \cdots + x_m \cdot \langle a_{1,m}, a_{2,m}, \ldots, a_{n,m}\rangle = \langle b_1, b_2, \ldots, b_n\rangle.$$

This latter condition is equivalent to the existence of a solution of the system of linear equations

$$\begin{aligned} a_{1,1}x_1 + a_{1,2}x_2 + \cdots + a_{1,m}x_m &= b_1 \\ a_{2,1}x_1 + a_{2,2}x_2 + \cdots + a_{2,m}x_m &= b_2 \\ &\cdots \\ a_{n,1}x_1 + a_{n,2}x_2 + \cdots + a_{n,m}x_m &= b_n. \end{aligned} \qquad (10\text{-}1)$$

The problem of solving such systems of n linear equations in m unknowns is not confined to the study of vector spaces. It is a problem that occurs in many branches and applications of mathematics.

The real numbers $a_{i,j}$ and b_i in equations (10-1) are called the *coefficients* of the equations. The system (10-1) is *consistent* if there exist real numbers $x_1, x_2, \ldots, x_m$ that satisfy the equations. Such a set of real numbers is called a *solution* of the system. If the system has no solutions, it is *inconsistent*. A complete analysis of a system of linear equations includes giving criteria for consistency and, when the system is consistent, describing a systematic method for finding all solutions.

(10.1) Definition. Let

$$\begin{aligned} a_{1,1}x_1 + a_{1,2}x_2 + \cdots + a_{1,m}x_m &= b_1 \\ a_{2,1}x_1 + a_{2,2}x_2 + \cdots + a_{2,m}x_m &= b_2 \\ &\cdots \\ a_{n,1}x_1 + a_{n,2}x_2 + \cdots + a_{n,m}x_m &= b_n \end{aligned}$$

and

$$\begin{aligned} d_{1,1}x_1 + d_{1,2}x_2 + \cdots + d_{1,m}x_m &= e_1 \\ d_{2,1}x_1 + d_{2,2}x_2 + \cdots + d_{2,m}x_m &= e_2 \\ &\cdots \\ d_{p,1}x_1 + d_{p,2}x_2 + \cdots + d_{p,m}x_m &= e_p \end{aligned}$$

be systems of n and p linear equations in m unknowns with real coefficients. The systems are *equivalent* if every solution of the first system is a solution of the second system, and vice versa.

For example, the system

$$\begin{aligned} 3x_1 - 2x_2 + x_3 &= -6 \\ 2x_1 + 5x_2 - x_3 &= 0 \\ 7x_1 - \tfrac{3}{2}x_2 + \tfrac{3}{2}x_3 &= -12 \end{aligned} \qquad (10\text{-}2)$$

is equivalent to the system

$$\begin{aligned} 3x_1 - 2x_2 + x_3 &= -6 \\ 2x_1 + 5x_2 - x_3 &= 0, \end{aligned} \tag{10-3}$$

since it can be shown that every set of three real numbers that satisfies the first two equations of (10-2) satisfies the third equation as well.

Our method for analyzing the system of equations (10-1) consists of replacing the given system by a new equivalent system whose consistency can be determined by inspection; and when it is consistent, all solutions can be easily computed. The first step in this process is to describe certain elementary operations on the equations that can be defined in terms of operations on a set of vectors in a real vector space.

Let $\langle \mathbf{U}_1, \mathbf{U}_2, \ldots, \mathbf{U}_n \rangle$ be an ordered n-tuple of vectors in a vector space $\mathcal{V}$. The three *elementary transformations* on the given set of vectors are described as follows:

Type I. Replace $\langle \mathbf{U}_1, \mathbf{U}_2, \ldots, \mathbf{U}_i, \ldots, \mathbf{U}_j, \ldots, \mathbf{U}_n \rangle$ by $\langle \mathbf{U}_1, \mathbf{U}_2, \ldots, \mathbf{U}_j, \ldots, \mathbf{U}_i, \ldots, \mathbf{U}_n \rangle$, where $1 \leq i < j \leq n$. That is, two of the vectors are interchanged in the given n-tuple.

Type II. Replace $\langle \mathbf{U}_1, \mathbf{U}_2, \ldots, \mathbf{U}_i, \ldots, \mathbf{U}_j, \ldots, \mathbf{U}_n \rangle$ by $\langle \mathbf{U}_1, \mathbf{U}_2, \ldots, \mathbf{U}_i, \ldots, c \cdot \mathbf{U}_i + \mathbf{U}_j, \ldots, \mathbf{U}_n \rangle$, where $i \neq j$ and c is a real number. Here, the vector $\mathbf{U}_j$ is replaced by the vector $c \cdot \mathbf{U}_i + \mathbf{U}_j$, with $i \neq j$.

Type III. Replace $\langle \mathbf{U}_1, \mathbf{U}_2, \ldots, \mathbf{U}_i, \ldots, \mathbf{U}_n \rangle$ by $\langle \mathbf{U}_1, \mathbf{U}_2, \ldots, c \cdot \mathbf{U}_i, \ldots, \mathbf{U}_n \rangle$, where c is a nonzero real number. Thus, a vector $\mathbf{U}_i$ is replaced by its scalar multiple $c \cdot \mathbf{U}_i$, where c is a nonzero real number.

Note that in each case every vector of the new n-tuple is a linear combination of the vectors in the original n-tuple. Moreover, it is easy to see that each of the original vectors is a linear combination of the vectors in the new n-tuple. This is obvious for an elementary transformation of Type I. For a Type II transformation, it is sufficient to show that $\mathbf{U}_j$ is a linear combination of the vectors $\mathbf{U}_1, \mathbf{U}_2, \ldots, \mathbf{U}_i, \ldots, c \cdot \mathbf{U}_i + \mathbf{U}_j, \ldots, \mathbf{U}_n$. This is indeed the case, since $\mathbf{U}_j = (-c) \cdot \mathbf{U}_i + 1 \cdot (c \cdot \mathbf{U}_i + \mathbf{U}_j)$. For Type III transformations, since $\mathbf{U}_i = (1/c) \cdot (c \cdot \mathbf{U}_i)$, $c \neq 0$, each vector in the original n-tuple is a linear combination of the new set of vectors obtained by a Type III elementary transformation. Thus, by Theorem 7.7, a given set of n vectors S in a vector space $\mathcal{V}$ spans the same subspace of $\mathcal{V}$ as the set T of vectors obtained from S by an elementary transformation. The following theorem is an immediate consequence of this result.

(10.2) Theorem. Let S be an ordered set of n vectors in a vector space $\mathcal{V}$, and let T be a set of vectors obtained from S by means of a sequence of elementary transformations. That is, there are ordered sets of vectors S_0, $S_1, \ldots, S_t$ such that S_0 is S and S_t is T, and for each k $(0 < k \leq t)$, the set S_k is obtained from the set S_{k-1} by an elementary transformation. Then the sets S and T span the same subspace of $\mathcal{V}$.

The system of linear equations (10-1) determines a subspace of the vector space $\mathcal{V}_{m+1}$ spanned by the vectors

$$\mathbf{U}_1 = \langle a_{1,1}, a_{1,2}, \ldots, a_{1,m}, b_1\rangle, \qquad \mathbf{U}_2 = \langle a_{2,1}, a_{2,2}, \ldots, a_{2,m}, b_2\rangle, \quad \ldots,$$
$$\mathbf{U}_n = \langle a_{n,1}, a_{n,2}, \ldots, a_{n,m}, b_n\rangle.$$

This subspace of $\mathcal{V}_{m+1}$ is called the *row space* of the system. For example, the row space of the system (10-2) is the subspace of $\mathcal{V}_4$ spanned by $\langle 3, -2, 1, -6\rangle$, $\langle 2, 5, -1, 0\rangle$, and $\langle 7, -\frac{3}{2}, \frac{3}{2}, -12\rangle$.

Suppose that a sequence of elementary transformations is performed on the vectors $\langle \mathbf{U}_1, \mathbf{U}_2, \ldots, \mathbf{U}_n\rangle$ spanning the row space of (10-1), yielding a new set $\langle \mathbf{U}_1^*, \mathbf{U}_2^*, \ldots, \mathbf{U}_n^*\rangle$, where $\mathbf{U}_i^* = \langle a_{i,1}^*, a_{i,2}^*, \ldots, a_{i,n}^*, b_i^*\rangle$, for $i = 1, 2, \ldots, n$. Thus, a new system of n linear equations in m unknowns is determined:

$$\begin{aligned} a_{1,1}^*x_1 + a_{1,2}^*x_2 + \cdots + a_{1,m}^*x_m &= b_1^* \\ a_{2,1}^*x_1 + a_{2,2}^*x_2 + \cdots + a_{2,m}^*x_m &= b_2^* \\ &\cdots \\ a_{n,1}^*x_1 + a_{n,2}^*x_2 + \cdots + a_{n,m}^*x_m &= b_n^*. \end{aligned} \tag{10-4}$$

The row space of this new system is spanned by the vectors $\mathbf{U}_1^*, \mathbf{U}_2^*, \ldots,$ $\mathbf{U}_n^*$. It follows from Theorem 10.2 that the systems (10-1) and (10-4) have the same row space. The elementary transformations performed on the vectors $\langle \mathbf{U}_1, \mathbf{U}_2, \ldots, \mathbf{U}_n\rangle$ of system (10-1) may be described directly in terms of the equations. A Type I elementary transformation interchanges two equations, a Type II transformation multiplies one of the equations by a constant and adds this equation to another equation, and a transformation of Type III multiplies one of the equations by a nonzero constant. Thus, the new system (10-4) is obtained from (10-1) by a sequence of elementary algebraic operations.

Example 1. Consider the system

$$\begin{aligned} \tfrac{1}{2}x_1 - 3x_2 + 2x_3 + x_4 &= 0 \\ 0x_1 + \tfrac{1}{3}x_2 + 5x_3 - 3x_4 &= 5 \\ 4x_1 + 6x_2 + 0x_3 - 2x_4 &= -1. \end{aligned} \tag{10-5}$$

The row space of system (10-5) is the subspace of $\mathcal{V}_5$ spanned by the vectors

$$\mathbf{U}_1 = \langle 1/2, -3, 2, 1, 0\rangle$$
$$\mathbf{U}_2 = \langle 0, 1/3, 5, -3, 5\rangle$$
$$\mathbf{U}_3 = \langle 4, 6, 0, -2, -1\rangle.$$

We perform the following sequence of elementary transformations on $\langle \mathbf{U}_1, \mathbf{U}_2, \mathbf{U}_3\rangle$. Multiply $\mathbf{U}_1$ by 2:

$$\left.\begin{matrix}\mathbf{U}_1\\ \mathbf{U}_2\\ \mathbf{U}_3\end{matrix}\right\} \to \left\{\begin{matrix}\langle 1, -6, 4, 2, 0\rangle & = \mathbf{U}_1^{(1)}\\ \langle 0, 1/3, 5, -3, 5\rangle & = \mathbf{U}_2^{(1)}\\ \langle 4, 6, 0, -2, -1\rangle & = \mathbf{U}_3^{(1)}\end{matrix}\right.$$

Multiply $\mathbf{U}_1^{(1)}$ by -4 and add to $\mathbf{U}_3^{(1)}$:

$$\left.\begin{matrix}\mathbf{U}_1^{(1)}\\ \mathbf{U}_2^{(1)}\\ \mathbf{U}_3^{(1)}\end{matrix}\right\} \to \left\{\begin{matrix}\langle 1, -6, 4, 2, 0\rangle & = \mathbf{U}_1^{(2)}\\ \langle 0, 1/3, 5, -3, 5\rangle & = \mathbf{U}_2^{(2)}\\ \langle 0, 30, -16, -10, -1\rangle & = \mathbf{U}_3^{(2)}\end{matrix}\right.$$

Multiply $\mathbf{U}_2^{(2)}$ by 3:

$$\left.\begin{matrix}\mathbf{U}_1^{(2)}\\ \mathbf{U}_2^{(2)}\\ \mathbf{U}_3^{(2)}\end{matrix}\right\} \to \left\{\begin{matrix}\langle 1, -6, 4, 2, 0\rangle & = \mathbf{U}_1^{(3)}\\ \langle 0, 1, 15, -9, 15\rangle & = \mathbf{U}_2^{(3)}\\ \langle 0, 30, -16, -10, -1\rangle & = \mathbf{U}_3^{(3)}\end{matrix}\right.$$

Multiply $\mathbf{U}_2^{(3)}$ by -30 and add to $\mathbf{U}_3^{(3)}$:

$$\left.\begin{matrix}\mathbf{U}_1^{(3)}\\ \mathbf{U}_2^{(3)}\\ \mathbf{U}_3^{(3)}\end{matrix}\right\} \to \left\{\begin{matrix}\langle 1, -6, 4, 2, 0\rangle & = \mathbf{U}_1^{(4)}\\ \langle 0, 1, 15, -9, 15\rangle & = \mathbf{U}_2^{(4)}\\ \langle 0, 0, -466, 260, -451\rangle & = \mathbf{U}_3^{(4)}\end{matrix}\right.$$

Multiply $\mathbf{U}_3^{(4)}$ by $-1/466$:

$$\left.\begin{matrix}\mathbf{U}_1^{(4)}\\ \mathbf{U}_2^{(4)}\\ \mathbf{U}_3^{(4)}\end{matrix}\right\} \to \left\{\begin{matrix}\langle 1, -6, 4, 2, 0\rangle & = \mathbf{U}_1^{(5)}\\ \langle 0, 1, 15, -9, 15\rangle & = \mathbf{U}_2^{(5)}\\ \langle 0, 0, 1, -130/233, 451/466\rangle & = \mathbf{U}_3^{(5)}.\end{matrix}\right.$$

The row space of the new system of equations,

$$\begin{aligned} x_1 - 6x_2 + 4x_3 + 2x_4 &= 0\\ x_2 + 15x_3 - 9x_4 &= 15\\ x_3 - \tfrac{130}{233}x_4 &= \tfrac{451}{466}, \end{aligned} \tag{10-6}$$

is spanned by $\langle 1, -6, 4, 2, 0\rangle$, $\langle 0, 1, 15, -9, 15\rangle$, and $\langle 0, 0, 1, -130/233, 451/466\rangle$. It is the same subspace of $\mathcal{V}_5$ as the row space of the original system (10-5).

In Section 11 we will prove that a sequence of elementary transformations replaces a system of linear equations by an equivalent system. Thus, in Example 1, the system (10-6) is equivalent to the system (10-5).

Exercises

10.1 Determine which of the following systems of equations are consistent. Find all solutions of the consistent systems.

(a)
$$\begin{aligned} 3x_1 - 5x_2 - 2x_3 &= 0 \\ x_1 + 9x_2 - x_3 &= 0 \\ 2x_1 + 4x_2 - 7x_3 &= 0 \end{aligned}$$

(b)
$$\begin{aligned} 6x_1 - 5x_2 &= 14 \\ 2x_1 + x_2 &= 0 \\ x_1 - 3x_2 &= 1 \end{aligned}$$

(c)
$$\begin{aligned} x_1 - 4x_2 + 2x_3 &= 10 \\ 3x_1 - x_2 + x_3 &= 5 \end{aligned}$$

(d)
$$\begin{aligned} -2x_1 + 4x_2 + 6x_3 &= 1 \\ x_1 \qquad\qquad - x_3 &= 1 \\ -x_1 + 4x_2 + 5x_3 &= 1 \end{aligned}$$

10.2 Prove that the systems of equations (10-2) and (10-3) are equivalent.

* **10.3** Suppose that the ordered set of vectors $\langle \mathbf{U}_1^*, \mathbf{U}_2^*, \ldots, \mathbf{U}_n^* \rangle$ is obtained from the ordered set $\langle \mathbf{U}_1, \mathbf{U}_2, \ldots, \mathbf{U}_n \rangle$ by an elementary transformation. Prove that there is an elementary transformation of the same type that takes the set $\langle \mathbf{U}_1^*, \mathbf{U}_2^*, \ldots, \mathbf{U}_n^* \rangle$ into $\langle \mathbf{U}_1, \mathbf{U}_2, \ldots, \mathbf{U}_n \rangle$.

10.4 Perform a sequence of elementary transformations on the vectors spanning the row space of equations (10-6) to obtain the vectors that span the row space of equations (10-5).

10.5 Prove that equivalence of systems of linear equations is an equivalence relation.

11 Systems of equations in echelon form

By Theorem 10.2, a system of linear equations obtained from a given system by a sequence of elementary transformations has the same row space as the given system. Then, by the following theorem, these systems are equivalent.

(11.1) **Theorem.** If two systems of linear equations in m unknowns have the same row space, the two systems are equivalent.

PROOF. Let the given systems be

$$\begin{aligned} a_{1,1}x_1 + a_{1,2}x_2 + \cdots + a_{1,m}x_m &= b_1 \\ a_{2,1}x_1 + a_{2,2}x_2 + \cdots + a_{2,m}x_m &= b_2 \\ &\cdots \\ a_{n,1}x_1 + a_{n,2}x_2 + \cdots + a_{n,m}x_m &= b_n \end{aligned} \tag{11-1}$$

and

$$\begin{aligned} d_{1,1}x_1 + d_{1,2}x_2 + \cdots + d_{1,m}x_m &= e_1 \\ d_{2,1}x_1 + d_{2,2}x_2 + \cdots + d_{2,m}x_m &= e_2 \\ &\cdots \\ d_{p,1}x_1 + d_{p,2}x_2 + \cdots + d_{p,m}x_m &= e_p. \end{aligned} \tag{11-2}$$

Let $x_1 = c_1$, $x_2 = c_2$, . . . , $x_m = c_m$ be a solution of (11-1). Since the row space of system (11-2) is the same as that of (11-1), it follows that each vector $\langle d_{i,1}, d_{i,2}, \ldots, d_{i,m}, e_i\rangle$ for $i = 1, 2, \ldots, p$ is a linear combination of the vectors $\langle a_{j,1}, a_{j,2}, \ldots, a_{j,m}, b_j\rangle$, $j = 1, 2, \ldots, n$. Thus, for $i = 1, 2, \ldots, p$, there exist real numbers $r_1, r_2, \ldots, r_n$ that depend on i such that

$$\begin{aligned}\langle d_{i,1}, d_{i,2}, \ldots, d_{i,m}, e_i\rangle \\ &= r_1 \cdot \langle a_{1,1}, a_{1,2}, \ldots, a_{1,m}, b_1\rangle \\ &\quad + r_2 \cdot \langle a_{2,1}, a_{2,2}, \ldots, a_{2,m}, b_2\rangle \\ &\quad + \cdots + r_n \cdot \langle a_{n,1}, a_{n,2}, \ldots, a_{n,m}, b_n\rangle \\ &= \langle r_1a_{1,1} + r_2a_{2,1} + \cdots + r_na_{n,1}, r_1a_{1,2} + r_2a_{2,2} \\ &\quad + \cdots + r_na_{n,2}, \ldots, r_1a_{1,m} + r_2a_{2,m} \\ &\quad + \cdots + r_na_{n,m}, r_1b_1 + r_2b_2 + \cdots + r_nb_n\rangle.\end{aligned}$$

Therefore,

$$d_{i,1} = r_1a_{1,1} + r_2a_{2,1} + \cdots + r_na_{n,1},$$

$$d_{i,2} = r_1a_{1,2} + r_2a_{2,2} + \cdots + r_na_{n,2}, \quad \ldots,$$

$$d_{i,m} = r_1a_{1,m} + r_2a_{2,m} + \cdots + r_na_{n,m},$$

and

$$e_i = r_1b_1 + r_2b_2 + \cdots + r_nb_n.$$

Hence,

$$\begin{aligned}d_{i,1}c_1 + d_{i,2}c_2 + \cdots + d_{i,m}c_m \\ &= (r_1a_{1,1} + r_2a_{2,1} + \cdots + r_na_{n,1})c_1 \\ &\quad + (r_1a_{1,2} + r_2a_{2,2} + \cdots + r_na_{n,2})c_2 \\ &\quad + \cdots + (r_1a_{1,m} + r_2a_{2,m} + \cdots + r_na_{n,m})c_m \\ &= r_1(a_{1,1}c_1 + a_{1,2}c_2 + \cdots + a_{1,m}c_m) \\ &\quad + r_2(a_{2,1}c_1 + a_{2,2}c_2 + \cdots + a_{2,m}c_m) \\ &\quad + \cdots + r_n(a_{n,1}c_1 + a_{n,2}c_2 + \cdots + a_{n,m}c_n).\end{aligned}$$

Since $c_1, c_2, \ldots, c_m$ is a solution of (11-1),

$$a_{j,1}c_1 + a_{j,2}c_2 + \cdots + a_{j,m}c_m = b_j,$$

for $j = 1, 2, \ldots, n$. Hence

$$d_{i,1}c_1 + d_{i,2}c_2 + \cdots + d_{i,m}c_m = r_1b_1 + r_2b_2 + \cdots + r_nb_n = e_i,$$

for $i = 1, 2, \ldots, p$. Therefore $c_1, c_2, \ldots, c_m$ is a solution of the system (11-2). Conversely, since each vector $\langle a_{j,1}, a_{j,2}, \ldots, a_{j,m}, b_j\rangle$ for $j = 1, 2, \ldots, n$ is a linear combination of the vectors $\langle d_{i,1}, d_{i,2}, \ldots, d_{i,m}, e_i\rangle$, $i = 1, 2, \ldots, p$, a similar argument shows that every solution of the system (11-2) is a solution of (11-1). Therefore, the systems are equivalent.

(11.2) Corollary. Let S' be a system of linear equations obtained from a system S of linear equations by a sequence of elementary transformations. Then the systems S and S' are equivalent.

PROOF. The vectors that span the row space of the system S' are obtained, by a sequence of elementary transformations, from the vectors that span the row space of the system S. By Theorem 10.2, the systems S and S' have the same row space. By Theorem 11.1, the systems S and S' are equivalent.

Thus, in Example 1, Section 10, the systems (10-6) and (10-5) have exactly the same solutions. The solutions of (10-6) are easily obtained. Every real solution is given by

$$\begin{aligned} x_4 &= r \\ x_3 &= \tfrac{451}{466} + \tfrac{130}{233}r \\ x_2 &= \tfrac{225}{466} + \tfrac{147}{233}r \\ x_1 &= -\tfrac{227}{233} - \tfrac{104}{233}r, \end{aligned}$$

where r is any real number. Our next step is to show that every system of linear equations can be carried into a new system with the advantages of (10-6) by a sequence of elementary transformations. The precise description of a system of n linear equations in m unknowns that has a special form clearly exhibiting the properties of the system is somewhat complicated. However, the concepts involved are quite simple, as a careful study of examples will show.

(11.3) Definition. A system of linear equations (10-1) is in *echelon form* if there exists an integer k, $0 \le k \le n$, with the following properties:

(a) If $k < i \le n$, then $a_{i,j} = 0$ for all j;

(b) If $k > 0$, then there exists an increasing sequence of positive integers $1 \le m_1 < m_2 < \cdots < m_k \le m$ such that $a_{i,j} = 0$ for $j < m_i$, and $a_{i,m_i} = 1 (1 \le i \le k)$.

Note that if the coefficients of $x_1, x_2, \ldots, x_m$ are zero in every equation of the system (10-1), then the system is in echelon form with $k = 0$. For example,

$$\begin{aligned} 0x_1 + 0x_2 &= -1 \\ 0x_1 + 0x_2 &= 2 \end{aligned}$$

is in echelon form. The system (10-6) is in echelon form with $k = n = 3$, $m_1 = 1$, $m_2 = 2$, $m_3 = 3$. The system

$$\begin{aligned} x_1 + 3x_2 + 0x_3 + 0x_4 &= 2 \\ 0x_1 + 0x_2 + x_3 + 6x_4 &= 1 \\ 0x_1 + 0x_2 + 0x_3 + 0x_4 &= 0 \end{aligned}$$

is in echelon form with $k = 2$, $m_1 = 1$, $m_2 = 3$. Notice that this system could be written

$$\begin{aligned} x_1 + 3x_2 + 0x_3 + 0x_4 &= 2 \\ x_3 + 6x_4 &= 1 \\ 0 &= 0. \end{aligned}$$

Except for the trivial case where $k = 0$, a typical system in echelon form can be written

$$\begin{aligned} x_{m_1} + a_{1,m_1+1}\, x_{m_1+1} + a_{1,m_1+2}\, x_{m_1+2} + \cdots + a_{1,m}x_m &= b_1 \\ x_{m_2} \quad + a_{2,m_2+1}\, x_{m_2+1} + \cdots + a_{2,m}x_m &= b_2 \\ \cdots \qquad & \\ x_{m_k} \quad + a_{k,m_k+1}\, x_{m_k+1} + \cdots + a_{k,m}x_m &= b_k \\ 0 &= b_{k+1} \\ \cdots & \\ 0 &= b_n. \end{aligned} \tag{11-3}$$

Of course, if $k = n$, the equations

$$\begin{aligned} 0 &= b_{k+1} \\ \cdots & \\ 0 &= b_n \end{aligned}$$

do not appear.

(11.4) Theorem. A system of linear equations can be transformed into an equivalent system in echelon form by a sequence of elementary transformations.

PROOF. As we observed in Section 10, we may describe directly, in terms of the equations, any elementary transformation on the vectors spanning the row space of a given system of equations. The proof of this theorem is by mathematical induction on the number n of equations in the given system (10-1). If $n = 1$, then the system consists of the single equation

$$a_{1,1}x_1 + a_{1,2}x_2 + \cdots + a_{1,m}x_m = b_1.$$

If $a_{i,j} = 0$ for $j = 1, 2, \ldots, m$, then this system is in echelon form with $k = 0$. Otherwise, let t be the least positive integer such that $a_{1,t} \neq 0$. Then a Type III elementary transformation, which multiplies the equation by $1/a_{1,t}$, puts the system in echelon form with $k = n = 1$ and $m_1 = t$. Therefore, suppose that $n > 1$ and that any system of $n - 1$ equations can be carried into echelon form by a sequence of elementary transformations. If $a_{i,j} = 0$ for all i and j in system (10-1), then the system is in echelon form with $k = 0$. Otherwise, let t be the least positive integer such that $a_{i,t} \neq 0$ for some i. Thus, if $j < t$, then $a_{i,j} = 0$ for $i = 1, 2, \ldots, n$.

Now if $a_{1,t} = 0$, a Type I transformation, which interchanges the first and ith equations, yields a system in which the coefficient of x_t in the first equation is $a_{i,t} \neq 0$. Moreover, for every equation, the coefficient of x_j is zero if $j < t$. The coefficient of x_t in the first equation can be changed to 1 by a Type III transformation, which multiplies the first equation by $1/a_{i,t}$. The system now has the form

$$\begin{aligned}
0x_1 + \cdots + 0x_{t-1} + 1x_t + a^*_{1,t+1}x_{t+1} + \cdots + a^*_{1,m}x_m &= b^*_1 \\
0x_1 + \cdots + 0x_{t-1} + a^*_{2,t}x_t + a^*_{2,t+1}x_{t+1} + \cdots + a^*_{2,m}x_m &= b^*_2 \\
&\cdots \\
0x_1 + \cdots + 0x_{t-1} + a^*_{n,t}x_t + a^*_{n,t+1}x_{t+1} + \cdots + a^*_{n,m}x_m &= b^*_n.
\end{aligned}$$

(Of course, if $t = 1$, the terms with coefficient 0 do not appear.) A sequence of Type II transformations that add to the ith equation the first equation multiplied by $-a^*_{i,t}$ yields a system in which the coefficient of x_t is zero in every equation except the first. The last $n - 1$ equations then have the form

$$\begin{aligned}
0x_1 + \cdots + 0x_{t-1} + 0x_t + a^{**}_{2,t+1}x_{t+1} + \cdots + a^{**}_{2,m}x_m &= b^{**}_2 \\
&\cdots \\
0x_1 + \cdots + 0x_{t-1} + 0x_t + a^{**}_{n,t+1}x_{t+1} + \cdots + a^{**}_{n,m}x_m &= b^{**}_n.
\end{aligned}$$

By the induction hypothesis, the latter system can be carried to echelon form by a sequence of elementary transformations, which may be regarded as transformations on the complete system of n equations that do not affect the first equation. Moreover, the coefficients of $x_1, \ldots, x_t$ remain zero when the last $n - 1$ equations undergo any elementary transformation. Therefore, the final system of n equations is in echelon form. The fact that the new system of equations is equivalent to the original system is a consequence of Corollary 11.2.

Example 1. Consider the system of equations

$$\begin{aligned}
\tfrac{1}{2}x_1 + \tfrac{3}{2}x_2 - \tfrac{1}{2}x_3 \qquad\quad + x_5 &= 1 \\
2x_1 + 6x_2 + x_3 + 6x_4 + 4x_5 &= 13 \\
-3x_1 - 9x_2 \qquad\quad - 6x_4 - 6x_5 &= -18.
\end{aligned} \tag{11-4}$$

We perform a sequence of elementary transformations to carry this system to echelon form. First, multiply the first equation by 2:

$$\begin{aligned}
x_1 + 3x_2 - x_3 \qquad\quad + 2x_5 &= 2 \\
2x_1 + 6x_2 + x_3 + 6x_4 + 4x_5 &= 13 \\
-3x_1 - 9x_2 \qquad\quad - 6x_4 - 6x_5 &= -18.
\end{aligned}$$

Multiply the first equation by -2 and add it to the second equation; then multiply the first equation by 3 and add it to the third equation:

$$\begin{aligned} x_1 + 3x_2 - x_3 \qquad\qquad + 2x_5 &= 2 \\ 3x_3 + 6x_4 \qquad &= 9 \\ -3x_3 - 6x_4 \qquad &= -12. \end{aligned}$$

Add the second equation to the third; then multiply the second equation by $\frac{1}{3}$:

$$\begin{aligned} x_1 + 3x_2 - x_3 \qquad\qquad + 2x_5 &= 2 \\ x_3 + 2x_4 \qquad &= 3 \\ 0 &= -3. \end{aligned} \tag{11-5}$$

The system (11-5) is in echelon form with $k = 2$, $m_1 = 1$, $m_2 = 3$. Since the third equation is never satisfied, there are no values for x_1, x_2, x_3, x_4, x_5 that satisfy the equations. That is, the equations are inconsistent. Thus, the original system (11-4), which is equivalent to (11-5), has no solution.

Theorem 11.4, which completes the description of the process for solving a system of linear equations, reduces the problem of solving general systems to that of solving systems in echelon form. Moreover, the proof of Theorem 11.4 provides the method for replacing a given system of equations by an equivalent system in echelon form. It is evident from the examples that systems in echelon form are easily solved.

In general, there are many echelon forms to which a system of equations may be carried by elementary transformations. However, by Corollary 11.2, all of these systems are equivalent.

Example 2. Consider the system of equations

$$\begin{aligned} x_1 + x_2 + x_3 &= 1 \\ x_1 + x_2 - x_3 &= 2 \\ x_1 - x_2 - x_3 &= 3. \end{aligned}$$

This system can be carried by elementary transformations into each of the following systems, both of which are in echelon form:

$$\begin{aligned} x_1 + x_2 - x_3 &= 2 \\ x_2 \qquad &= -\tfrac{1}{2} \\ x_3 &= -\tfrac{1}{2} \end{aligned} \qquad\qquad \begin{aligned} x_1 - x_2 - x_3 &= 3 \\ x_2 + x_3 &= -1 \\ x_3 &= -\tfrac{1}{2}. \end{aligned}$$

It is evident from either echelon form that the given system has a unique solution $x_3 = -\frac{1}{2}$, $x_2 = -\frac{1}{2}$, $x_1 = 2$.

Exercises

11.1 Put the systems of equations of Exercise 10.1 into echelon form, and then solve the systems.

11.2 Put the following systems of equations into echelon form. State the values of k and m_i, $i = 1, 2, \ldots, k$ (see Definition 11.3). Solve the systems.

(a)
$$\begin{aligned} 2x_1 - 7x_2 + 5x_3 - 8x_4 &= 7 \\ 4x_1 - 14x_2 + 10x_3 - 5x_4 &= 2 \end{aligned}$$

(b)
$$\begin{aligned} 4x_1 \qquad\quad + 6x_3 - 2x_4 &= 4 \\ 3x_1 - 7x_2 \qquad\quad + 2x_4 &= 5 \\ x_2 - 7x_3 + x_4 &= 2 \end{aligned}$$

(c)
$$\begin{aligned} 3x_1 \qquad\quad - x_3 &= 0 \\ x_1 + x_2 - 2x_3 &= 0 \\ 2x_1 - 2x_2 + 8x_3 &= 0 \\ 2x_1 - x_2 - 4x_3 &= 0 \end{aligned}$$

(d)
$$\begin{aligned} 5x_1 + 2x_2 - 7x_3 &= 1 \\ 7x_1 - x_2 + 2x_3 &= 0 \\ 2x_1 + 5x_2 - x_3 &= 5 \end{aligned}$$

11.3 In Example 2, find sequences of elementary transformations that carry the given system of equations to the echelon forms given in the example. Find other echelon forms for the given system.

12 Theory of linear systems; homogeneous systems

By the results of Section 11, the study of systems of linear equations can be replaced by the study of systems in echelon form. For systems in echelon form, we refer to the integer k of Definition 11.3 as the *associated integer* k.

(12.1) Theorem. Let S be a system of n equations in m unknowns, and let S be in echelon form with associated integer k. The dimension of the row space of S is either k or $k + 1$. The system is consistent if and only if this dimension is k. If the system is consistent, then its solution is unique if and only if $k = m$.

PROOF. The vectors that span the row space of a system S in echelon form are [see equations (11-3)]

$$\begin{aligned} \mathbf{U}_1 &= \langle 0, \ldots, 0, 1, a_{1,m_1+1}, \ldots, a_{1,m}, b_1 \rangle \\ \mathbf{U}_2 &= \langle 0, \ldots, 0, 1, a_{2,m_2+1}, \ldots, a_{2,m}, b_2 \rangle \\ &\ldots \\ \mathbf{U}_k &= \langle 0, \ldots, 0, 1, a_{k,m_k+1}, \ldots, a_{k,m}, b_k \rangle \\ \mathbf{U}_{k+1} &= \langle 0, \ldots, 0, b_{k+1} \rangle \\ &\ldots \\ \mathbf{U}_n &= \langle 0, \ldots, 0, b_n \rangle. \end{aligned}$$

It is convenient to consider the following three mutually exclusive cases: (1) $k = n$; (2) $k < n$ and $b_{k+1} = \cdots = b_n = 0$; (3) $k < n$ and some $b_r \neq 0$ where $k + 1 \leq r \leq n$. In case (1), the row space is spanned by $\mathbf{U}_1, \mathbf{U}_2, \ldots, \mathbf{U}_k$. In case (2), the last $n - k$ vectors are zero, so that again the row space is spanned by $\mathbf{U}_1, \mathbf{U}_2, \ldots, \mathbf{U}_k$. Thus, we may consider cases (1) and (2) together. Clearly, if $k = 0$, the row space is $\{\mathbf{0}\}$ and its dimension is $k = 0$. Therefore suppose that $k > 0$, and that

$$c_1 \cdot \mathbf{U}_1 + c_2 \cdot \mathbf{U}_2 + \cdots + c_k \cdot \mathbf{U}_k = \mathbf{0}$$

for real numbers $c_1, c_2, \ldots, c_k$. Since $m_1 < m_2 < \cdots < m_k$, it follows that

$$\begin{aligned} c_1 &= 0 \\ c_1 a_{1,m_2} + c_2 &= 0 \\ c_1 a_{1,m_3} + c_2 a_{2,m_3} + c_3 &= 0 \\ &\cdots \\ c_1 a_{1,m_k} + c_2 a_{2,m_k} + \cdots + c_{k-1} a_{k-1,m_k} + c_k &= 0. \end{aligned} \tag{12-1}$$

Equations (12-1) imply that $c_1 = c_2 = \cdots = c_k = 0$. Thus, the vectors $\mathbf{U}_1, \mathbf{U}_2, \ldots, \mathbf{U}_k$ are linearly independent and form a basis of the row space. Therefore, in cases (1) and (2), the dimension of the row space is k.

In case (3), some $b_r \neq 0$, where $k + 1 \leq r \leq n$. If

$$c_1 \cdot \mathbf{U}_1 + c_2 \cdot \mathbf{U}_2 + \cdots + c_k \cdot \mathbf{U}_k + c_{k+1} \cdot \mathbf{U}_r = \mathbf{0},$$

then, in addition to equations (12-1), we have the equation

$$c_1 b_1 + c_2 b_2 + \cdots + c_k b_k + c_{k+1} b_r = 0.$$

Therefore, $c_1 = c_2 = \cdots = c_k = 0$ and $c_{k+1} b_r = 0$. Since $b_r \neq 0$, this implies $c_{k+1} = 0$. Hence, the set $\{\mathbf{U}_1, \mathbf{U}_2, \ldots, \mathbf{U}_k, \mathbf{U}_r\}$ is linearly independent. (If $k = 0$, this set contains the single vector $\mathbf{U}_r$.) Since each $\mathbf{U}_s$ with $k + 1 \leq s \leq n$ is a scalar multiple of $\mathbf{U}_r (\mathbf{U}_s = (b_s/b_r) \cdot \mathbf{U}_r)$, the vectors $\mathbf{U}_1, \mathbf{U}_2, \ldots, \mathbf{U}_k, \mathbf{U}_r$ span the row space. Therefore, in case (3), the row space has a basis of $k + 1$ vectors. That is, the dimension of the row space is $k + 1$.

If the dimension of the row space of the system of equations S is k, then case (1) or (2) must hold. Therefore the given system has the form

$$\begin{aligned} x_{m_1} + a_{1,m_1+1} x_{m_1+1} + \cdots + a_{1,m} x_m &= b_1 \\ x_{m_2} + a_{2,m_2+1} x_{m_2+1} + \cdots + a_{2,m} x_m &= b_2 \\ &\cdots \\ x_{m_k} + a_{k,m_k+1} x_{m_k+1} + \cdots + a_{k,m} x_m &= b_k. \end{aligned} \tag{12-2}$$

By choosing arbitrary real values for the unknowns other than $x_{m_1}, x_{m_2}, \ldots, x_{m_k}$, and by solving the equations in turn for $x_{m_k}, x_{m_{k-1}}, \ldots, x_{m_1}$, we obtain a solution. Therefore, the system is consistent. However, if the dimension of the row space is $k + 1$, then the situation must be that of case (3). Thus, the system contains an equation $0 = b_r$, where $b_r \neq 0$. Since this is impossible, the equations are inconsistent.

If the system is consistent, then it is clear from equations (12-2) that the solution is unique if and only if no arbitrary choice for the values of some of the unknowns is possible, that is, if and only if the only unknowns are $x_{m_1}, x_{m_2}, \ldots, x_{m_k}$. The latter condition holds if and only if $x_{m_1} = x_1$, $x_{m_2} = x_2, \ldots, x_{m_k} = x_m$, that is, if and only if $k = m$.

The system of equations (10-1) is called *homogeneous* if $b_1 = b_2 = \cdots = b_n = 0$. Suppose that a homogeneous system is carried into echelon form by a sequence of elementary transformations. Let $b_1^*, b_2^*, \ldots, b_n^*$ be the right-hand members of the equations in this echelon form. By observing the effect of any elementary transformation on a homogeneous system of equations, it is clear that $b_1^* = b_2^* = \cdots = b_n^* = 0$. Therefore, either case (1) or (2) of Theorem 12.1 applies, and the system is consistent. It is obvious directly that $x_1 = 0, x_2 = 0, \ldots, x_m = 0$ is a solution of a homogeneous system. We have previously encountered problems where we wish to know whether a homogeneous system has a solution other than this trivial one. Theorem 12.2 provides the answer to this question.

(12.2) Theorem. A homogeneous system of n equations in m unknowns has a nontrivial solution if and only if the dimension k of its row space is less than m.

PROOF. By Theorem 10.2, a system of equations has the same row space as any echelon form for the system. Since a homogeneous system of equations is consistent, by Theorem 12.1, the dimension of its row space is the associated integer k of an echelon form for the system. By Definition 11.3, for any system of equations in echelon form, either $k = 0$ or $k \leq m_k \leq m$. Thus, it is always the case that $k \leq m$. By Theorem 12.1, a homogeneous system has a unique solution (which must be $x_1 = 0, x_2 = 0, \ldots, x_m = 0$) if and only if $k = m$. Therefore a homogeneous system has a solution other than $x_1 = 0, x_2 = 0, \ldots, x_m = 0$ if and only if $k < m$.

(12.3) Corollary. A homogeneous system of n equations in m unknowns has a nontrivial solution if $n < m$.

PROOF. The dimension of the row space of the system is the associated integer k of an echelon form for the system. By Definition 11.3, $k \leq n < m$. By Theorem 12.2, the system has a nontrivial solution.

The row space of a homongeneous system of linear equations

$$\begin{aligned} a_{1,1}x_1 + a_{1,2}x_2 + \cdots + a_{1,m}x_m &= 0 \\ a_{2,1}x_1 + a_{2,2}x_2 + \cdots + a_{2,m}x_m &= 0 \\ &\cdots \\ a_{n,1}x_1 + a_{n,2}x_2 + \cdots + a_{n,m}x_m &= 0 \end{aligned} \tag{12-3}$$

is the subspace of $\mathcal{V}_{m+1}$ spanned by the set of vectors $T = \{\langle a_{1,1}, a_{1,2}, \ldots, a_{1,m}, 0\rangle, \langle a_{2,1}, a_{2,2}, \ldots, a_{2,m}, 0\rangle, \ldots, \langle a_{n,1}, a_{n,2}, \ldots, a_{n,m}, 0\rangle\}$. Corresponding to each vector $\langle a_{i,1}, a_{i,2}, \ldots, a_{i,m}, 0\rangle$ in T, there is a unique vector $\langle a_{i,1}, a_{i,2}, \ldots, a_{i,m}\rangle$ in $\mathcal{V}_m$. Since the $(m + 1)$th component of each vector in T equals zero, a subset of T is a linearly independent set in $\mathcal{V}_{m+1}$ if and only if the corresponding subset of $T' = \{\langle a_{1,1}, a_{1,2}, \ldots, a_{1,m}\rangle, \langle a_{2,1}, a_{2,2}, \ldots, a_{2,m}\rangle, \ldots, \langle a_{n,1}, a_{n,2}, \ldots, a_{n,m}\rangle\}$ is a linearly independent set in $\mathcal{V}_m$. Therefore, the dimension k of the row space of equations (12-3) is the same as the dimension of the subspace $\mathcal{S}$ of $\mathcal{V}_m$ spanned by T'.

We next observe that a solution $x_1 = c_1, x_2 = c_2, \ldots, x_m = c_m$ of (12-3) may be regarded as a vector $\langle c_1, c_2, \ldots, c_m\rangle$ in $\mathcal{V}_m$. We shall refer to $\langle c_1, c_2, \ldots, c_m\rangle$ as a *solution vector* of (12-3). If $\langle c_1, c_2, \ldots, c_m\rangle$ and $\langle d_1, d_2, \ldots, d_m\rangle$ are solution vectors of (12-3), then

$$\sum_{j=1}^{m} a_{i,j}(c_j + d_j) = \sum_{j=1}^{m} a_{i,j}c_j + \sum_{j=1}^{m} a_{i,j}d_j = 0 + 0 = 0,$$

for $i = 1, 2, \ldots, n$. Hence, the sum

$$\langle c_1, c_2, \ldots, c_m\rangle + \langle d_1, d_2, \ldots, d_m\rangle = \langle c_1 + d_1, c_2 + d_2, \ldots, c_m + d_m\rangle$$

of two solution vectors is again a solution vector. Similarly, if t is a real number and $\langle c_1, c_2, \ldots, c_m\rangle$ is a solution vector of (12-3), then

$$t \cdot \langle c_1, c_2, \ldots, c_m\rangle = \langle tc_1, tc_2, \ldots, tc_m\rangle$$

is a solution vector, since

$$\sum_{j=1}^{m} a_{i,j}(tc_j) = t \sum_{j=1}^{m} a_{i,j}c_j = t\,0 = 0.$$

Therefore, the set of all solution vectors of (12-3) is a subspace $\mathfrak{I}$ of $\mathcal{V}_m$, called the *solution space* of (12-3).

We now regard $\mathcal{V}_m$ as a Euclidean vector space with the $E^{(m)}$-inner product (see Example 1, Section 9). Then a vector $\langle c_1, c_2, \ldots, c_m\rangle$ is in the solution space of (12-3) if and only if it is orthogonal to each vector in the set T' that spans the subspace $\mathcal{S}$ of $\mathcal{V}_m$ mentioned above. Moreover, $\langle c_1, c_2, \ldots, c_m\rangle$ is orthogonal to each vector in T' if and only if it is orthogonal to each vector in $\mathcal{S}$ (see Exercise 9.2). Therefore, the solution space $\mathfrak{I}$ of (12-3) is the orthogonal complement of $\mathcal{S}$ in $\mathcal{V}_m$, and $\mathcal{V}_m = \mathcal{S} \oplus \mathfrak{I}$ (see Exercise 9.3). Since the dimension of $\mathcal{S}$ is k, it now follows from Exercise 8.5

that the dimension of $\mathfrak{I}$ is $m - k$. Thus, we have proved the following useful result.

(12.4) Theorem. If k is the dimension of the row space of a homogeneous system of n linear equations in m unknowns, then the dimension of the solution space of the system is $m - k$.

By Corollary 8.8 and Theorem 12.4, any set of $m - k$ linearly independent vectors in the solution space of the equations (12-3) is a basis of this vector space. Thus, any solution vector of (12-3) is a linear combination of $m - k$ linearly independent solution vectors of (12-3).

Any solution $x_1 = r_1, x_2 = r_2, \ldots, x_m = r_m$ of the general system of linear equations (10-1) can also be regarded as a vector $\langle r_1, r_2, \ldots, r_m \rangle$ in $\mathcal{V}_m$. Replacing each b_i, $i = 1, 2, \ldots, n$, by 0 in the equations (10-1), we obtain the *associated homogeneous system* (12-3). The following theorem describes the structure of the solutions of the system (10-1).

(12.5) Theorem. Suppose that the system of linear equations (10-1) is consistent, and let $\langle r_1, r_2, \ldots, r_m \rangle$ be a fixed solution vector of (10-1). Then $\langle s_1, s_2, \ldots, s_m \rangle$ is a solution vector of (10-1) if and only if

$$\begin{aligned} \langle s_1, s_2, \ldots, s_m \rangle &= \langle r_1, r_2, \ldots, r_m \rangle + \langle c_1, c_2, \ldots, c_m \rangle \\ &= \langle r_1 + c_1, r_2 + c_2, \ldots, r_m + c_m \rangle, \end{aligned}$$

where $\langle c_1, c_2, \ldots, c_m \rangle$ is a solution vector of the associated homogeneous system (12-3).

PROOF. Let $\langle c_1, c_2, \ldots, c_m \rangle$ be a solution vector of the homogeneous system (12-3). Then, since $\langle r_1, r_2, \ldots, r_m \rangle$ is a solution vector of (10-1), we have

$$\sum_{j=1}^{m} a_{i,j}(r_j + c_j) = \sum_{j=1}^{m} a_{i,j}r_j + \sum_{j=1}^{m} a_{i,j}c_j = b_i + 0 = b_i,$$

for $i = 1, 2, \ldots, n$. Hence, $\langle r_1 + c_1, r_2 + c_2, \ldots, r_m + c_m \rangle$ is a solution vector of (10-1). Conversely, suppose that $\langle s_1, s_2, \ldots, s_m \rangle$ is any solution vector of (10-1). Then

$$\sum_{j=1}^{m} a_{i,j}(s_j - r_j) = \sum_{j=1}^{m} a_{i,j}s_j - \sum_{j=1}^{m} a_{i,j}r_j = b_i - b_i = 0,$$

for $i = 1, 2, \ldots, n$. Let $s_j - r_j = c_j$ for $j = 1, 2, \ldots, m$. Then

$$\langle s_1, s_2, \ldots, s_m \rangle - \langle r_1, r_2, \ldots, r_m \rangle = \langle c_1, c_2, \ldots, c_m \rangle$$

is a solution vector of the homogeneous system (12-3). That is,

$$\langle s_1, s_2, \ldots, s_m \rangle = \langle r_1, r_2, \ldots, r_m \rangle + \langle c_1, c_2, \ldots, c_m \rangle.$$

Combining the results of Theorems 12.4 and 12.5, we have the following: Any solution vector of a system of n linear equations in m unknowns is the sum of a fixed solution vector of this system and a linear combination of $m - k$ linearly independent solution vectors of the associated homogeneous system, where k is the dimension of the row space of the homogeneous system.

Exercises

12.1 Which of the following systems of equations are consistent? Find all solutions of the consistent systems.

(a) $$\begin{aligned} 3x_1 - 5x_2 + x_3 &= 1 \\ x_1 - 7x_2 + 2x_3 &= 0 \\ 3x_1 + 11x_2 - 4x_3 &= 5 \end{aligned}$$

(b) $$\begin{aligned} x_1 - 5x_2 + 4x_3 + x_4 &= 7 \\ 2x_1 + x_2 - 3x_3 - x_4 &= 1 \\ 3x_1 - 4x_2 + x_3 - 5x_4 &= 0 \\ x_1 + x_2 + x_3 + x_4 &= 1 \end{aligned}$$

(c) $$\begin{aligned} 3x_1 - 5x_2 &= 1/2 \\ 1/3 x_1 + x_2 &= 2/3 \\ 2x_1 - x_2 &= 1 \end{aligned}$$

(d) $$\begin{aligned} x_1 + 3x_2 - x_3 &= 11 \\ 2x_1 - x_2 - x_3 &= 0 \\ x_1 + 2x_2 + 6x_3 &= 7 \\ x_1 + x_2 + x_3 &= 9/2 \end{aligned}$$

12.2 Find nontrivial solutions of the following systems of homogeneous equations whenever they exist. Also find the solution space of each system.

(a) $$\begin{aligned} x_1 - 7/2 x_2 - 1/2 x_3 &= 0 \\ 3x_1 - 7x_2 + 2x_3 &= 0 \end{aligned}$$

(b) $$\begin{aligned} x_1 + x_2 - 2x_3 &= 0 \\ 4x_1 - 3x_2 + 4x_3 &= 0 \\ 2x_1 - x_2 + x_3 &= 0 \\ x_1 - 1/2 x_2 - 2x_3 &= 0 \end{aligned}$$

(c) $$\begin{aligned} - 2x_2 + 2x_3 &= 0 \\ 4x_1 - x_2 + 5x_3 &= 0 \\ 2x_1 + x_2 + x_3 &= 0 \end{aligned}$$

(d) $$\begin{aligned} x_1 - 4x_2 - 6x_3 &= 0 \\ 2x_1 + 5x_2 - x_3 &= 0 \\ 5x_1 - 2x_2 + x_3 &= 0 \end{aligned}$$

12.3 Which of the following sets of vectors in $\mathcal{V}_4$ are linearly dependent?

(a) $\{\langle -2, 1, 3, 6\rangle, \langle 0, 1, 4, -5\rangle, \langle 2, -3, 1, 1\rangle\}$;

(b) $\{\langle 1, 1, 1, 2\rangle, \langle 2, -1, 5, 0\rangle, \langle -1, -1, 2, 1\rangle, \langle 1, -1/2, 4, 3/2\rangle\}$;

(c) $\{\langle 0, -2, 2, 0\rangle, \langle 4, -1, 5, 0\rangle, \langle 2, 1, 1, 0\rangle\}$.

***12.4** Prove that a system of n linear equations in m unknowns (10-1) is consistent if and only if the dimension of its row space is the same as the dimension of the row space of the associated homogeneous system.

12.5 Let $\mathcal{S}$ be the subspace of $\mathcal{V}_5$ spanned by the vectors $\langle -2, 3, 0, -1, 0\rangle$, $\langle -4, 0, 1, 2, 7\rangle$, $\langle 8, 6, -3, -8, -21\rangle$. Regard $\mathcal{V}_5$ as a Euclidean vector space with the $E^{(5)}$-inner product. Find a basis of the orthogonal complement $\mathcal{T}$ of $\mathcal{S}$ in $\mathcal{V}_5$.

CHAPTER FOUR

Linear Transformations and Matrices

13 Linear transformations of $\mathcal{E}_2$ and $\mathcal{E}_3$

A rotation of a plane through an angle φ about the origin O of a rectangular Cartesian coordinate system carries each point P_i into a point P'_i such that P_i and P'_i are on the same circle with center at O, and the arc $P_iP'_i$ subtends the angle φ at O (Figure 26).

Let P be a point with coordinates (x, y) that is rotated through an angle φ into a point P' with coordinates (x', y'). Let r be the distance of P from the

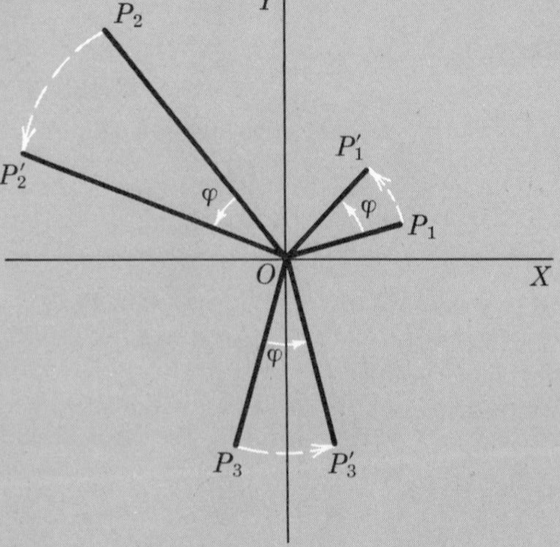

FIGURE 26

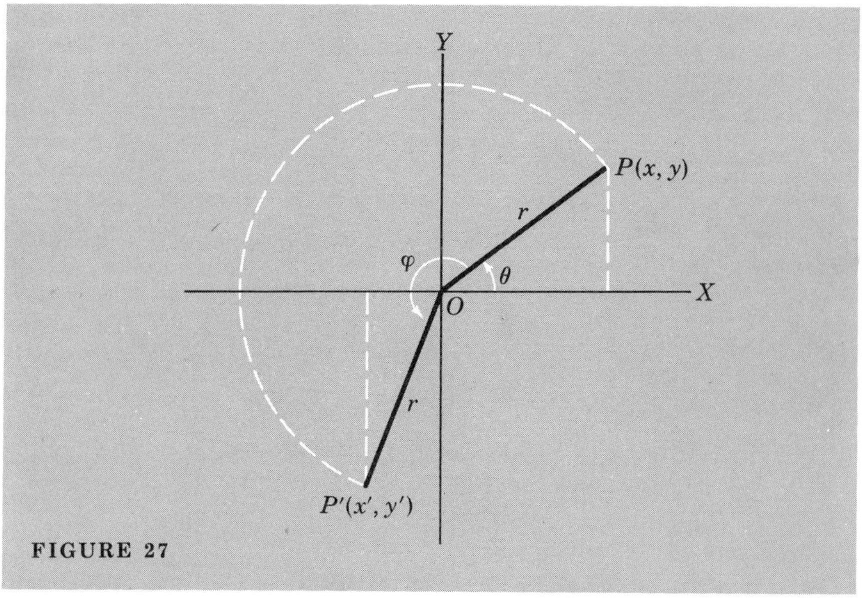

FIGURE 27

origin, and let θ be the angle from the X-axis to OP (Figure 27). Since

$$\frac{x}{r} = \cos\theta, \qquad \frac{y}{r} = \sin\theta,$$

$$\frac{x'}{r} = \cos(\varphi + \theta) = \cos\varphi\cos\theta - \sin\varphi\sin\theta$$

and

$$\frac{y'}{r} = \sin(\varphi + \theta) = \sin\varphi\cos\theta + \cos\varphi\sin\theta,$$

it follows that

$$\begin{aligned} x' &= x\cos\varphi - y\sin\varphi \\ y' &= x\sin\varphi + y\cos\varphi. \end{aligned} \qquad (13\text{-}1)$$

As in Section 7, we denote the set of all geometrical vectors in the plane by $\mathcal{E}_2$ (see Example 7, Section 7). Each vector $\mathbf{V}$ in $\mathcal{E}_2$ has coordinates $\langle x, y\rangle$, where $\mathbf{V}$ is represented by a directed line segment $\overrightarrow{OP}$ with initial point at the origin, and where the point P has coordinates (x, y). Corresponding to a rotation of the plane, there is a mapping of the vector space $\mathcal{E}_2$, which sends a vector $\mathbf{V}$ with coordinates $\langle x, y\rangle$ into a vector $\mathbf{V}'$ with coordinates

$$\langle x', y'\rangle = \langle x\cos\varphi - y\sin\varphi,\ x\sin\varphi + y\cos\varphi\rangle.$$

Thus $\mathbf{V}'$ is represented by $\overrightarrow{OP'}$, where the coordinates (x', y') of P' are given by the linear equations (13-1).

Let T_φ denote the mapping of $\mathcal{E}_2$ into $\mathcal{E}_2$ corresponding to a rotation of the plane through an angle φ. Then every vector $\mathbf{V}$ in $\mathcal{E}_2$ is carried into a unique vector $\mathbf{V}'$ in $\mathcal{E}_2$ by T_φ, and we write $T_\varphi(\mathbf{V}) = \mathbf{V}'$. Let $\mathbf{W}$ be a vector in $\mathcal{E}_2$ with coordinates $\langle s, t\rangle$. Then the coordinates of $\mathbf{V} + \mathbf{W}$ are $\langle x + s, y + t\rangle$, and the vector $T_\varphi(\mathbf{V} + \mathbf{W})$ has coordinates

$$\begin{aligned}\langle (x + s) \cos \varphi - (y + t) \sin \varphi, (x + s) \sin \varphi + (y + t) \cos \varphi\rangle \\ = \langle x \cos \varphi - y \sin \varphi, x \sin \varphi + y \cos \varphi\rangle \\ + \langle s \cos \varphi - t \sin \varphi, s \sin \varphi + t \cos \varphi\rangle,\end{aligned}$$

which is the sum of the coordinates of $T_\varphi(\mathbf{V})$ and $T_\varphi(\mathbf{W})$. Therefore,

$$T_\varphi(\mathbf{V} + \mathbf{W}) = T_\varphi(\mathbf{V}) + T_\varphi(\mathbf{W}). \tag{13-2}$$

Using a similar argument, the reader can easily show that

$$T_\varphi(r \cdot \mathbf{V}) = r \cdot T_\varphi(\mathbf{V}), \tag{13-3}$$

for every real number r. The vector $T_\varphi(\mathbf{V})$ is called the *image* of $\mathbf{V}$ by the mapping T_φ. By (13-2) and (13-3), the image of the sum of two vectors is the sum of the images, and the image of a scalar multiple of a vector is the same scalar multiple of the image. Thus, we say that T_φ "preserves" vector addition and scalar multiplication. Combining the identities (13-2) and (13-3), we obtain

$$T_\varphi(a \cdot \mathbf{V} + b \cdot \mathbf{W}) = a \cdot T_\varphi(\mathbf{V}) + b \cdot T_\varphi(\mathbf{W}), \tag{13-4}$$

for all $\mathbf{V}$, $\mathbf{W}$ in $\mathcal{E}_2$ and all real numbers a, b. A mapping of $\mathcal{E}_2$ into any real vector space $\mathcal{V}$ that has the property (13-4) is called a *linear transformation* of $\mathcal{E}_2$.

Let $\mathbf{U} = [\overrightarrow{OQ}]$ be a fixed nonzero vector of $\mathcal{E}_2$, and let $\mathbf{V} = [\overrightarrow{OP}]$ be any vector in $\mathcal{E}_2$, where O is the origin of a Cartesian coordinate system in a plane. Let θ be the angle between $\overrightarrow{OP}$ and $\overrightarrow{OQ}$. The projection of $\overrightarrow{OP}$ onto $\overrightarrow{OQ}$ is the directed line segment of length $|\,|OP|\cos \theta|$ along the line determined by $\overrightarrow{OQ}$ with the direction of $\overrightarrow{OQ}$ if θ is acute and with the direction opposite to $\overrightarrow{OQ}$ if θ is obtuse (Figure 28). Then $[(\mathbf{V} \circ \mathbf{U})/(\mathbf{U} \circ \mathbf{U})] \cdot \mathbf{U}$ is the vector that is represented by this projection (see Exercise 13.3). The mapping $P_\mathbf{U}$ of $\mathcal{E}_2$ defined by $P_\mathbf{U}(\mathbf{V}) = [(\mathbf{V} \circ \mathbf{U})/(\mathbf{U} \circ \mathbf{U})] \cdot \mathbf{U}$ is called the *orthogonal projection of* $\mathcal{E}_2$ into the subspace $\mathcal{S}$ of $\mathcal{E}_2$ spanned by the vector $\mathbf{U}$.

Using the identities satisfied by inner and scalar multiplication, we obtain

$$\begin{aligned}P_\mathbf{U}(\mathbf{V} + \mathbf{W}) &= \left(\frac{(\mathbf{V} + \mathbf{W}) \circ \mathbf{U}}{\mathbf{U} \circ \mathbf{U}}\right) \cdot \mathbf{U} = \left(\frac{\mathbf{V} \circ \mathbf{U}}{\mathbf{U} \circ \mathbf{U}} + \frac{\mathbf{W} \circ \mathbf{U}}{\mathbf{U} \circ \mathbf{U}}\right) \cdot \mathbf{U} \\ &= \left(\frac{\mathbf{V} \circ \mathbf{U}}{\mathbf{U} \circ \mathbf{U}}\right) \cdot \mathbf{U} + \left(\frac{\mathbf{W} \circ \mathbf{U}}{\mathbf{U} \circ \mathbf{U}}\right) \cdot \mathbf{U} = P_\mathbf{U}(\mathbf{V}) + P_\mathbf{U}(\mathbf{W}),\end{aligned}$$

and

$$P_{\mathbf{U}}(r \cdot \mathbf{V}) = \left(\frac{(r \cdot \mathbf{V}) \circ \mathbf{U}}{\mathbf{U} \circ \mathbf{U}}\right) \cdot \mathbf{U} = \left[r\left(\frac{\mathbf{V} \circ \mathbf{U}}{\mathbf{U} \circ \mathbf{U}}\right)\right] \cdot \mathbf{U}$$

$$= r \cdot \left[\left(\frac{\mathbf{V} \circ \mathbf{U}}{\mathbf{U} \circ \mathbf{U}}\right) \cdot \mathbf{U}\right] = r \cdot P_{\mathbf{U}}(\mathbf{V}).$$

Thus, the projection $P_{\mathbf{U}}$ of $\mathcal{E}_2$ into the subspace $\mathcal{S}$ spanned by $\mathbf{U}$ is a linear transformation of $\mathcal{E}_2$.

Let the fixed vector $\mathbf{U}$ have coordinates $\langle a, b\rangle$. Then if $\mathbf{V}$ has coordinates $\langle x, y\rangle$,

$$P_{\mathbf{U}}(\mathbf{V}) = P_{\mathbf{U}}(\langle x, y\rangle) = \left(\frac{\mathbf{V} \circ \mathbf{U}}{\mathbf{U} \circ \mathbf{U}}\right) \cdot \langle a, b\rangle = \left(\frac{xa + yb}{a^2 + b^2}\right) \cdot \langle a, b\rangle$$

$$= \left\langle \frac{a^2}{a^2 + b^2}\, x + \frac{ab}{a^2 + b^2}\, y,\ \frac{ab}{a^2 + b^2}\, x + \frac{b^2}{a^2 + b^2}\, y \right\rangle.$$

Thus, the coordinates of $P_{\mathbf{U}}(\mathbf{V})$ are $\langle x', y'\rangle$, where x' and y' are given by the linear equations

$$x' = \frac{a^2}{a^2 + b^2}\, x + \frac{ab}{a^2 + b^2}\, y$$

$$y' = \frac{ab}{a^2 + b^2}\, x + \frac{b^2}{a^2 + b^2}\, y.$$

Another example of a linear transformation of $\mathcal{E}_2$ is given by the mapping D_k, which sends a vector $\mathbf{V}$ into $k \cdot \mathbf{V}$. Clearly, each vector $\mathbf{V}$ in $\mathcal{E}_2$ is sent into a vector with length $|k||\mathbf{V}|$, having the direction of $\mathbf{V}$ if $k > 0$ and the direction opposite to that of $\mathbf{V}$ if $k < 0$. If $k = 0$, then each vector of $\mathcal{E}_2$ is sent into the zero vector. The proof that D_k is a linear transformation for every real number k is left as an exercise (Exercise 13.5).

FIGURE 28

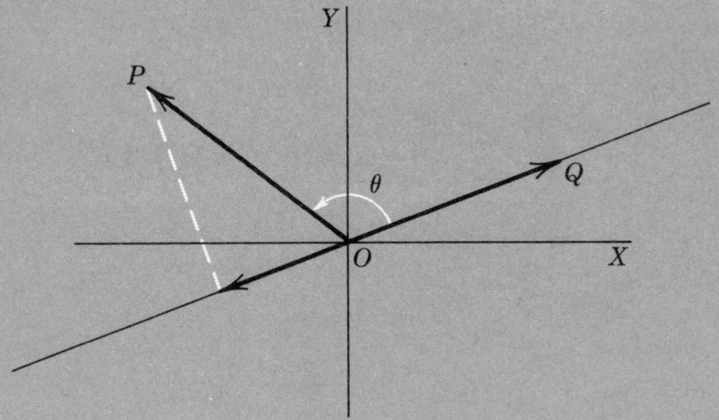

The examples given above can be modified to produce linear transformations of $\mathcal{E}_3$, that is, mappings of $\mathcal{E}_3$ into a real vector space $\mathcal{V}$ that have the property (13-4) [or the properties (13-2) and (13-3)]. A rotation of three-dimensional space about an axis is easily described if a Cartesian coordinate system is chosen so that the Z-axis is the axis of rotation and the sense of the rotation is from the positive direction of the X-axis to the positive direction of the Y-axis. Then a rotation through an angle φ sends a point P with coordinates (x, y, z) into a point P' with coordinates (x', y', z'), where

$$\begin{aligned} x' &= x \cos \varphi - y \sin \varphi \\ y' &= x \sin \varphi + y \cos \varphi \\ z' &= z. \end{aligned} \tag{13-5}$$

The corresponding mapping T_φ of $\mathcal{E}_3$ into $\mathcal{E}_3$, which sends a vector $\mathbf{V}$ with coordinates $\langle x, y, z\rangle$ into a vector $\mathbf{V}'$ with coordinates $\langle x', y', z'\rangle$, is a linear transformation of $\mathcal{E}_3$.

An orthogonal projection $P_\mathbf{U}$ of $\mathcal{E}_3$ into a subspace spanned by a single nonzero vector $\mathbf{U}$ is given by the formula

$$P_\mathbf{U}(\mathbf{V}) = \left(\frac{\mathbf{V} \circ \mathbf{U}}{\mathbf{U} \circ \mathbf{U}}\right) \cdot \mathbf{U},$$

which is the same as the one that describes a projection of $\mathcal{E}_2$. Let $\mathcal{S}$ be a subspace of $\mathcal{E}_3$ spanned by the nonzero orthogonal vectors $\mathbf{U}$ and $\mathbf{W}$. Then the mapping $P_\mathcal{S}$ of $\mathcal{E}_3$ given by

$$P_\mathcal{S}(\mathbf{V}) = \left(\frac{\mathbf{V} \circ \mathbf{U}}{\mathbf{U} \circ \mathbf{U}}\right) \cdot \mathbf{U} + \left(\frac{\mathbf{V} \circ \mathbf{W}}{\mathbf{W} \circ \mathbf{W}}\right) \cdot \mathbf{W}$$

is an orthogonal projection of $\mathcal{E}_3$ into $\mathcal{S}$. In particular, if $\mathbf{U}$ and $\mathbf{W}$ are the unit vectors $\mathbf{I}$ and $\mathbf{J}$ with the directions of the X- and Y-axis, respectively, then this projection sends a vector $\mathbf{V}$ with coordinates $\langle x, y, z\rangle$ into a vector $\mathbf{V}'$ with coordinates $\langle x, y, 0\rangle$. If the set of vectors in the XY-plane is regarded as $\mathcal{E}_2$, then the projection we have described is a linear transformation of $\mathcal{E}_3$ into $\mathcal{E}_2$.

Exercises

13.1 Let T_φ be the mapping of $\mathcal{E}_2$ into $\mathcal{E}_2$ corresponding to a rotation of the plane through an angle φ. Prove that $T_\varphi(r \cdot \mathbf{V}) = r \cdot T_\varphi(\mathbf{V})$ for every $\mathbf{V} \in \mathcal{E}_2$ and every real number r.

13.2 Show that the identities (13-2) and (13-3) imply the identity (13-4).

13.3 Let $\mathbf{U} \neq \mathbf{0}$ and $\mathbf{V}$ be vectors in $\mathcal{E}_2$ represented by the directed line segments $\overrightarrow{OQ}$ and $\overrightarrow{OP}$, respectively. Let θ be the angle between $\overrightarrow{OP}$ and $\overrightarrow{OQ}$. Prove that the length of the vector $[(\mathbf{V} \circ \mathbf{U})/(\mathbf{U} \circ \mathbf{U})] \cdot \mathbf{U}$ is $|\,|OP| \cos \theta|$, and that the direction is that of $\mathbf{U}$ if θ is acute and opposite to that of $\mathbf{U}$ if θ is obtuse.

13.4 Let $P_{\mathbf{U}}$ be the projection of $\mathcal{E}_2$ into the subspace of $\mathcal{E}_2$ spanned by a nonzero vector $\mathbf{U} \in \mathcal{E}_2$. Prove that the vector $\mathbf{V} - P_{\mathbf{U}}(\mathbf{V})$ is orthogonal to $\mathbf{U}$ for any vector $\mathbf{V} \in \mathcal{E}_2$.

13.5 Show that the mapping D_k, defined on page 77, is a linear transformation of $\mathcal{E}_2$ into $\mathcal{E}_2$ for every real number k.

13.6 Let L be a mapping of $\mathcal{E}_3$ into $\mathcal{E}_3$ that sends a vector $\mathbf{V}$ with coordinates $\langle x, y, z\rangle$ into a vector $L(\mathbf{V})$ with coordinates $\langle x', y', z'\rangle$, where

$$x' = a_{1,1}x + a_{1,2}y + a_{1,3}z$$

$$y' = a_{2,1}x + a_{2,2}y + a_{2,3}z$$

$$z' = a_{3,1}x + a_{3,2}y + a_{3,3}z,$$

for real numbers $a_{i,j}$; $i = 1, 2, 3$; $j = 1, 2, 3$. Prove that L is a linear transformation of $\mathcal{E}_3$ into $\mathcal{E}_3$.

13.7 Let $P_{\mathcal{S}}$ be the projection of $\mathcal{E}_3$ into the subspace $\mathcal{S}$ of $\mathcal{E}_3$ spanned by the nonzero orthogonal vectors $\mathbf{U}$ and $\mathbf{W}$. Derive the equations that give the coordinates $\langle x', y', z'\rangle$ of $P_{\mathcal{S}}(\mathbf{V})$ in terms of the coordinates $\langle x, y, z\rangle$ of $\mathbf{V}$. Find the special form of these equations when $\mathbf{U}$ and $\mathbf{W}$ are the unit vectors $\mathbf{I}$ and $\mathbf{J}$ with the directions of the X- and Y-axis, respectively. Prove that $\mathbf{V} - P_{\mathcal{S}}(\mathbf{V})$ is orthogonal to both $\mathbf{U}$ and $\mathbf{W}$.

14 Definition of a linear transformation

In the preceding section we introduced the notion of a linear transformation of $\mathcal{E}_2$ or $\mathcal{E}_3$. The concept of a linear transformation of a vector space $\mathcal{V}$ is the central idea in the study of linear algebra.

(14.1) Definition. A mapping L of a vector space $\mathcal{V}$ into a vector space $\mathcal{W}$, such that

$$L(a \cdot \mathbf{U} + b \cdot \mathbf{W}) = a \cdot L(\mathbf{U}) + b \cdot L(\mathbf{W}),$$

for all $\mathbf{U}$, $\mathbf{W}$ in $\mathcal{V}$ and all real numbers a, b, is called a *linear transformation* of $\mathcal{V}$ into $\mathcal{W}$.

A mapping L of $\mathcal{V}$ into $\mathcal{W}$ is a single-valued function of $\mathcal{V}$ into $\mathcal{W}$. That is, for each $\mathbf{U} \in \mathcal{V}$, $L(\mathbf{U})$ is a unique vector in $\mathcal{W}$. The vector $L(\mathbf{U})$ is called the *image* of $\mathbf{U}$ by L. In Definition 14.1, the vector space $\mathcal{W}$ may be taken to be the space $\mathcal{V}$. In this case, we say that L is a linear transformation of $\mathcal{V}$ into itself. The condition

$$L(a \cdot \mathbf{U} + b \cdot \mathbf{W}) = a \cdot L(\mathbf{U}) + b \cdot L(\mathbf{W}),$$

for all $\mathbf{U}$, $\mathbf{W}$ in $\mathcal{V}$ and all real numbers a, b, is easily seen to be equivalent to the two conditions

$$L(\mathbf{U} + \mathbf{W}) = L(\mathbf{U}) + L(\mathbf{W}) \tag{14-1}$$

and

$$L(a \cdot \mathbf{U}) = a \cdot L(\mathbf{U}), \tag{14-2}$$

for all $\mathbf{U}$, $\mathbf{W}$ in $\mathcal{V}$ and every real number a.

By (14-1),

$$L(\mathbf{0}) = L(\mathbf{0} + \mathbf{0}) = L(\mathbf{0}) + L(\mathbf{0}).$$

Subtracting the vector $L(\mathbf{0})$ from both sides of this equation, we find that $L(\mathbf{0})$ is the zero vector of $\mathcal{W}$. That is, $L(\mathbf{0}) = \mathbf{0}$ (where the same symbol $\mathbf{0}$ is used to denote both the zero vector in $\mathcal{V}$ and the zero vector in $\mathcal{W}$). By (14-2),

$$L(-\mathbf{U}) = L((-1) \cdot \mathbf{U}) = (-1) \cdot L(\mathbf{U}) = -L(\mathbf{U}).$$

Thus, the image of the negative of a vector is the negative of the image of the vector.

If $\mathcal{S}$ is a subspace of $\mathcal{V}$, then $L(\mathcal{S})$ is the set of all vectors in $\mathcal{W}$ that are images of vectors in $\mathcal{S}$. That is,

$$L(\mathcal{S}) = \{L(\mathbf{U}) \mid \mathbf{U} \in \mathcal{S}\}.$$

If $\mathfrak{I}$ is a subspace of $\mathcal{W}$, then $L^{-1}(\mathfrak{I})$ is the set of all vectors in $\mathcal{V}$ whose images by L are in $\mathfrak{I}$. Thus,

$$L^{-1}(\mathfrak{I}) = \{\mathbf{U} \mid L(\mathbf{U}) \in \mathfrak{I}\}.$$

The set of vectors $L(\mathcal{S})$ is called the *image* of $\mathcal{S}$, and $L^{-1}(\mathfrak{I})$ is called the *complete inverse image* of $\mathfrak{I}$.

(14.2) **Theorem.** Let L be a linear transformation of $\mathcal{V}$ into $\mathcal{W}$, and let $\mathcal{S}$ be a subspace of $\mathcal{V}$ and $\mathfrak{I}$ be a subspace of $\mathcal{W}$. Then $L(\mathcal{S})$ is a subspace of $\mathcal{W}$ and $L^{-1}(\mathfrak{I})$ is a subspace of $\mathcal{V}$.

PROOF. Since $\mathbf{0} \in \mathcal{S}$, $L(\mathcal{S})$ is nonempty. Suppose that $\mathbf{U}'$ and $\mathbf{W}'$ are in $L(\mathcal{S})$. Then $\mathbf{U}' = L(\mathbf{U})$ and $\mathbf{W}' = L(\mathbf{W})$ for some $\mathbf{U}, \mathbf{W} \in \mathcal{S}$. Since $\mathcal{S}$ is a subspace of $\mathcal{V}$, it follows that $\mathbf{U} + \mathbf{W} \in \mathcal{S}$ and $a \cdot \mathbf{U} \in \mathcal{S}$ for any real number a. Therefore, by (14-1) and (14-2),

$$\mathbf{U}' + \mathbf{W}' = L(\mathbf{U}) + L(\mathbf{W}) = L(\mathbf{U} + \mathbf{W}) \in L(\mathcal{S})$$

and

$$a \cdot \mathbf{U}' = a \cdot L(\mathbf{U}) = L(a \cdot \mathbf{U}) \in L(\mathcal{S}).$$

Hence, by Theorem 7.5, $L(\mathcal{S})$ is a subspace of $\mathcal{W}$.

Since $\mathbf{0} \in \mathfrak{I}$, and $L(\mathbf{0}) = \mathbf{0}$, it follows that $\mathbf{0} \in L^{-1}(\mathfrak{I})$. Thus, $L^{-1}(\mathfrak{I})$ is nonempty. Suppose that $\mathbf{U}$ and $\mathbf{W}$ are in $L^{-1}(\mathfrak{I})$. Then $L(\mathbf{U})$ and $L(\mathbf{W})$ are in $\mathfrak{I}$. Therefore, $L(\mathbf{U}) + L(\mathbf{W}) \in \mathfrak{I}$, and $a \cdot L(\mathbf{U}) \in \mathfrak{I}$ for any real number a, since $\mathfrak{I}$ is a subspace of $\mathcal{W}$. Again by (14-1) and (14-2),

$$L(\mathbf{U} + \mathbf{W}) = L(\mathbf{U}) + L(\mathbf{W}) \in \mathfrak{I}$$

and

$$L(a \cdot \mathbf{U}) = a \cdot L(\mathbf{U}) \in \mathfrak{I}.$$

Hence, $\mathbf{U} + \mathbf{W} \in L^{-1}(\mathfrak{I})$ and $a \cdot \mathbf{U} \in L^{-1}(\mathfrak{I})$. By Theorem 7.5, $L^{-1}(\mathfrak{I})$ is a subspace of $\mathcal{V}$.

If we take $\mathcal{S} = \mathcal{V}$ in Theorem 14.2, then $L(\mathcal{V})$ is a subspace of $\mathcal{W}$, which is called the *range space* of L. Let $\mathcal{J} = \{\mathbf{0}\}$ be the zero subspace of $\mathcal{W}$. Then, by Theorem 14.2, $L^{-1}(\{\mathbf{0}\})$ is a subspace of $\mathcal{V}$, which is called the *null space* or *kernel* of L.

Example 1. Let $P_{\mathbf{U}}$ be the orthogonal projection of $\mathcal{E}_2$ into the subspace $\mathcal{S}$ spanned by the nonzero vector $\mathbf{U} \in \mathcal{E}_2$. Then $P_{\mathbf{U}}$ is a mapping of $\mathcal{E}_2$ into $\mathcal{E}_2$. We proved in Section 13 that $P_{\mathbf{U}}$ is a linear transformation of $\mathcal{E}_2$. Now $\mathcal{S}$ is the set of all vectors $k \cdot \mathbf{U}$, where k is a real number. Since

$$P_{\mathbf{U}}(\mathbf{V}) = \left(\frac{\mathbf{V} \circ \mathbf{U}}{\mathbf{U} \circ \mathbf{U}}\right) \cdot \mathbf{U}$$

for $\mathbf{V} \in \mathcal{E}_2$, it follows that $P_{\mathbf{U}}(\mathcal{E}_2) \subseteq \mathcal{S}$. Moreover, for any real number k,

$$P_{\mathbf{U}}(k \cdot \mathbf{U}) = \left(\frac{(k \cdot \mathbf{U}) \circ \mathbf{U}}{\mathbf{U} \circ \mathbf{U}}\right) \cdot \mathbf{U} = \left(\frac{k(\mathbf{U} \circ \mathbf{U})}{\mathbf{U} \circ \mathbf{U}}\right) \cdot \mathbf{U} = k \cdot \mathbf{U}.$$

Therefore $P_{\mathbf{U}}(\mathcal{E}_2) = \mathcal{S}$, so that $\mathcal{S}$ is the range space of $P_{\mathbf{U}}$. Thus, we say that $P_{\mathbf{U}}$ is a linear transformation of $\mathcal{E}_2$ *onto* $\mathcal{S}$. Suppose that $P_{\mathbf{U}}(\mathbf{V}) = \mathbf{0}$. This implies $\mathbf{V} \circ \mathbf{U} = 0$, that is, $\mathbf{V}$ and $\mathbf{U}$ are orthogonal. Conversely, if $\mathbf{V} \circ \mathbf{U} = 0$, then $P_{\mathbf{U}}(\mathbf{V}) = \mathbf{0}$. Therefore, the null space of $P_{\mathbf{U}}$ is the set of all vectors in $\mathcal{E}_2$ that are orthogonal to the vector $\mathbf{U}$.

Example 2. Let L be the mapping of $\mathcal{V}_3$ into $\mathcal{V}_5$ defined by

$$L(\langle a_1, a_2, a_3\rangle) = \langle a_1 - a_2, 0, a_1 - a_3, a_2, 0\rangle.$$

The reader can verify that L is a linear transformation. Let $\mathcal{J}$ be the subspace of $\mathcal{V}_5$ with basis $\langle 1, 0, 0, 0, 0\rangle$, $\langle 0, 0, 1, 0, 0\rangle$, and $\langle 0, 0, 0, 1, 0\rangle$. Clearly, $L(\mathcal{V}_3) \subseteq \mathcal{J}$. Let

$$c_1 \cdot \langle 1, 0, 0, 0, 0\rangle + c_2 \cdot \langle 0, 0, 1, 0, 0\rangle + c_3 \cdot \langle 0, 0, 0, 1, 0\rangle = \langle c_1, 0, c_2, c_3, 0\rangle$$

be any element of $\mathcal{J}$. Then

$$L(\langle c_1 + c_3, c_3, c_1 + c_3 - c_2\rangle) = \langle c_1, 0, c_2, c_3, 0\rangle.$$

Therefore $L(\mathcal{V}_3) = \mathcal{J}$, and $\mathcal{J}$ is the range space of L. Suppose that $L(\langle a_1, a_2, a_3\rangle) = \langle 0, 0, 0, 0, 0\rangle$. Then

$$\begin{aligned} a_1 - a_2 &= 0 \\ a_1 - a_3 &= 0 \\ a_2 &= 0. \end{aligned}$$

This homogeneous system of equations has only the trivial solution $a_1 = a_2 = a_3 = 0$. Hence, the null space of L is $\{\langle 0, 0, 0\rangle\} = \{\mathbf{0}\}$.

Example 3. Let $\mathcal{V} = R[x]$ (see Example 1, Section 7). For

$$f(x) = a_n x^n + a_{n-1}x^{n-1} + \cdots + a_1 x + a_0 \in R[x],$$

let

$$D(f(x)) = na_n x^{n-1} + (n-1)a_{n-1}x^{n-2} + \cdots + 2a_2 x + a_1.$$

That is, $D(f(x))$ is the ordinary derivative of $f(x)$. It follows from the properties of the derivative that D is a linear transformation of $R[x]$ into $R[x]$. Since

$$D\left(\left(\frac{a_n}{n+1}\right)x^{n+1} + \left(\frac{a_{n-1}}{n}\right)x^n + \cdots + \left(\frac{a_1}{2}\right)x^2 + a_0x\right) = f(x)$$

for every $f(x) \in R[x]$, it follows that the range space of D is $R[x]$. Further, $D(g(x)) = 0$ if and only if $g(x)$ is a constant polynomial. Therefore, the null space of D is the set of all constant polynomials in $R[x]$.

(14.3) **Definition.** A linear transformation L of a vector space $\mathcal{V}$ into a vector space $\mathcal{W}$ is *nonsingular* if $L^{-1}(\{\mathbf{0}\}) = \{\mathbf{0}\}$; L is *singular* if $L^{-1}(\{\mathbf{0}\}) \neq \{\mathbf{0}\}$.

In Example 2, the linear transformation L of $\mathcal{V}_3$ into $\mathcal{V}_5$ is nonsingular. The linear transformations described in Examples 1 and 3 are singular. The following theorem gives a useful characterization of a nonsingular linear transformation.

(14.4) **Theorem.** A linear transformation L of a vector space $\mathcal{V}$ into a vector space $\mathcal{W}$ is nonsingular if and only if L is a one-to-one linear transformation of $\mathcal{V}$ onto $L(\mathcal{V})$.

PROOF. By a one-to-one linear transformation of $\mathcal{V}$ onto $L(\mathcal{V})$, we mean that L is a linear transformation that, at the same time, is a one-to-one correspondence of $\mathcal{V}$ onto $L(\mathcal{V})$. Suppose first that L is nonsingular. Assume that $L(\mathbf{U}) = L(\mathbf{W})$ for $\mathbf{U}, \mathbf{W} \in \mathcal{V}$. Then it follows from Definition 14.1 that

$$L(\mathbf{U} - \mathbf{W}) = L(\mathbf{U}) - L(\mathbf{W}) = \mathbf{0}.$$

Hence $\mathbf{U} - \mathbf{W} \in L^{-1}(\{\mathbf{0}\}) = \{\mathbf{0}\}$. That is, $\mathbf{U} - \mathbf{W} = \mathbf{0}$, so that $\mathbf{U} = \mathbf{W}$. This proves that different vectors in $\mathcal{V}$ are mapped onto different vectors in $L(\mathcal{V})$. Therefore, L is a one-to-one correspondence of $\mathcal{V}$ onto $L(\mathcal{V})$. Conversely, if L is one-to-one, then $\mathbf{0} \in \mathcal{V}$ is the only vector mapped onto $\mathbf{0} \in L(\mathcal{V})$. Hence, $L^{-1}(\{\mathbf{0}\}) = \{\mathbf{0}\}$, and L is nonsingular.

Another characterization of a nonsingular linear transformation can be given if $\mathcal{V}$ is finite dimensional.

(14.5) **Theorem.** Let L be a linear transformation of a finite dimensional vector space $\mathcal{V}$ into a vector space $\mathcal{W}$. Then L is nonsingular if and only if the dimension of $L(\mathcal{V})$ is equal to the dimension of $\mathcal{V}$.

PROOF. Let $S = \{\mathbf{U}_1, \mathbf{U}_2, \ldots, \mathbf{U}_n\}$ be a basis of $\mathcal{V}$, and consider the set $T = \{L(\mathbf{U}_1), L(\mathbf{U}_2), \ldots, L(\mathbf{U}_n)\} \subseteq L(\mathcal{V})$. Each vector $\mathbf{V} \in \mathcal{V}$ has an expression

$$\mathbf{V} = r_1 \cdot \mathbf{U}_1 + r_2 \cdot \mathbf{U}_2 + \cdots + r_n \cdot \mathbf{U}_n.$$

Therefore,

$$L(\mathbf{V}) = r_1 \cdot L(\mathbf{U}_1) + r_2 \cdot L(\mathbf{U}_2) + \cdots + r_n \cdot L(\mathbf{U}_n).$$

Hence, the set T spans $L(\mathcal{V})$.

Now suppose that L is nonsingular. If

$$\begin{aligned} \mathbf{0} &= r_1 \cdot L(\mathbf{U}_1) + r_2 \cdot L(\mathbf{U}_2) + \cdots + r_n \cdot L(\mathbf{U}_n) \\ &= L(r_1 \cdot \mathbf{U}_2 + r_2 \cdot \mathbf{U}_2 + \cdots + r_n \cdot \mathbf{U}_n), \end{aligned}$$

then, since $L^{-1}(\{\mathbf{0}\}) = \{\mathbf{0}\}$,

$$r_1 \cdot \mathbf{U}_1 + r_2 \cdot \mathbf{U}_2 + \cdots + r_n \cdot \mathbf{U}_n = \mathbf{0}.$$

This implies that $r_1 = r_2 = \cdots = r_n = 0$, since S is a basis of $\mathcal{V}$. Therefore T is a linearly independent set in $L(\mathcal{V})$ that spans $L(\mathcal{V})$. That is, T is a basis of $L(\mathcal{V})$. Hence, $\dim L(\mathcal{V}) = n = \dim \mathcal{V}$.

Conversely, assume that $\dim L(\mathcal{V}) = \dim \mathcal{V} = n$. Since T spans $L(\mathcal{V})$, it follows from Corollary 8.8 that T is a basis of $L(\mathcal{V})$. Therefore, if

$$\begin{aligned} \mathbf{0} = L(\mathbf{V}) &= L(r_1 \cdot \mathbf{U}_1 + r_2 \cdot \mathbf{U}_2 + \cdots + r_n \cdot \mathbf{U}_n) \\ &= r_1 \cdot L(\mathbf{U}_1) + r_2 \cdot L(\mathbf{U}_2) + \cdots + r_n \cdot L(\mathbf{U}_n), \end{aligned}$$

we have $r_1 = r_2 = \cdots = r_n = 0$; hence, $\mathbf{V} = \mathbf{0}$. We have proved that $L^{-1}(\{\mathbf{0}\}) = \{\mathbf{0}\}$. That is, L is nonsingular.

(14.6) Corollary. Let L be a linear transformation of a finite dimensional vector space $\mathcal{V}$ into itself. Then L is nonsingular if and only if $L(\mathcal{V}) = \mathcal{V}$.

PROOF. If L is nonsingular, then, by Theorem 14.5, the dimension of $L(\mathcal{V})$ is equal to the dimension of $\mathcal{V}$. Therefore $L(\mathcal{V}) = \mathcal{V}$ by Corollary 8.9. Conversely, if $L(\mathcal{V}) = \mathcal{V}$, then $\dim L(\mathcal{V}) = \dim \mathcal{V}$. Hence, by Theorem 14.5, L is nonsingular.

(14.7) Definition. If L is a nonsingular linear transformation of $\mathcal{V}$ into $\mathcal{W}$ such that $L(\mathcal{V}) = \mathcal{W}$, then L is called an *isomorphism* of $\mathcal{V}$ onto $\mathcal{W}$. We say that $\mathcal{V}$ is *isomorphic* to $\mathcal{W}$.

If $\mathcal{V}$ is isomorphic to $\mathcal{W}$, then $\mathcal{V}$ and $\mathcal{W}$ are essentially the same as algebraic systems. For not only is there a one-to-one correspondence between $\mathcal{V}$ and $\mathcal{W}$ (that is, $\mathcal{V}$ and $\mathcal{W}$ are equivalent as sets), but also the conditions (14-1) and (14-2) imply that the operations of addition and scalar multiplication are "preserved" by the correspondence. Any property of $\mathcal{V}$ that can be stated as an identity in terms of the operations of addition and scalar multiplication is also a property of $\mathcal{W}$, and vice versa. The following theorem shows the importance of Example 4, Section 7.

(14.8) Theorem. A finite dimensional vector space $\mathcal{V}$ of dimension n is isomorphic to $\mathcal{V}_n$.

PROOF. Let $\{\mathbf{U}_1, \mathbf{U}_2, \ldots, \mathbf{U}_n\}$ be a basis of $\mathcal{V}$. Then every vector $\mathbf{V} \in \mathcal{V}$ has a unique expression

$$\mathbf{V} = r_1 \cdot \mathbf{U}_1 + r_2 \cdot \mathbf{U}_2 + \cdots + r_n \cdot \mathbf{U}_n.$$

Define a mapping L of $\mathcal{V}$ into $\mathcal{V}_n$ by

$$L(\mathbf{V}) = L(r_1 \cdot \mathbf{U}_1 + r_2 \cdot \mathbf{U}_2 + \cdots + r_n \cdot \mathbf{U}_n) = \langle r_1, r_2, \ldots, r_n \rangle.$$

The proof that L is an isomorphism of $\mathcal{V}$ onto $\mathcal{V}_n$ is left as an exercise (Exercise 14.6).

It follows from the isomorphism of Theorem 14.8 that addition and scalar multiplication of vectors in a finite dimensional vector space $\mathcal{V}$ can be performed in terms of the coordinates of the vectors with respect to some basis of $\mathcal{V}$. Let $\{\mathbf{U}_1, \mathbf{U}_2, \ldots, \mathbf{U}_n\}$ be a basis of $\mathcal{V}$ and let

$$\mathbf{V} = r_1 \cdot \mathbf{U}_1 + r_2 \cdot \mathbf{U}_2 + \cdots + r_n \cdot \mathbf{U}_n,$$

$$\mathbf{W} = s_1 \cdot \mathbf{U}_1 + s_2 \cdot \mathbf{U}_2 + \cdots + s_n \cdot \mathbf{U}_n.$$

By the isomorphism of Theorem 14.8, $\mathbf{V}$ corresponds to $\langle r_1, r_2, \ldots, r_n \rangle \in \mathcal{V}_n$ and $\mathbf{W}$ corresponds to $\langle s_1, s_2, \ldots, s_n \rangle \in \mathcal{V}_n$. Hence $\mathbf{V} + \mathbf{W}$ corresponds to

$$\langle r_1, r_2, \ldots, r_n \rangle + \langle s_1, s_2, \ldots, s_n \rangle = \langle r_1 + s_1, r_2 + s_2, \ldots, r_n + s_n \rangle,$$

where $r_1 + s_1$, $r_2 + s_2$, $\ldots$, $r_n + s_n$ are the coordinates of $\mathbf{V} + \mathbf{W}$. Similarly, for any real number r, $r \cdot \mathbf{V}$ corresponds to

$$r \cdot \langle r_1, r_2, \ldots, r_n \rangle = \langle rr_1, rr_2, \ldots, rr_n \rangle,$$

where $rr_1, rr_2, \ldots, rr_n$ are the coordinates of $r \cdot \mathbf{V}$.

Exercises

14.1 Show that the condition $L(a \cdot \mathbf{U} + b \cdot \mathbf{W}) = a \cdot L(\mathbf{U}) + b \cdot L(\mathbf{W})$ in Definition 14.1 is equivalent to the two conditions (14-1) and (14-2).

14.2 Let L be a linear transformation of $\mathcal{V}$ into $\mathcal{W}$, and let $\mathcal{S}$ be a subspace of $\mathcal{V}$. Show that $L^{-1}(L(\mathcal{S})) \supseteq \mathcal{S}$. Show that $L^{-1}(L(\mathcal{V})) = L^{-1}(\mathcal{W})$.

14.3 Verify that the mapping L of $\mathcal{V}_3$ into $\mathcal{V}_5$ given in Example 2 is a linear transformation.

14.4 The mapping L of $\mathcal{E}_2$ into $\mathcal{E}_2$ that sends a vector $\mathbf{V}$ with coordinates $\langle x, y \rangle$ into a vector $L(\mathbf{V})$ with coordinates $\langle x', y' \rangle$, where

$$x' = ax + by$$

$$y' = cx + dy,$$

for real numbers a, b, c, d, is a linear transformation. Prove that L is nonsingular if and only if $ad - bc \neq 0$.

***14.5** Let L be an isomorphism of the vector space $\mathcal{V}$ onto the vector space $\mathcal{W}$. Let M be the mapping of $\mathcal{W}$ into $\mathcal{V}$ defined by $M(\mathbf{U}) = \mathbf{V}$ if $L(\mathbf{V}) = \mathbf{U}$. Prove that M is an isomorphism of $\mathcal{W}$ onto $\mathcal{V}$.

14.6 Complete the proof of Theorem 14.8.

14.7 Prove that $\mathcal{V}_n$ is not isomorphic to $\mathcal{V}_m$ if $n \neq m$.

***14.8** Let L be a linear transformation of a finite dimensional vector space $\mathcal{V}$ into a vector space $\mathcal{W}$. (a) Prove that $\dim L(\mathcal{V}) \leq \dim \mathcal{V}$. (b) Prove that $\dim L^{-1}(\{\mathbf{0}\}) + \dim L(\mathcal{V}) = \dim \mathcal{V}$ (which is a generalization of Theorem 14.5).

***14.9** Let L be a nonsingular linear transformation of a finite dimensional vector space $\mathcal{V}$ into a vector space $\mathcal{W}$, and let $\mathcal{S}$ be a subspace of $\mathcal{V}$. Prove that $\dim L(\mathcal{S}) = \dim \mathcal{S}$. Suppose that $\mathcal{S}$ is spanned by $\mathbf{U}_1, \mathbf{U}_2, \ldots, \mathbf{U}_k$. Prove that $L(\mathcal{S})$ is spanned by $L(\mathbf{U}_1), L(\mathbf{U}_2), \ldots, L(\mathbf{U}_k)$.

15 The algebra of linear transformations

Let $\mathfrak{M}$ be the set of all linear transformations of a vector space $\mathcal{V}$ into a vector space $\mathcal{W}$. Then operations of *addition* and *scalar multiplication* by a real number can be defined in $\mathfrak{M}$ in a natural way. If L and M are in $\mathfrak{M}$, then the mappings $L + M$ and $r \cdot L$ defined by the rules

$$(L + M)(\mathbf{U}) = L(\mathbf{U}) + M(\mathbf{U}) \tag{15-1}$$

$$(r \cdot L)(\mathbf{U}) = r \cdot L(\mathbf{U}), \tag{15-2}$$

for $\mathbf{U} \in \mathcal{V}$, are readily seen to be linear transformations of $\mathcal{V}$ into $\mathcal{W}$. The mapping $\mathbf{O}$ of $\mathcal{V}$ into $\mathcal{W}$ defined by $\mathbf{O}(\mathbf{U}) = \mathbf{0}$ for all $\mathbf{U} \in \mathcal{V}$ is called the *zero mapping*. The zero mapping is a linear transformation, and

$$(L + \mathbf{O})(\mathbf{U}) = L(\mathbf{U}) + \mathbf{O}(\mathbf{U}) = L(\mathbf{U}) + \mathbf{0} = L(\mathbf{U})$$

for all $L \in \mathfrak{M}$. Thus, $L + \mathbf{O} = L$. Similarly. $\mathbf{O} + L = L$. For $L \in \mathfrak{M}$, the mapping $-L$ is defined by $(-L)(\mathbf{U}) = -L(\mathbf{U})$ for $\mathbf{U} \in \mathcal{V}$. Then $-L \in \mathfrak{M}$ and

$$L + (-L) = (-L) + L = \mathbf{O}.$$

Using these definitions, it is a routine job to prove the following theorem by verifying that the conditions (a) through (j) of Definition 7.2 are satisfied.

(15.1) Theorem. Let $\mathfrak{M}$ be the set of all linear transformations of a vector space $\mathcal{V}$ into a vector space $\mathcal{W}$. Then $\mathfrak{M}$ is a vector space with respect to the operations of addition and scalar multiplication defined by (15-1) and (15-2).

Let $\mathcal{V}$, $\mathcal{W}$, and $\mathcal{P}$ be vector spaces, and suppose that L is a linear transformation of $\mathcal{V}$ into $\mathcal{W}$ and that M is a linear transformation of $\mathcal{W}$ into $\mathcal{P}$. For each $\mathbf{U} \in \mathcal{V}$, $L(\mathbf{U})$ is a unique vector in $\mathcal{W}$; hence $M(L(\mathbf{U}))$ is a unique vector in $\mathcal{P}$. Thus, if we define

$$(ML)(\mathbf{U}) = M(L(\mathbf{U})) \tag{15-3}$$

for $\mathbf{U} \in \mathcal{V}$, ML is a mapping of $\mathcal{V}$ into $\mathcal{P}$. Moreover, ML satisfies the linearity condition of Definition 14.1. Indeed,

$$\begin{aligned}(ML)(a \cdot \mathbf{U} + b \cdot \mathbf{W}) &= M(L(a \cdot \mathbf{U} + b \cdot \mathbf{W})) = M(a \cdot L(\mathbf{U}) + b \cdot L(\mathbf{W}))\\ &= a \cdot M(L(\mathbf{U})) + b \cdot M(L(\mathbf{W}))\\ &= a \cdot (ML)(\mathbf{U}) + b \cdot (ML)(\mathbf{W}),\end{aligned}$$

using the facts that L is a linear transformation of $\mathcal{V}$ and M is a linear transformation of $\mathcal{W}$. Thus, ML is a linear transformation of $\mathcal{V}$ into $\mathcal{P}$. If $\mathcal{V} = \mathcal{W} = \mathcal{P}$, so that L and M are linear transformations of $\mathcal{V}$ into itself, then ML is a linear transformation of $\mathcal{V}$ into itself. The rule (15-3) is the usual composition of mappings and is called *multiplication* of linear transformations. The linear transformation ML is called the *product* of L and M.

Example 1. The mappings L and M of $\mathcal{V}_5$ into itself defined by

$$L(\langle a_1, a_2, a_3, a_4, a_5\rangle) = \langle a_1 + 2a_2, 0, a_4 - a_5, 0, a_3\rangle$$

and

$$M(\langle a_1, a_2, a_3, a_4, a_5\rangle) = \langle a_1, a_1 + a_2, a_1 + a_2 + a_3, 5a_4, -a_5\rangle$$

are linear transformations. Then

$$\begin{aligned}(L + M)(\langle a_1, a_2, a_3, a_4, a_5\rangle) &= \langle a_1 + 2a_2, 0, a_4 - a_5, 0, a_3\rangle\\ &\quad + \langle a_1, a_1 + a_2, a_1 + a_2 + a_3, 5a_4, -a_5\rangle\\ &= \langle 2a_1 + 2a_2, a_1 + a_2, a_1 + a_2 + a_3 + a_4 - a_5, 5a_4,\\ &\quad a_3 - a_5\rangle,\\ (10 \cdot L)(\langle a_1, a_2, a_3, a_4, a_5\rangle) &= 10 \cdot \langle a_1 + 2a_2, 0, a_4 - a_5, 0, a_3\rangle\\ &= \langle 10a_1 + 20a_2, 0, 10a_4 - 10a_5, 0, 10a_3\rangle,\\ (ML)(\langle a_1, a_2, a_3, a_4, a_5\rangle) &= M(\langle a_1 + 2a_2, 0, a_4 - a_5, 0, a_3\rangle)\\ &= \langle a_1 + 2a_2, a_1 + 2a_2, a_1 + 2a_2 + a_4 - a_5, 0, -a_3\rangle,\\ (LM)(\langle a_1, a_2, a_3, a_4, a_5\rangle &= L(\langle a_1, a_1 + a_2, a_1 + a_2 + a_3, 5a_4, -a_5\rangle)\\ &= \langle 3a_1 + 2a_2, 0, 5a_4 + a_5, 0, a_1 + a_2 + a_3\rangle.\end{aligned}$$

Example 2. Let L be the linear transformation of $\mathcal{V}_3$ into $\mathcal{V}_5$ given in Example 2, Section 14. The mapping M of $\mathcal{V}_5$ into $\mathcal{V}_4$ defined by

$$M(\langle b_1, b_2, b_3, b_4, b_5\rangle) = \langle b_1, b_2, b_3, b_4\rangle$$

is a linear transformation. Then,

$$(ML)(\langle a_1, a_2, a_3\rangle) = M(\langle a_1 - a_2, 0, a_1 - a_3, a_2, 0\rangle)$$
$$= \langle a_1 - a_2, 0, a_1 - a_3, a_2\rangle.$$

Example 3. Let $P_{\mathbf{U}}$ be the projection of $\mathcal{E}_2$ onto the subspace $\mathcal{S}$ spanned by the nonzero vector $\mathbf{U}$ of $\mathcal{E}_2$. For $\mathbf{V} \in \mathcal{E}_2$,

$$P_{\mathbf{U}}^2(\mathbf{V}) = P_{\mathbf{U}}(P_{\mathbf{U}}(\mathbf{V})) = P_{\mathbf{U}}\left(\left(\frac{\mathbf{V} \circ \mathbf{U}}{\mathbf{U} \circ \mathbf{U}}\right) \cdot \mathbf{U}\right)$$
$$= \left(\frac{\mathbf{V} \circ \mathbf{U}}{\mathbf{U} \circ \mathbf{U}}\right) \cdot P_{\mathbf{U}}(\mathbf{U}) = \left(\frac{\mathbf{V} \circ \mathbf{U}}{\mathbf{U} \circ \mathbf{U}}\right) \cdot \mathbf{U} = P_{\mathbf{U}}(\mathbf{V}).$$

Hence, $P_{\mathbf{U}}^2 = P_{\mathbf{U}}$.

Suppose that in addition to the vector spaces $\mathcal{V}$, $\mathcal{W}$, $\mathcal{P}$ and the linear transformations L of $\mathcal{V}$ into $\mathcal{W}$ and M of $\mathcal{W}$ into $\mathcal{P}$ described above, there is a space $\mathcal{Q}$ and a linear transformation N of $\mathcal{P}$ into $\mathcal{Q}$. Then ML maps $\mathcal{V}$ into $\mathcal{P}$ and N maps $\mathcal{P}$ into $\mathcal{Q}$, so that $N(ML)$ is a linear transformation of $\mathcal{V}$ into $\mathcal{Q}$. Similarly, NM maps $\mathcal{W}$ into $\mathcal{Q}$, so that $(NM)L$ is also a linear transformation of $\mathcal{V}$ into $\mathcal{Q}$. It is an immediate consequence of (15-3) that $[N(ML)](\mathbf{U}) = [(NM)L](\mathbf{U})$ for all vectors $\mathbf{U} \in \mathcal{V}$. That is, the multiplication of linear transformations is associative:

$$N(ML) = (NM)L. \tag{15-4}$$

The mapping that sends each vector of a space $\mathcal{V}$ into itself is a linear transformation of $\mathcal{V}$ into $\mathcal{V}$ called the *identity transformation* of $\mathcal{V}$. This transformation will be denoted by $I_{\mathcal{V}}$ (or simply by I if a single vector space $\mathcal{V}$ is under discussion). Thus, $I_{\mathcal{V}}(\mathbf{U}) = \mathbf{U}$ for all $\mathbf{U} \in \mathcal{V}$. If L is any linear transformation of $\mathcal{V}$ into $\mathcal{W}$, then $L(\mathbf{U}) = I_{\mathcal{W}}(L(\mathbf{U})) = L(I_{\mathcal{V}}(\mathbf{U}))$ for all $\mathbf{U} \in \mathcal{V}$. Therefore,

$$L = I_{\mathcal{W}}L = LI_{\mathcal{V}}. \tag{15-5}$$

Suppose that L is an isomorphism of $\mathcal{V}$ onto $\mathcal{W}$. For $\mathbf{U} \in \mathcal{W}$, let $M(\mathbf{U})$ be the unique vector $\mathbf{V} \in \mathcal{V}$ such that $L(\mathbf{V}) = \mathbf{U}$. Then M is an isomorphism of $\mathcal{W}$ onto $\mathcal{V}$ (see Exercise 14.5). The linear transformation M is called the *inverse* of L, and we write $M = L^*$. (We use the notation L^* for the inverse of an isomorphism L of $\mathcal{V}$ onto $\mathcal{W}$ instead of the more conventional notation L^{-1} to avoid confusion with the notation for the complete inverse image of a subspace of $\mathcal{W}$.) It is a consequence of the definition of L^* that $L^*L = I_{\mathcal{V}}$ and $LL^* = I_{\mathcal{W}}$. The converse of this result is given by the following theorem.

(15.2) Theorem. Let L be a linear transformation of $\mathcal{V}$ into $\mathcal{W}$, and let M be a linear transformation of $\mathcal{W}$ into $\mathcal{V}$ such that $ML = I_{\mathcal{V}}$ and $LM = I_{\mathcal{W}}$. Then L is an isomorphism of $\mathcal{V}$ onto $\mathcal{W}$ and $M = L^*$.

PROOF. Let $\mathbf{V} \in L^{-1}(\{\mathbf{0}\})$. Then $L(\mathbf{V}) = \mathbf{0} \in \mathcal{W}$, and $ML(\mathbf{V}) = M(\mathbf{0}) = \mathbf{0} \in \mathcal{V}$. However, since $ML = I_{\mathcal{V}}$, it follows that $ML(\mathbf{V}) = \mathbf{V}$. Hence, $\mathbf{V} = \mathbf{0}$, and $L^{-1}(\{\mathbf{0}\}) = \{\mathbf{0}\}$. Thus, L is nonsingular. Let $\mathbf{U} \in \mathcal{W}$. Since $LM(\mathbf{U}) = I_{\mathcal{W}}(\mathbf{U}) = \mathbf{U}$, it follows that $M(\mathbf{U})$ is a vector in $\mathcal{V}$ such that $L(M(\mathbf{U})) = \mathbf{U}$. Therefore, $L(\mathcal{V}) = \mathcal{W}$. By Definition 14.7, L is an isomorphism of $\mathcal{V}$ onto $\mathcal{W}$. Since L is an isomorphism, the inverse transformation L^* exists. Thus, we have

$$L^* = L^*I_{\mathcal{W}} = L^*(LM) = (L^*L)M = I_{\mathcal{V}}M = M,$$

which completes the proof of the theorem.

If L is a nonsingular transformation of a finite dimensional vector space $\mathcal{V}$ into itself, then, by Corollary 14.6, $L(\mathcal{V}) = \mathcal{V}$. Hence, L is an isomorphism of $\mathcal{V}$ onto $\mathcal{V}$ (Definition 14.7), and the inverse transformation L^* exists and is an isomorphism. Therefore, L^* is nonsingular and $L^*(\mathcal{V}) = \mathcal{V}$. Let I be the identity transformation of $\mathcal{V}$. Then $L^*L = LL^* = I$. Conversely, by Theorem 15.2, if L and M are linear transformations of $\mathcal{V}$ into $\mathcal{V}$ such that $ML = LM = I$, then L and M are nonsingular and $M = L^*$.

Let $\mathfrak{M}$ be the set of all linear transformations of a vector space $\mathcal{V}$ (not necessarily finite dimensional) into itself. In this case all three operations—addition (15-1), scalar multiplication (15-2), and multiplication (15-3)—are defined in $\mathfrak{M}$. The identity transformation I is in $\mathfrak{M}$. Let $K, L, M \in \mathfrak{M}$, and let r be a real number. Then in addition to the associativity of multiplication in $\mathfrak{M}$ (15-4) and those properties of addition and scalar multiplication that are a consequence of the fact that $\mathfrak{M}$ is a vector space (Theorem 15.1), the following identities are satisfied:

$$K(L + M) = KL + KM \tag{15-6}$$

$$(K + L)M = KM + LM \tag{15-7}$$

$$r \cdot (LM) = (r \cdot L)M = L(r \cdot M) \tag{15-8}$$

$$L = IL = LI. \tag{15-9}$$

Exercises

15.1 Let L and M be linear transformations of a vector space $\mathcal{V}$ into a vector space $\mathcal{W}$. Prove that $L + M$ and $r \cdot L$, as defined by (15-1) and (15-2), are linear transformations of $\mathcal{V}$ into $\mathcal{W}$.

15.2 Let T_φ and $P_{\mathcal{U}}$ be the linear transformations of $\mathcal{E}_2$ into $\mathcal{E}_2$ defined in Section 13. Let $\mathbf{V} \in \mathcal{E}_2$ have coordinates $\langle x, y\rangle$ with respect to a rectangular Cartesian coordinate system for $\mathcal{E}_2$. Compute the coordinates of the following vectors in $\mathcal{E}_2$:

$$(T_\varphi + P_{\mathcal{U}})(\mathbf{V}); \quad (3 \cdot T_\varphi)(\mathbf{V}); \quad (-5 \cdot P_{\mathcal{U}})(\mathbf{V});$$

$$(T_\varphi P_{\mathcal{U}})(\mathbf{V}); \quad (P_{\mathcal{U}} T_\varphi)(\mathbf{V}); \quad (-T_\varphi)(\mathbf{V}); \quad (2 \cdot T_\varphi + 7 \cdot P_{\mathcal{U}})(\mathbf{V}).$$

15.3 Let $\mathfrak{M}$ be the set of all linear transformations of a vector space $\mathcal{V}$ into a vector space $\mathcal{W}$. Prove that the zero mapping $\mathbf{O}$ of $\mathcal{V}$ into $\mathcal{W}$ is in $\mathfrak{M}$. For $L \in \mathfrak{M}$, prove that $-L \in \mathfrak{M}$. Prove that $L + (-L) = (-L) + L = \mathbf{O}$.

15.4 Prove Theorem 15.1.

15.5 Let L be a linear transformation of $\mathcal{V}$ into $\mathcal{W}$, and let M be a linear transformation of $\mathcal{W}$ into $\mathcal{P}$. Prove that the range space of ML is contained in the range space of M. Under what condition are these range spaces the same subspace of $\mathcal{P}$? Prove that the null space of L is contained in the null space of ML. Under what condition are these null spaces the same subspace of $\mathcal{V}$?

15.6 In Example 2, show that the range space of ML is a proper subspace of the range space of M, that is, $ML(\mathcal{V}_3) \subset M(\mathcal{V}_5)$. Show that the null space of L is the same subspace of $\mathcal{V}_3$ as the null space of ML, that is $L^{-1}(\{\mathbf{0}\}) = (ML)^{-1}(\{\mathbf{0}\})$. Is ML a nonsingular transformation of $\mathcal{V}_3$ into $\mathcal{V}_4$? Is M a nonsingular transformation of $\mathcal{V}_5$ into $\mathcal{V}_4$? Is ML an isomorphism of $\mathcal{V}_3$ onto $\mathcal{V}_4$?

***15.7** Let L be a nonsingular linear transformation of $\mathcal{V}$ into $\mathcal{W}$, and let M be a nonsingular linear transformation of $\mathcal{W}$ into $\mathcal{P}$. Prove that ML is a nonsingular linear transformation of $\mathcal{V}$ into $\mathcal{P}$.

15.8 Let L be an isomorphism of $\mathcal{V}$ onto $\mathcal{W}$, and let L^* be the inverse of L. Prove that $L^*L = I_{\mathcal{V}}$ and $LL^* = I_{\mathcal{W}}$.

15.9 Let $\mathfrak{M}$ be the set of all linear transformations of a vector space $\mathcal{V}$ into itself. Let $K, L, M \in \mathfrak{M}$, and let I be the identity transformation of $\mathcal{V}$. Prove the identities (15-6), (15-7), (15-8), and (15-9).

16 The matrix of a linear transformation

In the remaining sections of this text, we will be concerned with linear transformations of finite dimensional vector spaces. Let $\mathcal{V}$ and $\mathcal{W}$ be finite dimensional vector spaces of dimensions n and m, respectively. Let $\{\mathbf{U}_1, \mathbf{U}_2, \ldots, \mathbf{U}_n\}$ be a basis of $\mathcal{V}$, and let $\{\mathbf{W}_1, \mathbf{W}_2, \ldots, \mathbf{W}_m\}$ be a basis of $\mathcal{W}$. Suppose that L is a linear transformation of $\mathcal{V}$ into $\mathcal{W}$. Then if $\mathbf{V}$ is any vector in $\mathcal{V}$,

$$\mathbf{V} = r_1 \cdot \mathbf{U}_1 + r_2 \cdot \mathbf{U}_2 + \cdots + r_n \cdot \mathbf{U}_n.$$

Therefore, by the linearity condition of Definition 14.1,

$$L(\mathbf{V}) = r_1 \cdot L(\mathbf{U}_1) + r_2 \cdot L(\mathbf{U}_2) + \cdots + r_n \cdot L(\mathbf{U}_n).$$

Thus, the linear transformation L is determined completely by its effect on the basis vectors of $\mathcal{V}$. Since $L(\mathbf{U}_i) \in \mathcal{W}$, we have

$$L(\mathbf{U}_i) = a_{1,i} \cdot \mathbf{W}_1 + a_{2,i} \cdot \mathbf{W}_2 + \cdots + a_{m,i} \cdot \mathbf{W}_m,$$

for $i = 1, 2, \ldots, n$. The numbers $a_{1,i}, a_{2,i}, \ldots, a_{m,i}$ are the coordinates of $L(\mathbf{U}_i)$ with respect to the basis $\{\mathbf{W}_1, \mathbf{W}_2, \ldots, \mathbf{W}_m\}$. Therefore, these numbers are uniquely determined by L. We have

$$\begin{aligned}L(\mathbf{V}) &= r_1 \cdot (a_{1,1} \cdot \mathbf{W}_1 + a_{2,1} \cdot \mathbf{W}_2 + \cdots + a_{m,1} \cdot \mathbf{W}_m) \\ &\quad + r_2 \cdot (a_{1,2} \cdot \mathbf{W}_1 + a_{2,2} \cdot \mathbf{W}_2 + \cdots + a_{m,2} \cdot \mathbf{W}_m) \\ &\quad + \cdots + r_n \cdot (a_{1,n} \cdot \mathbf{W}_1 + a_{2,n} \cdot \mathbf{W}_2 + \cdots + a_{m,n} \cdot \mathbf{W}_m) \\ &= (r_1a_{1,1} + r_2a_{1,2} + \cdots + r_na_{1,n}) \cdot \mathbf{W}_1 \\ &\quad + (r_1a_{2,1} + r_2a_{2,2} + \cdots + r_na_{2,n}) \cdot \mathbf{W}_2 \\ &\quad + \cdots + (r_1a_{m,1} + r_2a_{m,2} + \cdots + r_na_{m,n}) \cdot \mathbf{W}_m.\end{aligned}$$

Let the coordinates of $L(\mathbf{V})$ with respect to the basis $\{\mathbf{W}_1, \mathbf{W}_2, \ldots, \mathbf{W}_m\}$ of $\mathcal{W}$ be denoted by $s_1, s_2, \ldots, s_m$. Then the linear transformation L is given by the system of linear equations

$$\begin{aligned}a_{1,1}r_1 + a_{1,2}r_2 + \cdots + a_{1,n}r_n &= s_1 \\ a_{2,1}r_1 + a_{2,2}r_2 + \cdots + a_{2,n}r_n &= s_2 \\ \cdots \\ a_{m,1}r_1 + a_{m,2}r_2 + \cdots + a_{m,n}r_n &= s_m.\end{aligned} \tag{16-1}$$

With respect to the given bases in $\mathcal{V}$ and $\mathcal{W}$, the equations (16-1) give the coordinates of $L(\mathbf{V})$ in terms of the coordinates of $\mathbf{V}$. Thus, L is completely described by the rectangular array of real numbers

$$\begin{bmatrix} a_{1,1} & a_{1,2} & \cdots & a_{1,n} \\ a_{2,1} & a_{2,2} & \cdots & a_{2,n} \\ \cdot & \cdot & & \cdot \\ \cdot & \cdot & & \cdot \\ \cdot & \cdot & & \cdot \\ a_{m,1} & a_{m,2} & \cdots & a_{m,n} \end{bmatrix}, \tag{16-2}$$

which is called the *matrix* of L with respect to the given bases.

Example 1. Let L be the linear transformation of $\mathcal{V}_3$ into $\mathcal{V}_5$ described in Example 2 of Section 14. Select the basis $E^{(3)} = \{\mathbf{E}_1^{(3)}, \mathbf{E}_2^{(3)}, \mathbf{E}_3^{(3)}\}$ for $\mathcal{V}_3$ and the basis $E^{(5)} = \{\mathbf{E}_1^{(5)}, \mathbf{E}_2^{(5)}, \mathbf{E}_3^{(5)}, \mathbf{E}_4^{(5)}, \mathbf{E}_5^{(5)}\}$ for $\mathcal{V}_5$. Then

$$\begin{aligned}L(\mathbf{E}_1^{(3)}) &= L(\langle 1, 0, 0\rangle) = \langle 1, 0, 1, 0, 0\rangle \\ &= 1 \cdot \mathbf{E}_1^{(5)} + 0 \cdot \mathbf{E}_2^{(5)} + 1 \cdot \mathbf{E}_3^{(5)} + 0 \cdot \mathbf{E}_4^{(5)} + 0 \cdot \mathbf{E}_5^{(5)} \\ L(\mathbf{E}_2^{(3)}) &= L(\langle 0, 1, 0\rangle) = \langle -1, 0, 0, 1, 0\rangle \\ &= (-1) \cdot \mathbf{E}_1^{(5)} + 0 \cdot \mathbf{E}_2^{(5)} + 0 \cdot \mathbf{E}_3^{(5)} + 1 \cdot \mathbf{E}_4^{(5)} + 0 \cdot \mathbf{E}_5^{(5)} \\ L(\mathbf{E}_3^{(3)}) &= L(\langle 0, 0, 1\rangle) = \langle 0, 0, -1, 0, 0\rangle \\ &= 0 \cdot \mathbf{E}_1^{(5)} + 0 \cdot \mathbf{E}_2^{(5)} + (-1) \cdot \mathbf{E}_3^{(5)} + 0 \cdot \mathbf{E}_4^{(5)} + 0 \cdot \mathbf{E}_5^{(5)}.\end{aligned}$$

Therefore, the matrix of L, with respect to the bases $E^{(3)}$ and $E^{(5)}$, is

$$\begin{bmatrix} 1 & -1 & 0 \\ 0 & 0 & 0 \\ 1 & 0 & -1 \\ 0 & 1 & 0 \\ 0 & 0 & 0 \end{bmatrix}.$$

Hence if $\mathbf{V} = \langle r_1, r_2, r_3 \rangle$ is any vector in $\mathcal{V}_3$, then $L(\mathbf{V}) = \langle s_1, s_2, s_3, s_4, s_5 \rangle$, where

$$\begin{aligned} 1r_1 - 1r_2 + 0r_3 &= s_1 \\ 0r_1 + 0r_2 + 0r_3 &= s_2 \\ 1r_1 + 0r_2 - 1r_3 &= s_3 \\ 0r_1 + 1r_2 + 0r_3 &= s_4 \\ 0r_1 + 0r_2 + 0r_3 &= s_5. \end{aligned}$$

Suppose that we select different bases in $\mathcal{V}_3$ and $\mathcal{V}_5$, say $B = \{\langle 1, 0, 0 \rangle, \langle 1, 1, 0 \rangle, \langle 1, 1, 1 \rangle\}$ as a basis for $\mathcal{V}_3$ and $C = \{\langle 1, 0, 0, 0, 0 \rangle, \langle 1, 1, 0, 0, 0 \rangle, \langle 1, 1, 1, 0, 0 \rangle, \langle 1, 1, 1, 1, 0 \rangle, \langle 1, 1, 1, 1, 1 \rangle\}$ as a basis for $\mathcal{V}_5$. Then

$$\begin{aligned} L(\langle 1, 0, 0 \rangle) &= \langle 1, 0, 1, 0, 0 \rangle \\ &= 1 \cdot \langle 1, 0, 0, 0, 0 \rangle + (-1) \cdot \langle 1, 1, 0, 0, 0 \rangle \\ &\quad + 1 \cdot \langle 1, 1, 1, 0, 0 \rangle, \\ L(\langle 1, 1, 0 \rangle) &= \langle 0, 0, 1, 1, 0 \rangle \\ &= (-1) \cdot \langle 1, 1, 0, 0, 0 \rangle + 1 \cdot \langle 1, 1, 1, 1, 0 \rangle, \\ L(\langle 1, 1, 1 \rangle) &= \langle 0, 0, 0, 1, 0 \rangle \\ &= (-1) \cdot \langle 1, 1, 1, 0, 0 \rangle + 1 \cdot \langle 1, 1, 1, 1, 0 \rangle. \end{aligned}$$

Therefore, the matrix of L with respect to the bases B and C is

$$\begin{bmatrix} 1 & 0 & 0 \\ -1 & -1 & 0 \\ 1 & 0 & -1 \\ 0 & 1 & 1 \\ 0 & 0 & 0 \end{bmatrix}.$$

We have seen that the concept of a rectangular matrix arises naturally in the study of a linear transformation of a vector space. Computational problems involving linear transformations will be solved by operating with their associated matrices. Matrices have other useful applications, so that it is worthwhile to study them as mathematical objects in their own right.

(16.1) Definition. An m by n *real matrix* A is a rectangular array

$$A = \begin{bmatrix} a_{1,1} & a_{1,2} & \cdots & a_{1,n} \\ a_{2,1} & a_{2,2} & \cdots & a_{2,n} \\ \cdot & \cdot & & \cdot \\ \cdot & \cdot & & \cdot \\ \cdot & \cdot & & \cdot \\ a_{m,1} & a_{m,2} & \cdots & a_{m,n} \end{bmatrix}$$

of m rows and n columns, where the elements $a_{i,j}$ are real numbers.

The position of each element in the array is given by its subscripts; that is, the element $a_{i,j}$ is in the ith row and jth column. The number m of rows and the number n of columns are called the *dimensions* of the matrix. When the dimensions of a matrix are known, we will abbreviate our notation and write $A = [a_{i,j}]$ for an m by n matrix.

Two matrices are *equal* if they are identically the same; that is,

$$A = \begin{bmatrix} a_{1,1} & a_{1,2} & \cdots & a_{1,n} \\ a_{2,1} & a_{2,2} & \cdots & a_{2,n} \\ \cdot & \cdot & & \cdot \\ \cdot & \cdot & & \cdot \\ \cdot & \cdot & & \cdot \\ a_{m,1} & a_{m,2} & \cdots & a_{m,n} \end{bmatrix} \quad \text{and} \quad B = \begin{bmatrix} b_{1,1} & b_{1,2} & \cdots & b_{1,q} \\ b_{2,1} & b_{2,2} & \cdots & b_{2,q} \\ \cdot & \cdot & & \cdot \\ \cdot & \cdot & & \cdot \\ \cdot & \cdot & & \cdot \\ b_{p,1} & b_{p,2} & \cdots & b_{p,q} \end{bmatrix}$$

are equal if and only if $m = p$, $n = q$ (A and B have the same dimensions), and $a_{i,j} = b_{i,j}$ for $i = 1, 2, \ldots, m$ and $j = 1, 2, \ldots, n$.

The following theorem expresses the important relation between linear transformations and matrices.

(16.2) Theorem. Let $\mathcal{V}$ and $\mathcal{W}$ be vector spaces with bases $\{\mathbf{U}_1, \mathbf{U}_2, \ldots, \mathbf{U}_n\}$ and $\{\mathbf{W}_1, \mathbf{W}_2, \ldots, \mathbf{W}_m\}$, respectively, and let $\mathfrak{M}$ be the set of all linear transformations of $\mathcal{V}$ into $\mathcal{W}$. The correspondence that associates each linear transformation $L \in \mathfrak{M}$ with the matrix of L with respect to the given bases is a one-to-one correspondence of $\mathfrak{M}$ onto the set of all m by n real matrices.

PROOF. Let $L \in \mathfrak{M}$. The matrix of L with respect to the given bases in $\mathcal{V}$ and $\mathcal{W}$ is an m by n matrix A, where the elements of the jth column of A are the coordinates $a_{1,j}, a_{2,j}, \ldots, a_{m,j}$ of $L(\mathbf{U}_j)$ with respect to $\{\mathbf{W}_1, \mathbf{W}_2, \ldots, \mathbf{W}_m\}$. Therefore, each L uniquely determines an m by n matrix (by Theorem 8.5). Conversely, let $A = [a_{i,j}]$ be any m by n matrix. Then it can be shown that the mapping L of $\mathcal{V}$ into $\mathcal{W}$ defined by

$$L(r_1 \cdot \mathbf{U}_1 + r_2 \cdot \mathbf{U}_2 + \cdots + r_n \cdot \mathbf{U}_n) = s_1 \cdot \mathbf{W}_1 + s_2 \cdot \mathbf{W}_2 + \cdots + s_m \cdot \mathbf{W}_m,$$

where the r's and s's are related by equations (16-1), is a linear transformation of $\mathcal{V}$ into $\mathcal{W}$ with associated matrix A. (This portion of the proof is left as an exercise (Exercise 16.3).) For $L, M \in \mathfrak{M}$, suppose that the matrix of L is $A = [a_{i,j}]$ and the matrix of M is the m by n matrix $B = [b_{i,j}]$. Let $\mathbf{V} = r_1 \cdot \mathbf{U}_1 + r_2 \cdot \mathbf{U}_2 + \cdots + r_n \cdot \mathbf{U}_n$ be any vector in $\mathcal{V}$. Then the ith coordinate of $L(\mathbf{V})$ is $a_{i,1}r_1 + a_{i,2}r_2 + \cdots + a_{i,n}r_n$, and the ith coordinate of $M(\mathbf{V})$ is $b_{i,1}r_1 + b_{i,2}r_2 + \cdots + b_{i,n}r_n$, for $i = 1, 2, \ldots, m$. If $A = B$, then $a_{i,j} = b_{i,j}$, for all i, j. Therefore, $L(\mathbf{V}) = M(\mathbf{V})$ for all $\mathbf{V} \in \mathcal{V}$. Hence $L = M$, which shows that the correspondence described in the theorem is one-to-one, and completes the proof.

We now consider the important special case where L is a linear transformation of the vector space $\mathcal{V}$ into itself. Let $\{\mathbf{U}_1, \mathbf{U}_2, \ldots, \mathbf{U}_n\}$ be a basis of $\mathcal{V}$. Then the image $L(\mathbf{V})$ of a vector $\mathbf{V} = r_1 \cdot \mathbf{U}_1 + r_2 \cdot \mathbf{U}_2 + \cdots + r_n \cdot \mathbf{U}_n$ can be expressed in terms of this same basis. That is,

$$\begin{aligned} L(\mathbf{V}) &= r_1 \cdot L(\mathbf{U}_1) + r_2 \cdot L(\mathbf{U}_2) + \cdots + r_n \cdot L(\mathbf{U}_n) \\ &= s_1 \cdot \mathbf{U}_1 + s_2 \cdot \mathbf{U}_2 + \cdots + s_n \cdot \mathbf{U}_n. \end{aligned}$$

In particular, if we write $L(\mathbf{U}_i) = a_{1,i} \cdot \mathbf{U}_1 + a_{2,i} \cdot \mathbf{U}_2 + \cdots + a_{n,i} \cdot \mathbf{U}_n$, for $i = 1, 2, \ldots, n$, then, as before, we have L given by the linear equations (16-1) with $m = n$. By Theorem 16.2, there is a one-to-one correspondence between the set $\mathfrak{M}$ of all linear transformations of $\mathcal{V}$ into itself and the set of all square n by n matrices.

Example 2. Let L be a linear transformation of $\mathcal{V}_3$ into itself. Suppose that

$$L(\langle 1, 0, 0\rangle) = \langle a_{1,1}, a_{2,1}, a_{3,1}\rangle,$$

$$L(\langle 0, 1, 0\rangle) = \langle a_{1,2}, a_{2,2}, a_{3,2}\rangle,$$

and

$$L(\langle 0, 0, 1\rangle) = \langle a_{1,3}, a_{2,3}, a_{3,3}\rangle.$$

Then the matrix of L with respect to the basis $E^{(3)} = \{\langle 1, 0, 0\rangle, \langle 0, 1, 0\rangle, \langle 0, 0, 1\rangle\}$ is the 3 by 3 matrix

$$A = \begin{bmatrix} a_{1,1} & a_{1,2} & a_{1,3} \\ a_{2,1} & a_{2,2} & a_{2,3} \\ a_{3,1} & a_{3,2} & a_{3,3} \end{bmatrix}.$$

If $\langle r_1, r_2, r_3\rangle \in \mathcal{V}$, then $L(\langle r_1, r_2, r_3\rangle) = \langle s_1, s_2, s_3\rangle$, where

$$\begin{aligned} a_{1,1}r_1 + a_{1,2}r_2 + a_{1,3}r_3 &= s_1 \\ a_{2,1}r_1 + a_{2,2}r_2 + a_{2,3}r_3 &= s_2 \\ a_{3,1}r_1 + a_{3,2}r_2 + a_{3,3}r_3 &= s_3. \end{aligned}$$

Conversely, if

$$B = \begin{bmatrix} b_{1,1} & b_{1,2} & b_{1,3} \\ b_{2,1} & b_{2,2} & b_{2,3} \\ b_{3,1} & b_{3,2} & b_{3,3} \end{bmatrix}$$

is any 3 by 3 matrix, then the mapping M defined by $M(\langle r_1, r_2, r_3 \rangle) = \langle s_1, s_2, s_3 \rangle$, where

$$\begin{aligned} b_{1,1}r_1 + b_{1,2}r_2 + b_{1,3}r_3 &= s_1 \\ b_{2,1}r_1 + b_{2,2}r_2 + b_{2,3}r_3 &= s_2 \\ b_{3,1}r_1 + b_{3,2}r_2 + b_{3,3}r_3 &= s_3. \end{aligned}$$

is a linear transformation of $\mathcal{V}_3$ into itself.

Exercises

16.1 Let L be the linear transformation of $\mathcal{V}_3$ into $\mathcal{V}_5$ given in Example 2, Section 14, and let M be the linear transformation of $\mathcal{V}_5$ into $\mathcal{V}_4$ given in Example 2, Section 15. The matrix of L with respect to the bases $E^{(3)}$ and $E^{(5)}$ was computed in Example 1 of this section. Compute the matrix of M with respect to the bases $E^{(5)}$ and $E^{(4)}$; also compute the matrix of ML with respect to the bases $E^{(3)}$ and $E^{(4)}$.

16.2 Let L and M be the linear transformations of $\mathcal{V}_5$ into itself given in Example 1, Section 15. With respect to the basis $E^{(5)}$ of $\mathcal{V}_5$, find the matrices of the following linear transformations of $\mathcal{V}_5$ into itself: L, M, $L + M$, $10 \cdot L$, ML, LM.

***16.3** Let $\mathcal{V}$ be a vector space of dimension n with basis $\{\mathbf{U}_1, \mathbf{U}_2, \ldots, \mathbf{U}_n\}$. Let $\mathcal{W}$ be a vector space of dimension m with basis $\{\mathbf{W}_1, \mathbf{W}_2, \ldots, \mathbf{W}_m\}$. Let L be the mapping of $\mathcal{V}$ into $\mathcal{W}$ defined by

$$L(r_1 \cdot \mathbf{U}_1 + r_2 \cdot \mathbf{U}_2 + \cdots + r_n \cdot \mathbf{U}_n) = s_1 \cdot \mathbf{W}_1 + s_2 \cdot \mathbf{W}_2 + \cdots + s_m \cdot \mathbf{W}_m,$$

where

$$\begin{aligned} a_{1,1}r_1 + a_{1,2}r_2 + \cdots + a_{1,n}r_n &= s_1 \\ a_{2,1}r_1 + a_{2,2}r_2 + \cdots + a_{2,n}r_n &= s_2 \\ &\cdots \\ a_{m,1}r_1 + a_{m,2}r_2 + \cdots + a_{m,n}r_n &= s_m. \end{aligned}$$

Prove that L is a linear transformation of $\mathcal{V}$ into $\mathcal{W}$ with matrix

$$A = \begin{bmatrix} a_{1,1} & a_{1,2} & \cdots & a_{1,n} \\ a_{2,1} & a_{2,2} & \cdots & a_{2,n} \\ \cdot & \cdot & & \cdot \\ \cdot & \cdot & & \cdot \\ \cdot & \cdot & & \cdot \\ a_{m,1} & a_{m,2} & \cdots & a_{m,n} \end{bmatrix}.$$

16.4 Let L be the linear transformation of $\mathcal{E}_2$ into $\mathcal{E}_2$ with matrix

$$\begin{bmatrix} \frac{1}{2} & \frac{-\sqrt{3}}{2} \\ \frac{\sqrt{3}}{2} & \frac{1}{2} \end{bmatrix}$$

with respect to the basis $\langle \mathbf{I}, \mathbf{J} \rangle$ of $\mathcal{E}_2$. Show that $L = T_\varphi$, with $\varphi = 60°$, where T_φ is the linear transformation of $\mathcal{E}_2$ described in Section 13.

16.5 Let L be the linear transformation of $\mathcal{E}_2$ into $\mathcal{E}_2$ with matrix

$$\begin{bmatrix} 25/61 & -30/61 \\ -30/61 & 36/61 \end{bmatrix}$$

with respect to the basis $\langle \mathbf{I}, \mathbf{J} \rangle$ of $\mathcal{E}_2$. Show that L is the projection $P_\mathbf{U}$ of $\mathcal{E}_2$ onto the subspace of $\mathcal{E}_2$ spanned by $\mathbf{U}$, where $\mathbf{U}$ has coordinates $\langle 5, -6 \rangle$ with respect to the given basis.

16.6 Let L be the linear transformation of $\mathcal{V}_2$ into $\mathcal{V}_4$ with matrix

$$\begin{bmatrix} -1 & 3 \\ 0 & 2 \\ -4 & 3 \\ 1 & 0 \end{bmatrix}$$

with respect to the bases $E^{(2)}$ and $E^{(4)}$. Find $L(\mathbf{V})$ for the following vectors $\mathbf{V} \in \mathcal{V}_2$: $\langle -2, 3 \rangle$; $\langle 0, 1 \rangle$; $\langle -1, -5 \rangle$; $\langle 1, 0 \rangle$; $\langle \sqrt{2}, \sqrt{3} \rangle$.

17 The algebra of matrices

The definitions of the operations of addition, scalar multiplication, and multiplication of matrices are based on the corresponding operations for linear transformations.

(17.1) Definition. If $A = [a_{i,j}]$ and $B = [b_{i,j}]$ are m by n matrices, then the *sum* of A and B is the m by n matrix

$$A + B = C = \begin{bmatrix} a_{1,1} + b_{1,1} & a_{1,2} + b_{1,2} & \cdots & a_{1,n} + b_{1,n} \\ a_{2,1} + b_{2,1} & a_{2,2} + b_{2,2} & \cdots & a_{2,n} + b_{2,n} \\ & & \cdots & \\ a_{m,1} + b_{m,1} & a_{m,2} + b_{m,2} & \cdots & a_{m,n} + b_{m,n} \end{bmatrix}.$$

Thus, $C = A + B$ is an m by n matrix with elements $c_{i,j} = a_{i,j} + b_{i,j}$, for $i = 1, 2, \ldots, m$ and $j = 1, 2, \ldots, n$. (Note that two matrices can be added only if they have the same dimensions.)

It is easy to establish the connection between matrix addition and the addition of linear transformations. Let $\mathcal{V}$ and $\mathcal{W}$ be vector spaces of dimensions n and m, respectively, and let L and M be linear transformations of $\mathcal{V}$ into $\mathcal{W}$ such that $A = [a_{i,j}]$ is the matrix of L and $B = [b_{i,j}]$ is the matrix of M with respect to chosen bases in $\mathcal{V}$ and $\mathcal{W}$. Then A and B are m by n matrices, and the matrix of the linear transformation $L + M$ of $\mathcal{V}$ into $\mathcal{W}$ is the sum of the matrices, $A + B$, as defined in 17.1.

Since, by Definition 17.1, matrices are added element-by-element, it follows from the associative and commutative properties of addition of real numbers that matrix addition is associative and commutative. Thus, if A, B, and C are m by n matrices,

$$(A + B) + C = A + (B + C), \tag{17-1}$$

and

$$A + B = B + A. \tag{17-2}$$

It also follows from Definition 17.1 that, for any dimensions m and n, there is a *zero matrix* $\mathbf{O}$, which has the number 0 in every position. Then for any m by n matrix $A = [a_{i,j}]$, we have

$$A + \mathbf{O} = \mathbf{O} + A = A.$$

Let $A = [a_{i,j}]$ and $B = [b_{i,j}]$ be m by n matrices. The *negative* of A is the m by n matrix $-A = [-a_{i,j}]$, which has the negative of $a_{i,j}$ in every position. Further, subtraction of m by n matrices is defined by

$$B - A = B + (-A).$$

In particular,

$$A - A = A + (-A) = (-A) + A = \mathbf{O}.$$

(17.2) **Definition.** If $A = [a_{i,j}]$ is an m by n matrix, then the *scalar product* of a real number r and the matrix A is the m by n matrix

$$r \cdot A = \begin{bmatrix} ra_{1,1} & ra_{1,2} & \cdots & ra_{1,n} \\ ra_{2,1} & ra_{2,2} & \cdots & ra_{2,n} \\ & & \cdots & \\ ra_{m,1} & ra_{m,2} & \cdots & ra_{m,n} \end{bmatrix}.$$

Thus, $r \cdot A$ is the m by n matrix obtained from A by multiplying each element of A by the real number r.

If L is a linear transformation of $\mathcal{V}$ into $\mathcal{W}$ with matrix $A = [a_{i,j}]$ with respect to chosen bases in $\mathcal{V}$ and $\mathcal{W}$, then $r \cdot A$ is the matrix of the linear transformation $r \cdot L$ with respect to these bases.

Let A and B be m by n matrices, and let r and s be real numbers. Then

$$r \cdot (A + B) = r \cdot A + r \cdot B \tag{17-3}$$

$$(r + s) \cdot A = r \cdot A + s \cdot A \tag{17-4}$$

$$(rs) \cdot A = r \cdot (s \cdot A) = s \cdot (r \cdot A). \tag{17-5}$$

These identities follow easily from Definition 17.2, and their proof is left as an exercise (Exercise 17.5).

Example 1. Let

$$A = \begin{bmatrix} -2 & 0 & 3 & 5 & -1 \\ 6 & 7 & -2 & 0 & 1 \\ 5 & -10 & 6 & -2 & 1 \end{bmatrix} \qquad B = \begin{bmatrix} 0 & -7 & 4 & 3 & 2 \\ -1 & 2 & 0 & 1 & 2 \\ 5 & 6 & -3 & 4 & -9 \end{bmatrix}.$$

Then

$$(1/2) \cdot (A + B) = (1/2) \cdot \begin{bmatrix} -2 & -7 & 7 & 8 & 1 \\ 5 & 9 & -2 & 1 & 3 \\ 10 & -4 & 3 & 2 & -8 \end{bmatrix} = \begin{bmatrix} -1 & -7/2 & 7/2 & 4 & 1/2 \\ 5/2 & 9/2 & -1 & 1/2 & 3/2 \\ 5 & -2 & 3/2 & 1 & -4 \end{bmatrix}$$

$$6 \cdot (A - B) - 3 \cdot (A - B) = 3 \cdot (A - B) = 3 \cdot \begin{bmatrix} -2 & 7 & -1 & 2 & -3 \\ 7 & 5 & -2 & -1 & -1 \\ 0 & -16 & 9 & -6 & 10 \end{bmatrix}$$

$$= \begin{bmatrix} -6 & 21 & -3 & 6 & -9 \\ 21 & 15 & -6 & -3 & -3 \\ 0 & -48 & 27 & -18 & 30 \end{bmatrix}.$$

(17.3) Theorem. Let ${}_m\mathfrak{A}_n$ be the set of all m by n real matrices. Then ${}_m\mathfrak{A}_n$ is a finite dimensional vector space with respect to the operations of addition and scalar multiplication defined by 17.1 and 17.2. Moreover, ${}_m\mathfrak{A}_n$ is isomorphic to the vector space $\mathfrak{M}$ of all linear transformations of a vector space $\mathcal{V}$ of dimension n into a vector space $\mathcal{W}$ of dimension m.

PROOF. The fact that ${}_m\mathfrak{A}_n$ is a vector space is a consequence of the properties of addition and scalar multiplication given above. Let $E_{i,j}$ be the m by n matrix with the number 1 in the ith row and the jth column and zeros elsewhere. The set of mn matrices, $\{E_{i,j} \mid i = 1, 2, \ldots, m; j = 1, 2, \ldots, n\}$, is a linearly independent set, for, if

$$a_{1,1} \cdot E_{1,1} + \cdots + a_{1,n} \cdot E_{1,n} + a_{2,1} \cdot E_{2,1} + \cdots + a_{2,n} \cdot E_{2,n}$$
$$+ \cdots + a_{m,1} \cdot E_{m,1} + \cdots + a_{m,n} \cdot E_{m,n}$$

is the zero m by n matrix, then

$$\begin{bmatrix} a_{1,1} & a_{1,2} & \cdots & a_{1,n} \\ a_{2,1} & a_{2,2} & \cdots & a_{2,n} \\ \cdot & \cdot & & \cdot \\ \cdot & \cdot & & \cdot \\ \cdot & \cdot & & \cdot \\ a_{m,1} & a_{m,2} & \cdots & a_{m,n} \end{bmatrix} = \begin{bmatrix} 0 & 0 & \cdots & 0 \\ 0 & 0 & \cdots & 0 \\ \cdot & \cdot & & \cdot \\ \cdot & \cdot & & \cdot \\ \cdot & \cdot & & \cdot \\ 0 & 0 & \cdots & 0 \end{bmatrix}.$$

Therefore, $a_{i,j} = 0$ for all i, j. Moreover, if $A = [a_{i,j}]$ is any real m by n matrix, then

$$A = a_{1,1} \cdot E_{1,1} + \cdots + a_{1,n} \cdot E_{1,n} + a_{2,1} \cdot E_{2,1} + \cdots + a_{2,n} \cdot E_{2,n} + \cdots + a_{m,1} \cdot E_{m,1} + \cdots + a_{m,n} \cdot E_{m,n}.$$

Thus, $\{E_{i,j}\}$ spans ${}_m\mathfrak{A}_n$, and therefore is a basis. Hence ${}_m\mathfrak{A}_n$ is a vector space of dimension mn.

Let $\mathcal{V}$ be a vector space with basis $\{\mathbf{U}_1, \mathbf{U}_2, \ldots, \mathbf{U}_n\}$, and let $\mathcal{W}$ be a vector space with basis $\{\mathbf{W}_1, \mathbf{W}_2, \ldots, \mathbf{W}_m\}$. By Theorem 16.2, the correspondence that associates each linear transformation L of $\mathcal{V}$ into $\mathcal{W}$ with the matrix of L with respect to these bases is a one-to-one correspondence of $\mathcal{M}$ onto ${}_m\mathfrak{A}_n$. If A is the matrix of L and B is the matrix of a linear transformation M, then we have observed that $A + B$ is the matrix of $L + M$ and $r \cdot A$ is the matrix of $r \cdot L$. Thus, the correspondence of Theorem 16.2 is a one-to-one linear transformation of $\mathcal{M}$ onto ${}_m\mathfrak{A}_n$. That is, $\mathcal{M}$ is isomorphic to the vector space ${}_m\mathfrak{A}_n$.

Let $\mathfrak{A}_n$ denote the set of all n by n square matrices. Then it follows from Theorem 17.3 that $\mathfrak{A}_n$ is a vector space that is isomorphic to the vector space $\mathcal{M}$ of all linear transformations of a vector space $\mathcal{V}$ of dimension n into itself.

Let $\mathcal{V}$, $\mathcal{W}$, and $\mathcal{P}$ be vector spaces of dimensions n, m, and p, respectively, and let L be a linear transformation of $\mathcal{V}$ into $\mathcal{W}$ and M be a linear transformation of $\mathcal{W}$ into $\mathcal{P}$. Finally, suppose that the matrix of L is the m by n matrix $A = [a_{i,j}]$ and that the matrix of M is the p by m matrix $B = [b_{i,j}]$ with respect to chosen bases in $\mathcal{V}$, $\mathcal{W}$, and $\mathcal{P}$. If $\mathbf{V} \in \mathcal{V}$, equations (16-1),

$$\begin{aligned} a_{1,1}r_1 + a_{1,2}r_2 + \cdots + a_{1,n}r_n &= s_1 \\ a_{2,1}r_1 + a_{2,2}r_2 + \cdots + a_{2,n}r_n &= s_2 \\ &\cdots \\ a_{m,1}r_1 + a_{m,2}r_2 + \cdots + a_{m,n}r_n &= s_m, \end{aligned}$$

give the coordinates of $L(\mathbf{V}) \in \mathcal{W}$ in terms of the coordinates of $\mathbf{V}$. Similarly, the equations

$$\begin{aligned} b_{1,1}s_1 + b_{1,2}s_2 + \cdots + b_{1,m}s_m &= t_1 \\ b_{2,1}s_1 + b_{2,2}s_2 + \cdots + b_{2,m}s_m &= t_2 \\ &\cdots \\ b_{p,1}s_1 + b_{p,2}s_2 + \cdots + b_{p,m}s_m &= t_p \end{aligned} \tag{17-6}$$

give the coordinates $t_1, t_2, \ldots, t_p$ of $M(L(\mathbf{V})) \in \mathcal{P}$ in terms of the coordinates $s_1, s_2, \ldots, s_m$ of $L(\mathbf{V})$. Substituting the expressions for $s_1, s_2, \ldots, s_m$ from (16-1) into (17-6), we obtain the equations

$$\begin{aligned} &(b_{1,1}a_{1,1} + b_{1,2}a_{2,1} + \cdots + b_{1,m}a_{m,1})r_1 + \cdots \\ &\qquad + (b_{1,1}a_{1,n} + b_{1,2}a_{2,n} + \cdots + b_{1,m}a_{m,n})r_n = t_1 \\ &(b_{2,1}a_{1,1} + b_{2,2}a_{2,1} + \cdots + b_{2,m}a_{m,1})r_1 + \cdots \\ &\qquad + (b_{2,1}a_{1,n} + b_{2,2}a_{2,n} + \cdots + b_{2,m}a_{m,n})r_n = t_2 \\ &\qquad \cdots \\ &(b_{p,1}a_{1,1} + b_{p,2}a_{2,1} + \cdots + b_{p,m}a_{m,1})r_1 + \cdots \\ &\qquad + (b_{p,1}a_{1,n} + b_{p,2}a_{2,n} + \cdots + b_{p,n}a_{m,n})r_n = t_p, \end{aligned}$$

which give the coordinates of $ML(\mathbf{V})$ in terms of the coordinates of $\mathbf{V}$. Consequently, the matrix of the linear transformation ML of $\mathcal{V}$ into $\mathcal{P}$ is the p by n matrix $C = [c_{i,j}]$, where

$$c_{i,j} = b_{i,1}a_{1,j} + b_{i,2}a_{2,j} + \cdots + b_{i,m}a_{m,j} = \sum_{k=1}^{m} b_{i,k}a_{k,j}.$$

This rule for computing the matrix of the product of two linear transformations leads to the following definition of matrix multiplication.

(17.4) Definition. Let $A = [a_{i,j}]$ be an m by n matrix, and let $B = [b_{i,j}]$ be a p by m matrix. Then the *product BA* is the p by n matrix that has the number $\sum_{k=1}^{m} b_{i,k}a_{k,j}$ in the ith row and jth column for $i = 1, 2, \ldots, p$ and $j = 1, 2, \ldots, n$.

Thus, by Definition 17.4, two matrices can be multiplied only when the first matrix has the same number of columns as the second matrix has rows. Definition 17.4 is called the *row by column rule* for multiplying matrices. With this definition, our previous computations show that the matrix of the product of two linear transformations is the product of their matrices. This fact, together with Theorem 16.2, will enable us to conclude that matrix multiplication satisfies the same algebraic identities as the multiplication of linear transformations.

Example 2. Let

$$A = \begin{bmatrix} 0 & -1 \\ \frac{1}{2} & 3 \\ 7 & 4 \end{bmatrix}, \quad B = \begin{bmatrix} 5 & -3 & \frac{1}{3} \\ 0 & 2 & 1 \end{bmatrix}, \quad C = \begin{bmatrix} 4 & 1 & -2 \\ 1 & 0 & 10 \\ -1 & 6 & 0 \end{bmatrix}.$$

Then

$$AB = \begin{bmatrix} 0 & -2 & -1 \\ \frac{5}{2} & \frac{9}{2} & \frac{19}{6} \\ 35 & -13 & \frac{19}{3} \end{bmatrix}, \quad BA = \begin{bmatrix} \frac{5}{6} & -\frac{38}{3} \\ 8 & 10 \end{bmatrix}, \quad BC = \begin{bmatrix} \frac{50}{3} & 7 & -40 \\ 1 & 6 & 20 \end{bmatrix},$$

$$CA = \begin{bmatrix} -\frac{27}{2} & -9 \\ 70 & 39 \\ 3 & 19 \end{bmatrix}, \quad C^2 = \begin{bmatrix} 19 & -8 & 2 \\ -6 & 61 & -2 \\ 2 & -1 & 62 \end{bmatrix}.$$

The products AC and CB are not defined.

Example 3. Let L be a linear transformation of a vector space $\mathcal{V}$ of dimension n into a vector space $\mathcal{W}$ of dimension m, and let $A = [a_{i,j}]$ be the matrix of L with respect to chosen bases in each space. Then the system of equations (16-1), which give the coordinates $s_1, s_2, \ldots, s_m$ of $L(\mathbf{V})$, for $\mathbf{V} \in \mathcal{V}$, in terms of the coordinates $r_1, r_2, \ldots, r_n$ of $\mathbf{V}$, can be written as the single matrix equation

$$\begin{bmatrix} a_{1,1} & a_{1,2} & \cdots & a_{1,n} \\ a_{2,1} & a_{2,2} & \cdots & a_{2,n} \\ \cdot & \cdot & & \cdot \\ \cdot & \cdot & & \cdot \\ \cdot & \cdot & & \cdot \\ a_{m,1} & a_{m,2} & \cdots & a_{m,n} \end{bmatrix} \begin{bmatrix} r_1 \\ r_2 \\ \cdot \\ \cdot \\ \cdot \\ r_n \end{bmatrix} = \begin{bmatrix} s_1 \\ s_2 \\ \cdot \\ \cdot \\ \cdot \\ s_m \end{bmatrix}.$$

By (15-4), multiplication of linear transformations is associative. Then, as indicated above, the one-to-one correspondence between matrices and linear transformations (Theorem 16.2) and the fact that the matrix of the product of two linear transformations is the product of their matrices imply the associative law for matrix multiplication:

(17.5) Theorem. Let C be a q by p matrix, B be a p by m matrix, and A be an m by n matrix. Then

$$C(BA) = (CB)A.$$

Alternately, it can be proved directly from Definition 17.4 that matrix multiplication is associative.

The matrix of the identity transformation of a vector space $\mathcal{V}$ of dimension n into itself with respect to any basis of $\mathcal{V}$ is the n by n matrix

$$I_n = \begin{bmatrix} 1 & 0 & 0 & \dots & 0 & 0 \\ 0 & 1 & 0 & \dots & 0 & 0 \\ \cdot & \cdot & \cdot & & \cdot & \cdot \\ \cdot & \cdot & \cdot & & \cdot & \cdot \\ \cdot & \cdot & \cdot & & \cdot & \cdot \\ 0 & 0 & 0 & \dots & 0 & 1 \end{bmatrix},$$

which has 1 in the ith row and ith column for $i = 1, 2, \dots, n$, and zero elsewhere. Such a matrix is called an *identity matrix*. There is an identity matrix I_n for each positive integer n. If $A = [a_{i,j}]$ is an m by n matrix, then, from the definition of matrix multiplication,

$$A = I_m A = A I_n.$$

Both the sum and product of any pair of matrices in $\mathfrak{A}_n$, the set of all n by n square matrices, is defined. Let A, B, and C be in $\mathfrak{A}_n$, and let r be a real number. Then matrix multiplication in $\mathfrak{A}_n$ is related to addition and scalar multiplication by the following identities:

$$A(B + C) = AB + AC \qquad (17\text{-}7)$$

$$(A + B)C = AC + BC \qquad (17\text{-}8)$$

$$r \cdot (AB) = (r \cdot A)B = A(r \cdot B). \qquad (17\text{-}9)$$

However, matrix multiplication in $\mathfrak{A}_n$ is not commutative.

Example 4. The matrices

$$A = \begin{bmatrix} 0 & -1 & 2 \\ \tfrac{1}{2} & 6 & 0 \\ 5 & -3 & 1 \end{bmatrix} \quad \text{and} \quad B = \begin{bmatrix} 2 & 1 & 1 \\ -5 & 0 & 3 \\ -1 & 1 & 0 \end{bmatrix}$$

are in $\mathfrak{A}_3$.

$$AB = \begin{bmatrix} 3 & 2 & -3 \\ -29 & \tfrac{1}{2} & 3\tfrac{1}{2} \\ 24 & 6 & -4 \end{bmatrix} \qquad BA = \begin{bmatrix} 1\tfrac{1}{2} & 1 & 5 \\ 15 & -4 & -7 \\ \tfrac{1}{2} & 7 & -2 \end{bmatrix}.$$

In Section 15, we proved that L is a nonsingular transformation of a finite dimensional vector space $\mathcal{V}$ into itself if and only if there exists a transformation M of $\mathcal{V}$ into $\mathcal{V}$ such that $ML = LM = I_{\mathcal{V}}$. Let $\mathcal{V}$ have dimension n, and let A and B be the matrices of L and M, respectively, for some given basis of $\mathcal{V}$. Then by the one-to-one correspondence between the set of linear transformations of $\mathcal{V}$ into $\mathcal{V}$ and the set $\mathfrak{A}_n$ of n by n matrices, ML, LM, and $I_{\mathcal{V}}$ correspond to BA, AB, and I_n, respectively. Therefore, $BA = AB = I_n$, which suggests the following definition:

(17.6) **Definition.** A square n by n matrix A is *nonsingular* if there exists an n by n matrix B such that $BA = AB = I_n$. Otherwise, the matrix is *singular*.

Thus, the matrix of a nonsingular linear transformation L of $\mathcal{V}$ into itself is a nonsingular matrix. Conversely, a nonsingular matrix defines a nonsingular linear transformation. There is at most one matrix B that satisfies the condition of Definition 17.6. Indeed, if $BA = AB = I_n$ and $CA = AC = I_n$, then

$$C = CI_n = C(AB) = (CA)B = I_nB = B.$$

Thus, the matrix B is unique, and is called the *inverse* of A. It is customary to write $B = A^{-1}$. (Later, in Chapter Five, we will develop a method for computing the inverse of a nonsingular matrix.) Appealing once more to the correspondence between linear transformations and matrices, it is not difficult to show that if either of the equations $AB = I_n$ or $BA = I_n$ holds, then so does the other one. That is, an n by n matrix A is nonsingular if and only if there is an n by n matrix B such that either $AB = I_n$ or $BA = I_n$. The proof is left as an exercise (Exercise 17.13).

Example 5. Show that the matrix

$$A = \begin{bmatrix} -2 & 1 \\ 4 & -3 \end{bmatrix}$$

is nonsingular and find A^{-1}. If

$$B = \begin{bmatrix} b_{1,1} & b_{1,2} \\ b_{2,1} & b_{2,2} \end{bmatrix}$$

is a matrix such that

$$AB = \begin{bmatrix} 1 & 0 \\ 0 & 1 \end{bmatrix},$$

then

$$\begin{aligned} -2b_{1,1} + b_{2,1} \qquad\qquad\qquad &= 1 \\ -2b_{1,2} + b_{2,2} &= 0 \\ 4b_{1,1} - 3b_{2,1} \qquad\qquad\qquad &= 0 \\ 4b_{1,2} - 3b_{2,2} &= 1. \end{aligned}$$

Solving this system of equations by the methods of Chapter Three, we find $b_{1,1} = -3/2$, $b_{2,1} = -2$, $b_{1,2} = -1/2$, $b_{2,2} = -1$. Therefore,

$$A^{-1} = B = \begin{bmatrix} -3/2 & -1/2 \\ -2 & -1 \end{bmatrix}$$

and

$$AB = \begin{bmatrix} -2 & 1 \\ 4 & -3 \end{bmatrix} \begin{bmatrix} -3/2 & -1/2 \\ -2 & -1 \end{bmatrix} = \begin{bmatrix} 1 & 0 \\ 0 & 1 \end{bmatrix} = \begin{bmatrix} -3/2 & -1/2 \\ -2 & -1 \end{bmatrix} \begin{bmatrix} -2 & 1 \\ 4 & -3 \end{bmatrix} = BA.$$

We conclude this section by stating two useful properties of nonsingular matrices, the first of which follows immediately from Definition 17.6.

(17.7) The inverse of a nonsingular matrix is nonsingular.

(17.8) The product of two nonsingular n by n matrices is a nonsingular n by n matrix.

PROOF. Let A and B be nonsingular n by n matrices. Then A^{-1} and B^{-1} are n by n matrices such that

$$(B^{-1}A^{-1})(AB) = I_n = (AB)(B^{-1}A^{-1}).$$

Hence AB is nonsingular, and $(AB)^{-1} = B^{-1}A^{-1}$.

Exercises

17.1 Let L and M be linear transformations of $\mathcal{V}$ into $\mathcal{W}$ with matrices $A = [a_{i,j}]$ and $B = [b_{i,j}]$, respectively, with respect to given bases in $\mathcal{V}$ and $\mathcal{W}$. Prove that the matrix of the linear transformation $L + M$ of $\mathcal{V}$ into $\mathcal{W}$ is $A + B$. Also, prove that $-A$ is the matrix of $-L$.

17.2 Prove that matrix addition is associative and commutative.

17.3 Let

$$A = \begin{bmatrix} 2 & 0 & -1 & 5 \\ 7 & -6 & 3 & 1 \end{bmatrix}, \quad B = \begin{bmatrix} 1/2 & 7/5 & -2 & -1/10 \\ -3/5 & 5/2 & 7/10 & 5 \end{bmatrix}, \quad C = \begin{bmatrix} 1 & 1/3 & 2 & 0 \\ 0 & 3/2 & 1 & 17 \end{bmatrix}.$$

Compute the following matrices: $(A - B) + C$; $A - (B + C)$; $A + B$; $A + (C - B)$; $5 \cdot A + 10 \cdot B + \sqrt{2} \cdot C$; $20 \cdot (A - B)$.

17.4 Let L be a linear transformation of $\mathcal{V}$ into $\mathcal{W}$ with matrix $A = [a_{i,j}]$ with respect to given bases in $\mathcal{V}$ and $\mathcal{W}$. Prove that the matrix of $r \cdot L$ is $r \cdot A$.

17.5 Prove the identities (17-3), (17-4), and (17-5).

17.6 Find the 3 by 5 matrix X that is the solution of the following matrix equations:

(a) $$\begin{bmatrix} 1 & -5 & 2 & 6 & -1 \\ -2 & 1 & 0 & 3 & 0 \\ 0 & 10 & 4 & 2 & -1 \end{bmatrix} - 5 \cdot X = \begin{bmatrix} 1 & 0 & 0 & 0 & 0 \\ 0 & 1 & 0 & 0 & 0 \\ 0 & 0 & 1 & 0 & 0 \end{bmatrix};$$

(b) $$(1/7) \cdot X + \begin{bmatrix} 3 & -11 & 7 & 2 & 1 \\ 0 & 0 & 0 & 0 & 0 \\ -1 & 5 & 17 & 1 & 4 \end{bmatrix} = \begin{bmatrix} -6 & 6 & 3 & 10 & 2 \\ 1 & 4 & 0 & -1 & 7 \\ -16 & 3 & -1 & 0 & 4 \end{bmatrix}.$$

***17.7** Let $\mathfrak{M}$ be the vector space of all linear transformations of a vector space $\mathcal{V}$ of dimension n into a vector space $\mathcal{W}$ of dimension m. Prove that $\mathfrak{M}$ has dimension mn.

17.8 Let $A = [1 \quad -2 \quad 3 \quad 0]$,

$$B = \begin{bmatrix} 2 & 5 \\ -3 & -1 \\ 0 & 1 \\ 6 & 0 \end{bmatrix}, \qquad C = \begin{bmatrix} 0 & 1 & -1 & 10 \\ 2 & 6 & -1 & 5 \end{bmatrix}.$$

Compute the following matrices: $A(BC)$; BC; CB; $AB - 3 \cdot [2 \quad 1]$;

$$\begin{bmatrix} -3 & 1 \\ 2 & 5 \end{bmatrix} + 6 \cdot (CB).$$

17.9 Prove the associative law of matrix multiplication directly from Definition 17.4.

***17.10** A *diagonal matrix* is an m by n matrix $A = [a_{i,j}]$ such that $a_{i,j} = 0$ if $i \neq j$. Let $A = [a_{i,j}]$ be an m by n diagonal matrix, and let $B = [b_{i,j}]$ be any n by p matrix. Let $C = [c_{i,j}]$ be the m by p matrix AB. Prove that $c_{i,j} = a_{i,i}b_{i,j}$, for $i = 1, 2, \ldots, m$ and $j = 1, 2, \ldots, p$.

***17.11** A *scalar matrix* is a square diagonal matrix with equal diagonal elements. Prove that an n by n scalar matrix is a scalar multiple of I_n. Let $A = [a_{i,j}]$ be the n by n scalar matrix such that $a_{i,i} = r$, for $i = 1, 2, \ldots, n$. Let $B = [b_{i,j}]$ be any n by p matrix. Prove that $AB = r \cdot B$.

***17.12** Let $A = [a_{i,j}]$ be an m by n matrix, and let $B = [b_{i,j}]$ and $C = [c_{i,j}]$ be n by p matrices. Prove that $A(B + C) = AB + AC$. Also, prove that $r \cdot (AB) = (r \cdot A)B = A(r \cdot B)$. If $A = [a_{i,j}]$ and $B = [b_{i,j}]$ are m by n matrices and $C = [c_{i,j}]$ is an n by p matrix, prove that $(A + B)C = AC + BC$. The identities (17-7), (17-8), and (17-9) for n by n square matrices are special cases of the results of this exercise.

17.13 Let A be an n by n matrix. Prove that A is nonsingular if and only if there exists an n by n matrix B such that either $AB = I_n$ or $BA = I_n$.

17.14 Prove that a nonzero scalar matrix is nonsingular.

17.15 Show that the following matrices are nonsingular and find their inverses:

(a) $\begin{bmatrix} -7 & 2 \\ 0 & 1 \end{bmatrix}$; (b) $\begin{bmatrix} \frac{1}{3} & \frac{1}{2} \\ \frac{2}{5} & \frac{1}{4} \end{bmatrix}$; (c) $\begin{bmatrix} 1 & 0 & 2 \\ -3 & 4 & 0 \\ 0 & 0 & 1 \end{bmatrix}$.

***17.16** Let $A = [a_{i,j}]$ be an m by n matrix. The *transpose of* A is the n by m matrix $B = [b_{i,j}]$, where $b_{i,j} = a_{j,i}$ for $i = 1, 2, \ldots, n$ and $j = 1, 2, \ldots, m$. Thus, the rows of B are the columns of A and the columns of B are the rows of A. The transpose of a matrix A is denoted by A'. Prove the following statements:

(a) For any m by n matrix A, $(A')' = A$.

(b) If A is an m by n matrix and B is an n by p matrix, then $(AB)' = B'A'$.

(c) If A is a nonsingular n by n matrix, then A' is a nonsingular n by n matrix and $(A')^{-1} = (A^{-1})'$.

(d) If D is a square diagonal matrix, then $D' = D$.

(e) If A and B are m by n matrices and r and s are real numbers, then $(r \cdot A + s \cdot B)' = r \cdot A' + s \cdot B'$.

18 Applications to systems of linear equations

A system of n linear equations in m unknowns,

$$\begin{aligned} a_{1,1}x_1 + a_{1,2}x_2 + \cdots + a_{1,m}x_m &= b_1 \\ a_{2,1}x_1 + a_{2,2}x_2 + \cdots + a_{2,m}x_m &= b_2 \\ &\cdots \\ a_{n,1}x_1 + a_{n,2}x_2 + \cdots + a_{n,m}x_m &= b_n, \end{aligned} \tag{18-1}$$

can be written as a single matrix equation, using Definition 17.4 for matrix multiplication. Let

$$A = \begin{bmatrix} a_{1,1} & a_{1,2} & \cdots & a_{1,m} \\ a_{2,1} & a_{2,2} & \cdots & a_{2,m} \\ \cdot & \cdot & & \cdot \\ \cdot & \cdot & & \cdot \\ \cdot & \cdot & & \cdot \\ a_{n,1} & a_{n,2} & \cdots & a_{n,m} \end{bmatrix}, \quad X = \begin{bmatrix} x_1 \\ x_2 \\ \cdot \\ \cdot \\ \cdot \\ x_m \end{bmatrix}, \quad \text{and} \quad B = \begin{bmatrix} b_1 \\ b_2 \\ \cdot \\ \cdot \\ \cdot \\ b_n \end{bmatrix}.$$

Then, the system (18-1) can be written compactly as the matrix equation

$$AX = B.$$

Using this notation, a solution of the system is an m by 1 matrix

$$C = \begin{bmatrix} c_1 \\ c_2 \\ \cdot \\ \cdot \\ \cdot \\ c_m \end{bmatrix},$$

such that $AC = B$.

The n by m matrix $A = [a_{i,j}]$ of system (18-1) is called the *matrix of coefficients*, and the n by $(m + 1)$ matrix

$$A^* = \begin{bmatrix} a_{1,1} & a_{1,2} & \cdots & a_{1,m} & b_1 \\ a_{2,1} & a_{2,2} & \cdots & a_{2,m} & b_2 \\ \cdot & \cdot & & \cdot & \cdot \\ \cdot & \cdot & & \cdot & \cdot \\ \cdot & \cdot & & \cdot & \cdot \\ a_{n,1} & a_{n,2} & \cdots & a_{n,m} & b_n \end{bmatrix}$$

is called the *augmented matrix of coefficients*. Thus, the row space of the system is the subspace of $\mathcal{V}_{m+1}$ that is spanned by the vectors $\langle a_{i,1}, a_{i,2}, \ldots, a_{i,m}, b_i\rangle$, $i = 1, 2, \ldots, n$, which are the rows of the augmented matrix of coefficients. According to the procedure developed in Chapter Three, the system of equations (18-1) can be replaced by an equivalent system in echelon form by performing a sequence of elementary transformations on the set of vectors $\{\langle a_{i,1}, a_{i,2}, \ldots, a_{i,m}, b_i\rangle \mid i = 1, 2, \ldots, n\}$, which span the row space of the system. Since these transformations are performed on the rows of the augmented matrix A^*, they can be regarded as transformations of A^*. Accordingly, they are called *elementary row transformations* of the matrix A^*.

Example 1. The system of equations

$$\begin{aligned} 2x_1 - x_2 + 3x_3 &= 1 \\ x_1 + 5x_2 + x_4 &= 0 \\ -3x_1 + 2x_2 - x_3 + 6x_4 &= 4 \end{aligned}$$

can be written as the single matrix equation

$$\begin{bmatrix} 2 & -1 & 3 & 0 \\ 1 & 5 & 0 & 1 \\ -3 & 2 & -1 & 6 \end{bmatrix} \begin{bmatrix} x_1 \\ x_2 \\ x_3 \\ x_4 \end{bmatrix} = \begin{bmatrix} 1 \\ 0 \\ 4 \end{bmatrix}.$$

The matrix of coefficients is the matrix

$$A = \begin{bmatrix} 2 & -1 & 3 & 0 \\ 1 & 5 & 0 & 1 \\ -3 & 2 & -1 & 6 \end{bmatrix},$$

and the augmented matrix of coefficients is the matrix

$$A^* = \begin{bmatrix} 2 & -1 & 3 & 0 & 1 \\ 1 & 5 & 0 & 1 & 0 \\ -3 & 2 & -1 & 6 & 4 \end{bmatrix}.$$

The following sequence of elementary row transformations carries A^* to echelon form:

$$\begin{bmatrix} 2 & -1 & 3 & 0 & 1 \\ 1 & 5 & 0 & 1 & 0 \\ -3 & 2 & -1 & 6 & 4 \end{bmatrix} \xrightarrow{\text{Type I}} \begin{bmatrix} 1 & 5 & 0 & 1 & 0 \\ 2 & -1 & 3 & 0 & 1 \\ -3 & 2 & -1 & 6 & 4 \end{bmatrix} \xrightarrow{\text{Type II}}$$

$$\begin{bmatrix} 1 & 5 & 0 & 1 & 0 \\ 0 & -11 & 3 & -2 & 1 \\ -3 & 2 & -1 & 6 & 4 \end{bmatrix} \xrightarrow{\text{Type II}} \begin{bmatrix} 1 & 5 & 0 & 1 & 0 \\ 0 & -11 & 3 & -2 & 1 \\ 0 & 17 & -1 & 9 & 4 \end{bmatrix} \xrightarrow{\text{Type III}}$$

$$\begin{bmatrix} 1 & 5 & 0 & 1 & 0 \\ 0 & 1 & -3/11 & 2/11 & -1/11 \\ 0 & 17 & -1 & 9 & 4 \end{bmatrix} \xrightarrow{\text{Type II}} \begin{bmatrix} 1 & 5 & 0 & 1 & 0 \\ 0 & 1 & -3/11 & 2/11 & -1/11 \\ 0 & 0 & 40/11 & 65/11 & 61/11 \end{bmatrix}$$

$$\xrightarrow{\text{Type III}} \begin{bmatrix} 1 & 5 & 0 & 1 & 0 \\ 0 & 1 & -3/11 & 2/11 & -1/11 \\ 0 & 0 & 1 & 13/8 & 61/40 \end{bmatrix}.$$

Thus, the given system of equations is equivalent to the system

$$\begin{aligned} x_1 + 5x_2 \qquad\quad + \quad x_4 &= 0 \\ x_2 - 3/11\,x_3 + 2/11\,x_4 &= -1/11 \\ x_3 + 13/8\,x_4 &= 61/40. \end{aligned}$$

Therefore, every solution of the system is given by $x_4 = r$, $x_3 = 61/40 - 13/8\,r$, $x_2 = 143/440 - 5/8\,r$, $x_1 = -143/88 + 17/8\,r$, where r is any real number.

It will be useful to apply the terminology that we have introduced in the discussion of systems of linear equations to rectangular matrices in general.

(18.1) **Definition.** Let $A = [a_{i,j}]$ be an n by m matrix. The *row space* of A is the subspace of $\mathcal{V}_m$ spanned by the vectors $\langle a_{i,1}, a_{i,2}, \ldots, a_{i,m}\rangle$, $i = 1, 2, \ldots, n$, which are the rows of A. An *elementary row transformation* of A is an elementary transformation on the set of vectors in $\mathcal{V}_m$ that are the rows of A.

We can now translate into matrix language the results of Chapter Three.

(18.2) **Theorem.** If B is a matrix obtained from the matrix A by a sequence of elementary row transformations, then B and A have the same row space.

PROOF. Theorem 18.2 is an immediate consequence of Theorem 10.2.

Since Definition 11.3 of a system of linear equations in echelon form involves only a description of the matrix $A = [a_{i,j}]$ of coefficients of the system, it can be used to define an n by m matrix in echelon form. For example, the following matrices are in echelon form:

$$\begin{bmatrix} 0 & 1 & -3 & 1 \\ 0 & 0 & 1 & 0 \\ 0 & 0 & 0 & 1 \end{bmatrix}, \qquad k = 3,\ m_1 = 2,\ m_2 = 3,\ m_3 = 4;$$

$$\begin{bmatrix} 1 & 0 & 0 & -3 \\ 0 & 0 & 0 & 1 \\ 0 & 0 & 0 & 0 \\ 0 & 0 & 0 & 0 \end{bmatrix}, \qquad k = 2,\ m_1 = 1,\ m_2 = 4; \qquad \begin{bmatrix} 0 & 0 \\ 0 & 0 \end{bmatrix}, \qquad k = 0;$$

$$\begin{bmatrix} 0 & 1 & 6 & -5 & 0 \\ 0 & 0 & 1 & -2 & 1 \end{bmatrix}, \qquad k = 2,\ m_1 = 2,\ m_2 = 3.$$

The following theorem is the matrix form of Theorem 11.4.

(18.3) Theorem. An n by m matrix $A = [a_{i,j}]$ can be transformed into a matrix in echelon form by a sequence of elementary row transformations.

Example 2. Transform the matrix

$$A = \begin{bmatrix} -2 & -5 & 0 \\ 3 & 1 & 2 \\ 0 & 6 & -7 \\ -4 & 3 & 1 \end{bmatrix}$$

into echelon form by elementary row transformations.

$$\begin{bmatrix} -2 & -5 & 0 \\ 3 & 1 & 2 \\ 0 & 6 & -7 \\ -4 & 3 & 1 \end{bmatrix} \xrightarrow{\text{Type III}} \begin{bmatrix} 1 & 5/2 & 0 \\ 3 & 1 & 2 \\ 0 & 6 & -7 \\ -4 & 3 & 1 \end{bmatrix} \xrightarrow{\text{Type II}} \begin{bmatrix} 1 & 5/2 & 0 \\ 0 & -13/2 & 2 \\ 0 & 6 & -7 \\ -4 & 3 & 1 \end{bmatrix}$$

$$\xrightarrow{\text{Type II}} \begin{bmatrix} 1 & 5/2 & 0 \\ 0 & -13/2 & 2 \\ 0 & 6 & -7 \\ 0 & 13 & 1 \end{bmatrix} \xrightarrow{\text{Type III}} \begin{bmatrix} 1 & 5/2 & 0 \\ 0 & 1 & -4/13 \\ 0 & 6 & -7 \\ 0 & 13 & 1 \end{bmatrix} \xrightarrow{\text{Type II}} \begin{bmatrix} 1 & 5/2 & 0 \\ 0 & 1 & -4/13 \\ 0 & 0 & -67/13 \\ 0 & 13 & 1 \end{bmatrix}$$

$$\xrightarrow{\text{Type II}} \begin{bmatrix} 1 & 5/2 & 0 \\ 0 & 1 & -4/13 \\ 0 & 0 & -67/13 \\ 0 & 0 & 5 \end{bmatrix} \xrightarrow{\text{Type III}} \begin{bmatrix} 1 & 5/2 & 0 \\ 0 & 1 & -4/13 \\ 0 & 0 & 1 \\ 0 & 0 & 5 \end{bmatrix} \xrightarrow{\text{Type II}} \begin{bmatrix} 1 & 5/2 & 0 \\ 0 & 1 & -4/13 \\ 0 & 0 & 1 \\ 0 & 0 & 0 \end{bmatrix}.$$

In this echelon form, $k = 3$, $m_1 = 1$, $m_2 = 2$, $m_3 = 3$.

The results of Section 12 on systems of linear equations can conveniently be restated in terms of the following concept:

(18.4) **Definition.** The *row rank* of an n by m matrix $A = [a_{i,j}]$ is the dimension of the row space of A.

As a consequence of Theorem 18.2, if a matrix B is obtained from a matrix A by a sequence of elementary row transformations, then the row rank of B is equal to the row rank of A. Moreover, from the proof of Theorem 12.1, if a matrix A is in echelon form, then the row rank of A is the associated integer k of the echelon form.

(18.5) **Theorem.** Let $AX = B$ be a system of n linear equations in m unknowns. The system is consistent if and only if the row rank of the augmented matrix A^* is equal to the row rank of the matrix of coefficients A. If the system is consistent, then its solution is unique if and only if the row rank of A is equal to m.

PROOF. If the augmented matrix A^* is carried into echelon form A_1^* by elementary row transformations, then the matrix A that consists of the first n columns of A^* is automatically carried into echelon form A_1. Moreover, the system of equations $AX = B$ is carried into an equivalent system $A_1X = B_1$ in echelon form, where the matrix B_1 is the $(m + 1)$st column of the echelon form A_1^*. By Theorem 18.2, as noted above, the row rank of A = the row rank of $A_1 = k$, where k is the integer associated with the echelon form A_1. In Theorem 12.1, the integer k is the integer associated with the system of equations $A_1X = B_1$ in echelon form. Also, the dimension of the row space of the system $A_1X = B_1$ is equal to the row rank of A_1^*. Moreover, the row rank of A^* = the row rank of A_1^*, which is k or $k + 1$, since A_1^* is the matrix A_1 augmented either by an additional column of zeros or by a column having 1 in the $(k + 1)$st row and zeros elsewhere. By Theorem 12.1, the system $A_1X = B_1$ is consistent if and only if the row rank of $A_1^* = k$ = the row rank of A_1. Thus, the equivalent system $AX = B$ is consistent if and only if the row rank of A^* = the row rank of A.

If $A_1X = B_1$ is consistent, then, by Theorem 12.1, this system has a unique solution if and only k = the row rank of A_1 = the row rank of $A_1^* = m$. Thus, $AX = B$ has a unique solution if and only if k = the row rank of A = the row rank of $A^* = m$.

The system of equations $AX = B$ is homogeneous if

$$B = \begin{bmatrix} 0 \\ 0 \\ \cdot \\ \cdot \\ \cdot \\ 0 \end{bmatrix}.$$

As a corollary of Theorem 18.5, we obtain the following version of Theorem 12.2.

(18.6) **Corollary.** A homogeneous system $AX = \mathbf{O}$ of n equations in m unknowns has a nontrivial solution if and only if the row rank of A is less than m.

The proof of 18.6 is left as an exercise (Exercise 18.4). Corollary 18.6 has the following application.

(18.7) **Theorem.** A square n by n matrix $A = [a_{i,j}]$ is nonsingular if and only if the row rank of A is n.

PROOF. Suppose first that A is nonsingular.
Let

$$C = \begin{bmatrix} c_1 \\ c_2 \\ \cdot \\ \cdot \\ \cdot \\ c_n \end{bmatrix}, \quad \text{such that} \quad AC = \begin{bmatrix} 0 \\ 0 \\ \cdot \\ \cdot \\ \cdot \\ 0 \end{bmatrix}.$$

Then

$$C = I_nC = (A^{-1}A)C = A^{-1}(AC) = A^{-1}\begin{bmatrix} 0 \\ 0 \\ \cdot \\ \cdot \\ \cdot \\ 0 \end{bmatrix} = \begin{bmatrix} 0 \\ 0 \\ \cdot \\ \cdot \\ \cdot \\ 0 \end{bmatrix}.$$

Therefore, the homogeneous system of equations

$$A\begin{bmatrix} x_1 \\ x_2 \\ \cdot \\ \cdot \\ \cdot \\ x_n \end{bmatrix} = \begin{bmatrix} 0 \\ 0 \\ \cdot \\ \cdot \\ \cdot \\ 0 \end{bmatrix} \tag{18-2}$$

has only the trivial solution. By Corollary 18.6, the row rank of A is n.

Conversely, suppose that the row rank of $A = n$. By Corollary 18.6, the homogeneous system of equations (18-2) has only the trivial solution $x_1 = x_2 = \cdots = x_n = 0$. Thus, the linear transformation L of $\mathcal{V}_n$ into $\mathcal{V}_n$ defined by the matrix A (for any fixed basis of $\mathcal{V}_n$) has kernel $\{\mathbf{0}\}$. Therefore L is nonsingular, and its matrix A is nonsingular.

(18.8) Theorem. Let

$$A\begin{bmatrix} x_1 \\ x_2 \\ \cdot \\ \cdot \\ \cdot \\ x_n \end{bmatrix} = \begin{bmatrix} b_1 \\ b_2 \\ \cdot \\ \cdot \\ \cdot \\ b_n \end{bmatrix}$$

be a system of n linear equations in n unknowns. The system has a unique solution if and only if the n by n matrix A is nonsingular. When A is nonsingular, the solution is given by

$$\begin{bmatrix} c_1 \\ c_2 \\ \cdot \\ \cdot \\ \cdot \\ c_n \end{bmatrix} = A^{-1}\begin{bmatrix} b_1 \\ b_2 \\ \cdot \\ \cdot \\ \cdot \\ b_n \end{bmatrix}.$$

The proof of Theorem 18.8 is left as an exercise (Exercise 18.6).

Example 3. By Example 5, Section 17, the system of equations

$$-2x_1 + x_2 = 4$$
$$4x_1 - 3x_2 = -7$$

has a nonsingular matrix

$$A = \begin{bmatrix} -2 & 1 \\ 4 & -3 \end{bmatrix}$$

with inverse

$$A^{-1} = \begin{bmatrix} -3/2 & -1/2 \\ -2 & -1 \end{bmatrix}.$$

Thus, the unique solution of the system is given by

$$\begin{bmatrix} c_1 \\ c_2 \end{bmatrix} = \begin{bmatrix} -3/2 & -1/2 \\ -2 & -1 \end{bmatrix} \begin{bmatrix} 4 \\ -7 \end{bmatrix} = \begin{bmatrix} -5/2 \\ -1 \end{bmatrix}.$$

That is, the solution is $x_1 = c_1 = -5/2$, $x_2 = c_2 = -1$.

Let L be a linear transformation of an n-dimensional vector space $\mathcal{V}$ into an m-dimensional space $\mathcal{W}$ that has matrix $A = [a_{i,j}]$ with respect to given bases in the two spaces. Then L is given by the matrix equation

$$A \begin{bmatrix} r_1 \\ r_2 \\ \cdot \\ \cdot \\ \cdot \\ r_n \end{bmatrix} = \begin{bmatrix} s_1 \\ s_2 \\ \cdot \\ \cdot \\ \cdot \\ s_m \end{bmatrix},$$

where the coordinates of $\mathbf{V} \in \mathcal{V}$ are $r_1, r_2, \ldots, r_n$ with respect to the given basis in $\mathcal{V}$, and the coordinates of $L(\mathbf{V}) = \mathbf{W} \in \mathcal{W}$ are $s_1, s_2, \ldots, s_m$ with respect to the given basis in $\mathcal{W}$ (see Example 3, Section 17). The set of all vectors in $\mathcal{V}$ that are sent into a fixed vector $\mathbf{W} \in \mathcal{W}$ by L is found by solving the system of linear equations $AX = S$, where

$$X = \begin{bmatrix} x_1 \\ x_2 \\ \cdot \\ \cdot \\ \cdot \\ x_n \end{bmatrix}, \quad \text{and} \quad S = \begin{bmatrix} s_1 \\ s_2 \\ \cdot \\ \cdot \\ \cdot \\ s_m \end{bmatrix}.$$

In particular, the null space of L is the solution space of the homogeneous system $AX = \mathbf{O}$. Therefore, it follows from the results of Chapter Three that any vector in $\mathcal{V}$ that is sent into a given vector $\mathbf{W} \in \mathcal{W}$ is the sum of a fixed vector that is sent into $\mathbf{W}$ and a linear combination of the vectors in a basis for the null space of L.

Exercises

18.1 Transform the following matrices into echelon form by elementary row transformations:

$$\text{(a)} \begin{bmatrix} 2 & -1 & 0 & 1 & 2 & 2 \\ 1 & 3 & 4 & -3 & -1 & 4 \\ 3 & 2 & 4 & 2 & 3 & 2 \end{bmatrix}; \quad \text{(b)} \begin{bmatrix} \frac{1}{2} & \frac{2}{3} & -1 \\ 0 & 5 & \frac{3}{2} \\ 3 & 14 & -3 \end{bmatrix}; \quad \text{(c)} \begin{bmatrix} 2 & -1 & 1 \\ 1 & 1 & -2 \\ 4 & -3 & 4 \\ 2 & -1 & -4 \end{bmatrix}.$$

What is the row rank of each matrix?

18.2 Solve the systems of equations that have the matrices of Exercise 18.1 as augmented matrices of coefficients. Solve the homogeneous systems of equations that have these matrices as matrices of coefficients.

18.3 Prove that the row rank of an n by m matrix A is less than or equal to the smaller of the dimensions.

18.4 Prove Corollary 18.6.

18.5 Which of the following matrices are nonsingular?

$$\text{(a)} \begin{bmatrix} 1 & -2 & 3 & 0 \\ 4 & -1 & \frac{7}{2} & 1 \\ 4 & 2 & 1 & 0 \\ 2 & 0 & \frac{8}{5} & 1 \end{bmatrix}; \qquad \text{(b)} \begin{bmatrix} \frac{1}{2} & -2 & 0 \\ 1 & 3 & 2 \\ 6 & 12 & -1 \end{bmatrix};$$

$$\text{(c)} \begin{bmatrix} -1 & 1 & -1 & 1 \\ 2 & -3 & 4 & 1 \\ 1 & -1 & 1 & -1 \\ 0 & 0 & 0 & 1 \end{bmatrix}; \qquad \text{(d)} \begin{bmatrix} 0 & 0 & 0 & 0 & 1 \\ 0 & 1 & 0 & 0 & 0 \\ 0 & 0 & 1 & 0 & 0 \\ 1 & 0 & 0 & 0 & 0 \\ 0 & 0 & 0 & 1 & 0 \end{bmatrix}.$$

18.6 Prove Theorem 18.8.

18.7 The following systems of equations have nonsingular matrices of coefficients. Solve the systems by finding the inverse of each matrix of coefficients as in Example 3.

(a)
$$\begin{aligned} x_1 - 3x_2 &= 1 \\ 5x_1 + x_2 &= 0; \end{aligned}$$

(b)
$$\begin{aligned} x_1 + x_2 + x_3 &= 1 \\ x_2 + x_3 &= 2 \\ x_3 &= 3. \end{aligned}$$

18.8 Let $AX = B$ be a system of n linear equations in m unknowns. That is, A is an n by m matrix, B is an n by 1 matrix, and

$$X = \begin{bmatrix} x_1 \\ x_2 \\ \cdot \\ \cdot \\ \cdot \\ x_m \end{bmatrix}.$$

Let P be a nonsingular n by n matrix. Prove that the system of equations $(PA)X = PB$ is equivalent to the system $AX = B$.

18.9 Find the set of all vectors in $\mathcal{V}_6$ that are mapped into the vector $\langle 1, 2, -3\rangle \in \mathcal{V}_3$ by the linear transformation L that has the matrix of Exercise 18.1(a) with respect to the bases $E^{(6)}$ and $E^{(3)}$ in $\mathcal{V}_6$ and $\mathcal{V}_3$, respectively.

18.10 Let the matrix of Exercise 18.1(b) be the matrix of a linear transformation L of $\mathcal{V}_3$ into itself with respect to the basis $E^{(3)}$. Find the null space of L.

CHAPTER FIVE

Equivalence of Matrices

19 Change of basis

The matrix of a linear transformation of a finite dimensional vector space $\mathcal{V}$ into a finite dimensional vector space $\mathcal{W}$ depends on the particular choice of bases in each vector space. In this chapter we study the relations between different matrices associated with the same linear transformation. We begin this discussion by finding the equations that connect the coordinates of a given vector relative to two different bases in a vector space $\mathcal{V}$.

(19.1) **Theorem.** Let $\{\mathbf{U}_1, \mathbf{U}_2, \ldots, \mathbf{U}_k\}$ be a set of vectors in a vector space $\mathcal{V}$ of dimension n. Let $\mathbf{U}_i$ have coordinates $\langle r_{i,1}, r_{i,2}, \ldots, r_{i,n}\rangle$ for $i = 1, 2, \ldots, k$ with respect to some basis of $\mathcal{V}$. Then the row rank of the k by n matrix $R = [r_{i,j}]$ is equal to the dimension of the subspace $\mathcal{S}$ spanned by $\{\mathbf{U}_1, \mathbf{U}_2, \ldots, \mathbf{U}_k\}$.

PROOF. By the isomorphism between $\mathcal{V}$ and the n-tuple space $\mathcal{V}_n$, the vector $\mathbf{U}_i$ corresponds to the vector $\langle r_{i,1}, r_{i,2}, \ldots, r_{i,n}\rangle$, $i = 1, 2, \ldots, k$ (see Theorem 14.8). Therefore the subspace $\mathcal{S}$ of $\mathcal{V}$ spanned by $\{\mathbf{U}_1, \mathbf{U}_2, \ldots, \mathbf{U}_k\}$ is isomorphic to the row space of the matrix $R = [r_{i,j}]$. Hence, the dimension of $\mathcal{S}$ is equal to the dimension of the row space of R, which is the row rank of R.

(19.2) **Corollary.** Let $\{\mathbf{U}_1, \mathbf{U}_2, \ldots, \mathbf{U}_n\}$ be a set of n vectors in a vector space $\mathcal{V}$ of dimension n. Let $\mathbf{U}_i$ have coordinates $\langle r_{i,1}, r_{i,2}, \ldots, r_{i,n}\rangle$ for $i = 1, 2, \ldots, n$ with respect to some basis of $\mathcal{V}$. Then the n by n matrix $R = [r_{i,j}]$ is nonsingular if and only if $\{\mathbf{U}_1, \mathbf{U}_2, \ldots, \mathbf{U}_n\}$ is a basis of $\mathcal{V}$.

PROOF. If $R = [r_{i,j}]$ is nonsingular, then, by Theorem 18.7, R has row rank n. Then, by Theorem 19.1, the subspace $\mathcal{S}$ of $\mathcal{V}$ spanned by $\{\mathbf{U}_1, \mathbf{U}_2, \ldots, \mathbf{U}_n\}$ has dimension n. Hence, by Corollary 8.9, $\mathcal{S} = \mathcal{V}$. Thus, $\{\mathbf{U}_1, \mathbf{U}_2, \ldots, \mathbf{U}_n\}$ spans $\mathcal{V}$ and is a basis of $\mathcal{V}$ by Corollary 8.8. Conversely, if $\{\mathbf{U}_1, \mathbf{U}_2, \ldots, \mathbf{U}_n\}$ is a basis of $\mathcal{V}$, then, by Theorem 19.1, the row rank of R is n. Finally, by Theorem 18.7, R is nonsingular.

Suppose that $\{\mathbf{U}_1, \mathbf{U}_2, \ldots, \mathbf{U}_n\}$ is a basis of the vector space $\mathcal{V}$ and that $\{\bar{\mathbf{U}}_1, \bar{\mathbf{U}}_2, \ldots, \bar{\mathbf{U}}_n\}$ is any set of n vectors in $\mathcal{V}$. Then, since $\{\mathbf{U}_1, \mathbf{U}_2, \ldots, \mathbf{U}_n\}$ is a basis of $\mathcal{V}$, we have

$$
\begin{aligned}
\bar{\mathbf{U}}_1 &= p_{1,1} \cdot \mathbf{U}_1 + p_{1,2} \cdot \mathbf{U}_2 + \cdots + p_{1,n} \cdot \mathbf{U}_n \\
\bar{\mathbf{U}}_2 &= p_{2,1} \cdot \mathbf{U}_1 + p_{2,2} \cdot \mathbf{U}_2 + \cdots + p_{2,n} \cdot \mathbf{U}_n \\
&\cdots \\
\bar{\mathbf{U}}_n &= p_{n,1} \cdot \mathbf{U}_1 + p_{n,2} \cdot \mathbf{U}_2 + \cdots + p_{n,n} \cdot \mathbf{U}_n.
\end{aligned} \tag{19-1}
$$

The coordinates of $\bar{\mathbf{U}}_i$ with respect to the basis $\{\mathbf{U}_1, \mathbf{U}_2, \ldots, \mathbf{U}_n\}$ are $\langle p_{i,1}, p_{i,2}, \ldots, p_{i,n}\rangle$ for $i = 1, 2, \ldots, n$. By Corollary 19.2, $\{\bar{\mathbf{U}}_1, \bar{\mathbf{U}}_2, \ldots, \bar{\mathbf{U}}_n\}$ is a basis of $\mathcal{V}$ if and only if the matrix $P = [p_{i,j}]$ is nonsingular.

Now assume that $\{\bar{\mathbf{U}}_1, \bar{\mathbf{U}}_2, \ldots, \bar{\mathbf{U}}_n\}$ is a basis of $\mathcal{V}$ related to the basis $\{\mathbf{U}_1, \mathbf{U}_2, \ldots, \mathbf{U}_n\}$ by the equations (19-1). In this situation, we call the nonsingular matrix $P = [p_{i,j}]$ the *matrix of the change of basis* from the $\mathbf{U}$-basis to the $\bar{\mathbf{U}}$-basis. Let $\mathbf{V} \in \mathcal{V}$, and suppose that $\mathbf{V}$ has coordinates $\langle a_1, a_2, \ldots, a_n\rangle$ with respect to the $\mathbf{U}$-basis and coordinates $\langle \bar{a}_1, \bar{a}_2, \ldots, \bar{a}_n\rangle$ with respect to the $\bar{\mathbf{U}}$-basis. Then

$$\mathbf{V} = \bar{a}_1 \cdot \bar{\mathbf{U}}_1 + \bar{a}_2 \cdot \bar{\mathbf{U}}_2 + \cdots + \bar{a}_n \cdot \bar{\mathbf{U}}_n.$$

By the remarks following Theorem 14.8,

$$
\begin{aligned}
\langle a_1, a_2, \ldots, a_n\rangle &= \bar{a}_1 \cdot \langle p_{1,1}, p_{1,2}, \ldots, p_{1,n}\rangle + \bar{a}_2 \cdot \langle p_{2,1}, p_{2,2}, \ldots, p_{2,n}\rangle \\
&\quad + \cdots + \bar{a}_n \cdot \langle p_{n,1}, p_{n,2}, \ldots, p_{n,n}\rangle \\
&= \langle \bar{a}_1 p_{1,1} + \bar{a}_2 p_{2,1} + \cdots + \bar{a}_n p_{n,1}, \bar{a}_1 p_{1,2} + \bar{a}_2 p_{2,2} \\
&\quad + \cdots + \bar{a}_n p_{n,2}, \ldots, \bar{a}_1 p_{1,n} + \bar{a}_2 p_{2,n} + \cdots \\
&\quad + \bar{a}_n p_{n,n}\rangle.
\end{aligned}
$$

Hence,

$$
\begin{aligned}
a_1 &= \bar{a}_1 p_{1,1} + \bar{a}_2 p_{2,1} + \cdots + \bar{a}_n p_{n,1} \\
a_2 &= \bar{a}_1 p_{1,2} + \bar{a}_2 p_{2,2} + \cdots + \bar{a}_n p_{n,2} \\
&\cdots \\
a_n &= \bar{a}_1 p_{1,n} + \bar{a}_2 p_{2,n} + \cdots + \bar{a}_n p_{n,n}.
\end{aligned} \tag{19-2}
$$

Equations (19-2) can be written compactly as a single matrix equation in either of the two following ways:

$$[a_1 \quad a_2 \quad \ldots \quad a_n] = [\bar{a}_1 \quad \bar{a}_2 \quad \ldots \quad \bar{a}_n]P, \tag{19-3}$$

or

$$\begin{bmatrix} a_1 \\ a_2 \\ \cdot \\ \cdot \\ \cdot \\ a_n \end{bmatrix} = P' \begin{bmatrix} \bar{a}_1 \\ \bar{a}_2 \\ \cdot \\ \cdot \\ \cdot \\ \bar{a}_n \end{bmatrix}, \tag{19-4}$$

where P' is the transpose of the matrix P (see Exercise 17.16). Moreover $P = [p_{i,j}]$ is the matrix of the change of basis. Since P is nonsingular, equation (19-3) can be multiplied by P^{-1} to obtain

$$[\bar{a}_1 \quad \bar{a}_2 \quad \ldots \quad \bar{a}_n] = [a_1 \quad a_2 \quad \ldots \quad a_n]P^{-1}, \tag{19-5}$$

which can be written in the form

$$\begin{bmatrix} \bar{a}_1 \\ \bar{a}_2 \\ \cdot \\ \cdot \\ \cdot \\ \bar{a}_n \end{bmatrix} = (P^{-1})' \begin{bmatrix} a_1 \\ a_2 \\ \cdot \\ \cdot \\ \cdot \\ a_n \end{bmatrix}. \tag{19-6}$$

Example 1. In $\mathcal{E}_3$, let the vectors **U**, **V**, **W** have coordinates $\langle 2, -1, 3\rangle$, $\langle 4, 0, 1\rangle$, $\langle 1, -1, 8\rangle$, respectively, with respect to the basis $\{\mathbf{I}, \mathbf{J}, \mathbf{K}\}$. Then

$$\begin{aligned} \mathbf{U} &= 2\cdot\mathbf{I} + (-1)\cdot\mathbf{J} + 3\cdot\mathbf{K} \\ \mathbf{V} &= 4\cdot\mathbf{I} \qquad + 0\cdot\mathbf{J} + 1\cdot\mathbf{K} \\ \mathbf{W} &= 1\cdot\mathbf{I} + (-1)\cdot\mathbf{J} + 8\cdot\mathbf{K}. \end{aligned}$$

The matrix P of equations (19-1) is

$$P = \begin{bmatrix} 2 & -1 & 3 \\ 4 & 0 & 1 \\ 1 & -1 & 8 \end{bmatrix},$$

which can be carried to echelon form

$$P^* = \begin{bmatrix} 1 & -1 & 8 \\ 0 & 1 & -13 \\ 0 & 0 & 1 \end{bmatrix}$$

by elementary row transformations. Therefore, the row rank of P = the row rank of $P^* = 3$. By Theorem 18.7, P is nonsingular. Hence $\{\mathbf{U}, \mathbf{V}, \mathbf{W}\}$ is a basis of $\mathcal{E}_3$. Let $\mathbf{T}$ have coordinates $\langle -5, 7, 9\rangle$ with respect to $\{\mathbf{I}, \mathbf{J}, \mathbf{K}\}$. If $\mathbf{T}$ has coordinates $\langle \bar{a}_1, \bar{a}_2, \bar{a}_3\rangle$ with respect to $\{\mathbf{U}, \mathbf{V}, \mathbf{W}\}$, then, by (19-4),

$$\begin{bmatrix} -5 \\ 7 \\ 9 \end{bmatrix} = \begin{bmatrix} 2 & 4 & 1 \\ -1 & 0 & -1 \\ 3 & 1 & 8 \end{bmatrix} \begin{bmatrix} \bar{a}_1 \\ \bar{a}_2 \\ \bar{a}_3 \end{bmatrix}.$$

Solving this system of equations for $\bar{a}_1$, $\bar{a}_2$, and $\bar{a}_3$ by the methods of Chapter Three, we find $\langle \bar{a}_1, \bar{a}_2, \bar{a}_3\rangle = \langle -\frac{86}{7}, \frac{25}{7}, \frac{37}{7}\rangle$.

Example 2. Let $\langle \mathbf{I}, \mathbf{J}\rangle$ be a rectangular Cartesian coordinate system in $\mathcal{E}_2$. Define vectors $\bar{\mathbf{I}}$ and $\bar{\mathbf{J}}$ by the equations

$$\bar{\mathbf{I}} = (\cos\theta)\mathbf{I} + (-\sin\theta)\mathbf{J}$$
$$\bar{\mathbf{J}} = (\sin\theta)\mathbf{I} + (\cos\theta)\mathbf{J},$$

for some fixed angle θ. It is easy to discover that the matrix

$$P = \begin{bmatrix} \cos\theta & -\sin\theta \\ \sin\theta & \cos\theta \end{bmatrix}$$

has an inverse

$$P^{-1} = \begin{bmatrix} \cos\theta & \sin\theta \\ -\sin\theta & \cos\theta \end{bmatrix}.$$

Thus, P is nonsingular, and $\{\bar{\mathbf{I}}, \bar{\mathbf{J}}\}$ is a basis of $\mathcal{E}_2$. We find

$$|\bar{\mathbf{I}}| = \sqrt{\cos^2\theta + \sin^2\theta} = 1, \qquad |\bar{\mathbf{J}}| = \sqrt{\sin^2\theta + \cos^2\theta} = 1,$$

and

$$\bar{\mathbf{I}} \circ \bar{\mathbf{J}} = \cos\theta\sin\theta + (-\sin\theta)\cos\theta = 0.$$

Hence, $\langle \bar{\mathbf{I}}, \bar{\mathbf{J}}\rangle$ is a rectangular Cartesian coordinate system for $\mathcal{E}_2$. If $\mathbf{V} \in \mathcal{E}_2$ has coordinates $\langle x, y\rangle$ with respect to $\langle \mathbf{I}, \mathbf{J}\rangle$ and coordinates $\langle \bar{x}, \bar{y}\rangle$ with respect to $\langle \bar{\mathbf{I}}, \bar{\mathbf{J}}\rangle$, then

$$[\bar{x} \quad \bar{y}] = [x \quad y] \begin{bmatrix} \cos\theta & \sin\theta \\ -\sin\theta & \cos\theta \end{bmatrix}, \tag{19-7}$$

which is the matrix version of the equations of rotation of a rectangular Cartesian coordinate system through an angle θ.

Exercises

19.1 Prove that $\{\mathbf{U}_1, \mathbf{U}_2, \mathbf{U}_3, \mathbf{U}_4\}$ is a basis of $\mathcal{V}_4$, where $\mathbf{U}_1 = \langle -2, 3, 4, 1\rangle$, $\mathbf{U}_2 = \langle 0, -1, 6, 3\rangle$, $\mathbf{U}_3 = \langle 1, 1, 4, 2\rangle$, and $\mathbf{U}_4 = \langle -5, 6, -1, 0\rangle$. Find the dimension of the subspace $\mathcal{S}$ of $\mathcal{V}_4$ spanned by the following sets of vectors:

(a) $\{\mathbf{U}_1 - 2 \cdot \mathbf{U}_2 + \mathbf{U}_3,\ 3 \cdot \mathbf{U}_1 - \mathbf{U}_3,\ -6 \cdot \mathbf{U}_2 + 4 \cdot \mathbf{U}_3\}$;

(b) $\{\mathbf{U}_1 - \mathbf{U}_2 + \mathbf{U}_3 - \mathbf{U}_4,\ \mathbf{U}_1 - \mathbf{U}_3 + \mathbf{U}_4,\ \mathbf{U}_2 - \mathbf{U}_3 + \mathbf{U}_4,\ \mathbf{U}_3 - \mathbf{U}_4\}$;

(c) $\{\sqrt{2} \cdot \mathbf{U}_1 + \sqrt{3} \cdot \mathbf{U}_2 + \sqrt{5} \cdot \mathbf{U}_3 + \sqrt{7} \cdot \mathbf{U}_4,\ \sqrt{7} \cdot \mathbf{U}_1 + \sqrt{5} \cdot \mathbf{U}_2 + \sqrt{3} \cdot \mathbf{U}_3 + \sqrt{2} \cdot \mathbf{U}_4\}$.

19.2 Prove that $\{\langle 1, 0, 0\rangle, \langle 1, 1, 0\rangle, \langle 1, 1, 1\rangle\}$ and $\{\langle 1, 2, -1\rangle, \langle 3, -1, 4\rangle, \langle 2, 0, 1\rangle\}$ are bases of $\mathcal{V}_3$. Find the matrix of the change of basis from the first basis to the second basis. Find the coordinates of the vector $\mathbf{U} = \langle 7, -3, 4\rangle$ with respect to each basis.

19.3 Let $\langle \mathbf{I}, \mathbf{J}\rangle$ be a rectangular Cartesian coordinate system in $\mathcal{E}_2$. Define vectors $\bar{\mathbf{I}}$, $\bar{\mathbf{J}}$ by the equations

$$\bar{\mathbf{I}} = p_{1,1} \cdot \mathbf{I} + p_{1,2} \cdot \mathbf{J}$$

$$\bar{\mathbf{J}} = p_{2,1} \cdot \mathbf{I} + p_{2,2} \cdot \mathbf{J},$$

where the matrix

$$P = \begin{bmatrix} p_{1,1} & p_{1,2} \\ p_{2,1} & p_{2,2} \end{bmatrix}$$

is nonsingular and $P^{-1} = P'$. Prove that $\langle \bar{\mathbf{I}}, \bar{\mathbf{J}}\rangle$ is a rectangular Cartesian coordinate system for $\mathcal{E}_2$.

***19.4** Let $\{\mathbf{U}_1, \mathbf{U}_2, \ldots, \mathbf{U}_n\}$ be an orthonormal basis of a Euclidean vector space $\mathcal{E}$. Let $\{\bar{\mathbf{U}}_1, \bar{\mathbf{U}}_2, \ldots, \bar{\mathbf{U}}_n\}$ be a second ba is of $\mathcal{E}$, and let $P = [p_{i,j}]$ be the matrix of the change of basis from the $\mathbf{U}$-basis to the $\bar{\mathbf{U}}$-basis. Prove that the $\bar{\mathbf{U}}$-basis is orthonormal if and only if $P^{-1} = P'$.

20 Matrices of linear transformations with respect to different bases

In the following discussion, $\mathcal{V}$ is an n-dimensional vector space with basis $\{\mathbf{U}_1, \mathbf{U}_2, \ldots, \mathbf{U}_n\}$ and $\mathcal{W}$ is an m-dimensional space with basis $\{\mathbf{W}_1, \mathbf{W}_2, \ldots, \mathbf{W}_m\}$. We assume that L is a linear transformation of $\mathcal{V}$ into $\mathcal{W}$ that has matrix A with respect to the given bases, and we investigate the effect of a change of basis in each space on the matrix A.

Suppose first that $\{\bar{\mathbf{U}}_1, \bar{\mathbf{U}}_2, \ldots, \bar{\mathbf{U}}_n\}$ and $\{\bar{\mathbf{W}}_1, \bar{\mathbf{W}}_2, \ldots, \bar{\mathbf{W}}_m\}$ are second bases of $\mathcal{V}$ and $\mathcal{W}$, respectively. Let $\mathbf{V}$ be any vector in $\mathcal{V}$ that has coordinates $\langle r_1, r_2, \ldots, r_n\rangle$ with respect to the basis $\{\mathbf{U}_1, \mathbf{U}_2, \ldots, \mathbf{U}_n\}$ and coordinates $\langle \bar{r}_1, \bar{r}_2, \ldots, \bar{r}_n\rangle$ with respect to the basis $\{\bar{\mathbf{U}}_1, \bar{\mathbf{U}}_2, \ldots, \bar{\mathbf{U}}_n\}$. Denote the coordinates of $L(\mathbf{V})$ with respect to the basis $\{\mathbf{W}_1, \mathbf{W}_2, \ldots, \mathbf{W}_m\}$ by $\langle s_1, s_2, \ldots, s_m\rangle$ and the coordinates of $L(\mathbf{V})$ with respect to $\{\bar{\mathbf{W}}_1, \bar{\mathbf{W}}_2, \ldots, \bar{\mathbf{W}}_m\}$ by $\langle \bar{s}_1, \bar{s}_2, \ldots, \bar{s}_m \rangle$. Then,

$$\begin{bmatrix} s_1 \\ s_2 \\ \cdot \\ \cdot \\ \cdot \\ s_m \end{bmatrix} = A \begin{bmatrix} r_1 \\ r_2 \\ \cdot \\ \cdot \\ \cdot \\ r_n \end{bmatrix},$$

where A is the m by n matrix of L with respect to the first bases in $\mathcal{V}$ and $\mathcal{W}$ (see Example 3, Section 17). Let P be the matrix of the change of basis from the $\mathbf{U}$-basis to the $\bar{\mathbf{U}}$-basis in $\mathcal{V}$, and let Q be the matrix of the change of basis from the $\mathbf{W}$-basis to the $\bar{\mathbf{W}}$-basis in $\mathcal{W}$. Then, by the results of Section 19,

$$\begin{bmatrix} r_1 \\ r_2 \\ \cdot \\ \cdot \\ \cdot \\ r_n \end{bmatrix} = P' \begin{bmatrix} \bar{r}_1 \\ \bar{r}_2 \\ \cdot \\ \cdot \\ \cdot \\ \bar{r}_n \end{bmatrix} \quad \text{and} \quad \begin{bmatrix} \bar{s}_1 \\ \bar{s}_2 \\ \cdot \\ \cdot \\ \cdot \\ \bar{s}_m \end{bmatrix} = (Q^{-1})' \begin{bmatrix} s_1 \\ s_2 \\ \cdot \\ \cdot \\ \cdot \\ s_m \end{bmatrix}.$$

Therefore,

$$\begin{bmatrix} \bar{s}_1 \\ \bar{s}_2 \\ \cdot \\ \cdot \\ \cdot \\ \bar{s}_m \end{bmatrix} = (Q^{-1})' \begin{bmatrix} s_1 \\ s_2 \\ \cdot \\ \cdot \\ \cdot \\ s_m \end{bmatrix} = (Q^{-1})'A \begin{bmatrix} r_1 \\ r_1 \\ \cdot \\ \cdot \\ \cdot \\ r_n \end{bmatrix} = (Q^{-1})'AP' \begin{bmatrix} \bar{r}_1 \\ \bar{r}_2 \\ \cdot \\ \cdot \\ \cdot \\ \bar{r}_n \end{bmatrix}.$$

Hence, the matrix of the linear transformation L with respect to the second bases in $\mathcal{V}$ and $\mathcal{W}$ is $(Q^{-1})'AP'$, where $(Q^{-1})'$ and P' are nonsingular matrices.

Now suppose that B is an m by n matrix and that there exist a nonsingular m by m matrix E and a nonsingular n by n matrix F such that $B = EAF$. By the results of Section 19, a new basis $\{\bar{\mathbf{U}}_1, \bar{\mathbf{U}}_2, \ldots, \bar{\mathbf{U}}_n\}$ can be defined in $\mathcal{V}$, using the nonsingular matrix F' as the matrix of the change of basis. Then the coordinates $\langle \bar{r}_1, \bar{r}_2, \ldots, \bar{r}_n \rangle$ of $\mathbf{V}$ with respect to this new basis are related to the coordinates $\langle r_1, r_2, \ldots, r_n \rangle$ of $\mathbf{V}$ with respect to the basis $\{\mathbf{U}_1, \mathbf{U}_2, \ldots, \mathbf{U}_n\}$ by

$$\begin{bmatrix} r_1 \\ r_2 \\ \cdot \\ \cdot \\ \cdot \\ r_n \end{bmatrix} = (F')' \begin{bmatrix} \bar{r}_1 \\ \bar{r}_2 \\ \cdot \\ \cdot \\ \cdot \\ \bar{r}_n \end{bmatrix} = F \begin{bmatrix} \bar{r}_1 \\ \bar{r}_2 \\ \cdot \\ \cdot \\ \cdot \\ \bar{r}_n \end{bmatrix}.$$

Similarly, a new basis $\{\overline{\mathbf{W}}_1, \overline{\mathbf{W}}_2, \ldots, \overline{\mathbf{W}}_m\}$ can be defined in $\mathcal{W}$, using the nonsingular matrix $(E')^{-1}$ as the matrix of the change of basis, such that the coordinates $\langle \bar{s}_1, \bar{s}_2, \ldots, \bar{s}_m \rangle$ of $L(\mathbf{V})$ with respect to this basis are given by

$$\begin{bmatrix} \bar{s}_1 \\ \bar{s}_1 \\ \cdot \\ \cdot \\ \cdot \\ \bar{s}_m \end{bmatrix} = (((E')^{-1})^{-1})' \begin{bmatrix} s_1 \\ s_2 \\ \cdot \\ \cdot \\ \cdot \\ s_m \end{bmatrix} = E \begin{bmatrix} s_2 \\ s_2 \\ \cdot \\ \cdot \\ \cdot \\ s_m \end{bmatrix},$$

where $\langle s_1, s_2, \ldots, s_m \rangle$ are the coordinates of $L(\mathbf{V})$ with respect to $\{\mathbf{W}_1, \mathbf{W}_2, \ldots, \mathbf{W}_m\}$. Hence,

$$\begin{bmatrix} \bar{s}_1 \\ \bar{s}_2 \\ \cdot \\ \cdot \\ \cdot \\ \bar{s}_m \end{bmatrix} = E \begin{bmatrix} s_1 \\ s_2 \\ \cdot \\ \cdot \\ \cdot \\ s_m \end{bmatrix} = EA \begin{bmatrix} r_1 \\ r_2 \\ \cdot \\ \cdot \\ \cdot \\ r_n \end{bmatrix} = EAF \begin{bmatrix} \bar{r}_1 \\ \bar{r}_2 \\ \cdot \\ \cdot \\ \cdot \\ \bar{r}_n \end{bmatrix} = B \begin{bmatrix} \bar{r}_1 \\ \bar{r}_2 \\ \cdot \\ \cdot \\ \cdot \\ \bar{r}_n \end{bmatrix}.$$

Therefore, there is a suitable change of basis in each space $\mathcal{V}$ and $\mathcal{W}$ such that B is the matrix of the linear transformation L with respect to these new bases. These results are summarized in the following theorem:

(20.1) **Theorem.** Let A and B be m by n matrices, and let $\mathcal{V}$ be an n-dimensional vector space and $\mathcal{W}$ be an m-dimensional vector space. The matrices A and B are matrices of the same linear transformation L of $\mathcal{V}$ into $\mathcal{W}$ (with respect to suitable bases in these spaces) if and only if there exist nonsingular matrices E and F such that $B = EAF$.

Theorem 20.1, in turn, leads to the following definition:

(20.2) Definition. Let A and B be m by n matrices. The matrix B is *equivalent* to the matrix A if there exist a nonsingular m by m matrix E and a nonsingular n by n matrix F such that $B = EAF$.

The relation between m by n matrices defined in 20.2 is called *equivalence of rectangular matrices*. It is readily verified that this relation is an equivalence relation on the set ${}_m\mathfrak{A}_n$ of all m by n matrices whose elements are real numbers. Thus, by the symmetric property of an equivalence relation, we can simply say that the matrices A and B are equivalent. In terms of the concept of equivalence of matrices, Theorem 20.1 states that two m by n matrices are matrices of the same linear transformation if and only if they are equivalent.

Suppose that a given m by n matrix A is equivalent to an m by n matrix B, which has a particularly simple form. Let L be the linear transformation of $\mathcal{V}$ into $\mathcal{W}$ defined by the matrix A relative to chosen bases in $\mathcal{V}$ and $\mathcal{W}$. Then the matrix A of L can be simplified by referring L to new bases in $\mathcal{V}$ and $\mathcal{W}$. Moreover, certain properties of L that are reflected in its corresponding matrices become apparent.

Example 1. Let L be the linear transformation of $\mathcal{V}_4$ into $\mathcal{V}_3$ that has the matrix

$$A = \begin{bmatrix} 0 & -3 & -1 & 1 \\ 1 & 5 & 4 & -1 \\ 1 & 2 & 3 & 0 \end{bmatrix}$$

with respect to the bases $E^{(4)}$ and $E^{(3)}$ in $\mathcal{V}_4$ and $\mathcal{V}_3$, respectively. Then any vector $\langle r_1, r_2, r_3, r_4\rangle \in \mathcal{V}_4$ is sent into the vector $\langle s_1, s_2, s_3\rangle \in \mathcal{V}_3$, where

$$\begin{bmatrix} s_1 \\ s_2 \\ s_3 \end{bmatrix} = \begin{bmatrix} 0 & -3 & -1 & 1 \\ 1 & 5 & 4 & -1 \\ 1 & 2 & 3 & 0 \end{bmatrix} \begin{bmatrix} r_1 \\ r_2 \\ r_3 \\ r_4 \end{bmatrix} = \begin{bmatrix} -3r_2 - r_3 + r_4 \\ r_1 + 5r_2 + 4r_3 - r_4 \\ r_1 + 2r_2 + 3r_3 \end{bmatrix}.$$

Thus, $L(\langle r_1, r_2, r_3, r_4\rangle) = \langle -3r_2 - r_3 + r_4, r_1 + 5r_2 + 4r_3 - r_4, r_1 + 2r_2 + 3r_3\rangle$. The matrix

$$E = \begin{bmatrix} 0 & 1 & 0 \\ -\frac{1}{3} & 0 & 0 \\ -1 & -1 & 1 \end{bmatrix}$$

is nonsingular with

$$E^{-1} = \begin{bmatrix} 0 & -3 & 0 \\ 1 & 0 & 0 \\ 1 & -3 & 1 \end{bmatrix}.$$

The matrix

$$F = \begin{bmatrix} 1 & -5 & -\tfrac{7}{3} & -\tfrac{2}{3} \\ 0 & 1 & -\tfrac{1}{3} & \tfrac{1}{3} \\ 0 & 0 & 1 & 0 \\ 0 & 0 & 0 & 1 \end{bmatrix}$$

is nonsingular with

$$F^{-1} = \begin{bmatrix} 1 & 5 & 4 & -1 \\ 0 & 1 & \tfrac{1}{3} & -\tfrac{1}{3} \\ 0 & 0 & 1 & 0 \\ 0 & 0 & 0 & 1 \end{bmatrix}.$$

Define a new basis in $\mathcal{V}_4$, using the matrix F':

$$\begin{aligned} \bar{\mathbf{U}}_1 &= 1 \cdot \mathbf{E}_1^{(4)} \\ \bar{\mathbf{U}}_2 &= (-5) \cdot \mathbf{E}_1^{(4)} + 1 \cdot \mathbf{E}_2^{(4)} \\ \bar{\mathbf{U}}_3 &= (-\tfrac{7}{3}) \cdot \mathbf{E}_1^{(4)} + (-\tfrac{1}{3}) \cdot \mathbf{E}_2^{(4)} + 1 \cdot \mathbf{E}_3^{(4)} \\ \bar{\mathbf{U}}_4 &= (-\tfrac{2}{3}) \cdot \mathbf{E}_1^{(4)} + (\tfrac{1}{3}) \cdot \mathbf{E}_2^{(4)} + 1 \cdot \mathbf{E}_4^{(4)}. \end{aligned}$$

Thus, $\bar{\mathbf{U}}_1 = \langle 1, 0, 0, 0\rangle$, $\bar{\mathbf{U}}_2 = \langle -5, 1, 0, 0\rangle$, $\bar{\mathbf{U}}_3 = \langle -\tfrac{7}{3}, -\tfrac{1}{3}, 1, 0\rangle$ and $\bar{\mathbf{U}}_4 = \langle -\tfrac{2}{3}, \tfrac{1}{3}, 0, 1\rangle$. Define a new basis in $\mathcal{V}_3$, using the matrix $(E')^{-1} = (E^{-1})'$:

$$\begin{aligned} \bar{\mathbf{W}}_1 &= 1 \cdot \mathbf{E}_2^{(3)} + 1 \cdot \mathbf{E}_3^{(3)} \\ \bar{\mathbf{W}}_2 &= (-3) \cdot \mathbf{E}_1^{(3)} + (-3) \cdot \mathbf{E}_3^{(3)} \\ \bar{\mathbf{W}}_3 &= 1 \cdot \mathbf{E}_3^{(3)}. \end{aligned}$$

Hence $\bar{\mathbf{W}}_1 = \langle 0, 1, 1\rangle$, $\bar{\mathbf{W}}_2 = \langle -3, 0, -3\rangle$, and $\bar{\mathbf{W}}_3 = \langle 0, 0, 1\rangle$. With respect to the bases $\{\bar{\mathbf{U}}_1, \bar{\mathbf{U}}_2, \bar{\mathbf{U}}_3, \bar{\mathbf{U}}_4\}$ and $\{\bar{\mathbf{W}}_1, \bar{\mathbf{W}}_2, \bar{\mathbf{W}}_3\}$ in $\mathcal{V}_4$ and $\mathcal{V}_3$, the linear transformation L has matrix

$$B = EAF = \begin{bmatrix} 0 & 1 & 0 \\ -\tfrac{1}{3} & 0 & 0 \\ -1 & -1 & 1 \end{bmatrix} \begin{bmatrix} 0 & -3 & -1 & 1 \\ 1 & 5 & 4 & -1 \\ 1 & 2 & 3 & 0 \end{bmatrix} \begin{bmatrix} 1 & -5 & -\tfrac{7}{3} & -\tfrac{2}{3} \\ 0 & 1 & -\tfrac{1}{3} & \tfrac{1}{3} \\ 0 & 0 & 1 & 0 \\ 0 & 0 & 0 & 1 \end{bmatrix}$$

$$= \begin{bmatrix} 1 & 0 & 0 & 0 \\ 0 & 1 & 0 & 0 \\ 0 & 0 & 0 & 0 \end{bmatrix}.$$

A vector $\mathbf{V} \in \mathcal{V}_4$ with coordinates $\langle \bar{r}_1, \bar{r}_2, \bar{r}_3, \bar{r}_4\rangle$ with respect to the basis $\{\bar{\mathbf{U}}_1, \bar{\mathbf{U}}_2, \bar{\mathbf{U}}_3, \bar{\mathbf{U}}_4\}$ is sent into the vector $L(\mathbf{V})$ with coordinates $\langle \bar{s}_1, \bar{s}_2, \bar{s}_3\rangle$ with respect to the basis $\{\bar{\mathbf{W}}_1, \bar{\mathbf{W}}_2, \bar{\mathbf{W}}_3\}$, where

$$\begin{bmatrix} \bar{s}_1 \\ \bar{s}_2 \\ \bar{s}_3 \end{bmatrix} = \begin{bmatrix} 1 & 0 & 0 & 0 \\ 0 & 1 & 0 & 0 \\ 0 & 0 & 0 & 0 \end{bmatrix} \begin{bmatrix} \bar{r}_1 \\ \bar{r}_2 \\ \bar{r}_3 \\ \bar{r}_4 \end{bmatrix} = \begin{bmatrix} \bar{r}_1 \\ \bar{r}_2 \\ 0 \end{bmatrix}.$$

For example, if

$$\mathbf{V} = 3 \cdot \bar{\mathbf{U}}_1 + (-6) \cdot \bar{\mathbf{U}}_2 + (\tfrac{1}{2}) \cdot \bar{\mathbf{U}}_3 + (-5) \cdot \bar{\mathbf{U}}_4,$$

then

$$L(\mathbf{V}) = 3 \cdot \bar{\mathbf{W}}_1 + (-6) \cdot \bar{\mathbf{W}}_2 + 0 \cdot \bar{\mathbf{W}}_3 = 3 \cdot \langle 0, 1, 1 \rangle + (-6) \cdot \langle -3, 0, -3 \rangle$$
$$= \langle 18, 3, 21 \rangle.$$

It is evident from the simple form of the matrix B of L that the range space $L(\mathcal{V}_4)$ is the subspace of $\mathcal{V}_3$ of dimension two spanned by $\bar{\mathbf{W}}_1$ and $\bar{\mathbf{W}}_2$. The null space $L^{-1}(\{\mathbf{0}\})$ of L is the subspace of $\mathcal{V}_4$ of dimension two spanned by $\bar{\mathbf{U}}_3$ and $\bar{\mathbf{U}}_4$.

We turn next to the situation where L is a linear transformation of an n-dimensional vector space $\mathcal{V}$ into itself. The matrix of L with respect to a basis $\{\mathbf{U}_1, \mathbf{U}_2, \ldots, \mathbf{U}_n\}$ of $\mathcal{V}$ is an n by n matrix A. If $\mathbf{V} \in \mathcal{V}$, and if $\mathbf{V}$ has coordinates $\langle r_1, r_2, \ldots, r_n \rangle$ with respect to this basis, then $L(\mathbf{V})$ has coordinates $\langle s_1, s_2, \ldots, s_n \rangle$ with respect to this same basis, where

$$\begin{bmatrix} s_1 \\ s_2 \\ \cdot \\ \cdot \\ \cdot \\ s_n \end{bmatrix} = A \begin{bmatrix} r_1 \\ r_2 \\ \cdot \\ \cdot \\ \cdot \\ r_n \end{bmatrix}.$$

If $\{\bar{\mathbf{U}}_1, \bar{\mathbf{U}}_2, \ldots, \bar{\mathbf{U}}_n\}$ is a second basis of $\mathcal{V}$, and if P is the matrix of the change of basis from the $\mathbf{U}$-basis to the $\bar{\mathbf{U}}$-basis, then

$$\begin{bmatrix} r_1 \\ r_2 \\ \cdot \\ \cdot \\ \cdot \\ r_n \end{bmatrix} = P' \begin{bmatrix} \bar{r}_1 \\ \bar{r}_2 \\ \cdot \\ \cdot \\ \cdot \\ \bar{r}_n \end{bmatrix} \quad \text{and} \quad \begin{bmatrix} s_1 \\ s_2 \\ \cdot \\ \cdot \\ \cdot \\ s_n \end{bmatrix} = P' \begin{bmatrix} \bar{s}_1 \\ \bar{s}_2 \\ \cdot \\ \cdot \\ \cdot \\ \bar{s}_n \end{bmatrix},$$

where **V** has coordinates $\langle \bar{r}_1, \bar{r}_2, \ldots, \bar{r}_n \rangle$ and $L(\mathbf{V})$ has coordinates $\langle \bar{s}_1, \bar{s}_2, \ldots, \bar{s}_n \rangle$ with respect to the second basis. Thus, we have

$$\begin{bmatrix} \bar{s}_1 \\ \bar{s}_2 \\ \cdot \\ \cdot \\ \cdot \\ \bar{s}_n \end{bmatrix} = (P')^{-1} \begin{bmatrix} s_1 \\ s_2 \\ \cdot \\ \cdot \\ \cdot \\ s_n \end{bmatrix} = (P')^{-1}A \begin{bmatrix} r_1 \\ r_2 \\ \cdot \\ \cdot \\ \cdot \\ r_n \end{bmatrix} = (P')^{-1}AP' \begin{bmatrix} \bar{r}_1 \\ \bar{r}_2 \\ \cdot \\ \cdot \\ \cdot \\ \bar{r}_n \end{bmatrix}.$$

Conversely, if B is an n by n matrix, and if there exists a nonsingular n by n matrix Q such that $B = Q^{-1}AQ$, then a new basis can be defined in $\mathcal{V}$ by means of Q' so that B is the matrix of L with respect to this new basis.

(20.3) Theorem. Let A and B be n by n matrices, and let $\mathcal{V}$ be an n-dimensional vector space. The matrices A and B are matrices of the same linear transformation L of $\mathcal{V}$ into itself (with respect to suitable bases in $\mathcal{V}$) if and only if there exists a nonsingular matrix Q such that $B = Q^{-1}AQ$.

An important relation between square matrices is suggested by Theorem 20.3:

(20.4) Definition. Let A and B be n by n matrices. The matrix B is *similar* to the matrix A if there exists a nonsingular matrix Q such that $B = Q^{-1}AQ$.

Similarity is an equivalence relation on the set $\mathfrak{A}_n$ of all n by n matrices. By Theorem 20.3, two n by n matrices are similar if and only if they are matrices of the same linear transformation of an n-dimensional vector space $\mathcal{V}$ into itself. The analysis of a linear transformation of $\mathcal{V}$ into itself is accomplished by finding a simple form for an n by n matrix under the relation of similarity.

Exercises

20.1 Let L be the linear transformation of $\mathcal{V}_3$ into $\mathcal{V}_2$ that has matrix

$$A = \begin{bmatrix} -1 & 2 & 0 \\ 1 & 0 & 1 \end{bmatrix}$$

with respect to the bases $\{\langle 1, -2, 3\rangle, \langle 0, 1, -1\rangle, \langle 0, 0, 2\rangle\}$ in $\mathcal{V}_3$ and $\{\langle 5, 1\rangle, \langle 2, 3\rangle\}$ in $\mathcal{V}_2$. Find the matrix of L with respect to the bases $E^{(3)}$ in $\mathcal{V}_3$ and $E^{(2)}$ in $\mathcal{V}_2$.

20.2 Let L be the linear transformation of $\mathcal{V}_3$ into $\mathcal{V}_4$ that has matrix

$$A = \begin{bmatrix} -1 & 2 & 1 \\ 0 & 1 & -3 \\ 7 & 1 & 0 \\ -6 & 2 & 1 \end{bmatrix}$$

with respect to the bases $E^{(3)}$ in $\mathcal{V}_3$ and $E^{(4)}$ in $\mathcal{V}_4$. Let E and F be the nonsingular matrices given in Example 1. Find the bases in $\mathcal{V}_3$ and $\mathcal{V}_4$ such that L has matrix FAE with respect to these bases.

20.3 Prove that Definition 20.2 defines an equivalence relation on the set ${}_m\mathfrak{A}_n$ of all m by n matrices.

20.4 Show that in the set $\mathfrak{A}_n$ of all n by n matrices, every nonsingular matrix P is equivalent to the identity matrix I_n.

20.5 Let $A \in {}_m\mathfrak{A}_n$, and let $\mathbf{O}$ be the zero matrix in ${}_m\mathfrak{A}_n$. Prove that A is equivalent to $\mathbf{O}$ if and only if $A = \mathbf{O}$.

20.6 Let A and B be in ${}_m\mathfrak{A}_n$. Prove that A is equivalent to B if and only if A' is equivalent to B' in ${}_n\mathfrak{A}_m$.

20.7 The matrix of the change of basis from the basis $E^{(3)}$ in $\mathcal{V}_3$ to the basis $\{\langle 1, 2, 3\rangle, \langle 3, 2, 1\rangle, \langle 1, 2, 1\rangle\}$ in $\mathcal{V}_3$ is

$$P = \begin{bmatrix} 1 & 2 & 3 \\ 3 & 2 & 1 \\ 1 & 2 & 1 \end{bmatrix},$$

where

$$P^{-1} = \begin{bmatrix} 0 & \tfrac{1}{2} & -\tfrac{1}{2} \\ -\tfrac{1}{4} & -\tfrac{1}{4} & 1 \\ \tfrac{1}{2} & 0 & -\tfrac{1}{2} \end{bmatrix}.$$

Let L be the linear transformation of $\mathcal{V}_3$ into itself that has matrix

$$A = \begin{bmatrix} 3 & 1 & 3 \\ 1 & -1 & 0 \\ 0 & 0 & 1 \end{bmatrix}$$

with respect to the basis $E^{(3)}$. Find the matrix of L with respect to the basis $\{\langle 1, 2, 3\rangle, \langle 3, 2, 1\rangle, \langle 1, 2, 1\rangle\}$. Find the coordinates of $L(\mathbf{E}_1{}^{(3)})$, $L(\mathbf{E}_2{}^{(3)})$, and $L(\mathbf{E}_3{}^{(3)})$ with respect to each basis.

20.8 Prove that similarity is an equivalence relation on $\mathfrak{A}_n$.

20.9 If two matrices in $\mathfrak{A}_n$ are similar, then they are equivalent (Definition 20.2). Show by an example that the converse of this statement is false.

***20.10** Suppose that

$$P^{-1}AP = \begin{bmatrix} k_1 & 0 & \cdots & 0 \\ 0 & k_2 & \cdot & \cdot \\ \cdot & \cdot & \cdot & \cdot \\ \cdot & \cdot & \cdot & \cdot \\ \cdot & & \cdot & 0 \\ 0 & \cdots & 0 & k_n \end{bmatrix}$$

for $A \in \mathfrak{A}_n$ and $P = [p_{i,j}]$ is a nonsingular matrix in $\mathfrak{A}_n$. Prove that

$$A \begin{bmatrix} p_{1,j} \\ p_{2,j} \\ \cdot \\ \cdot \\ \cdot \\ p_{n,j} \end{bmatrix} = k_j \cdot \begin{bmatrix} p_{1,j} \\ p_{2,j} \\ \cdot \\ \cdot \\ \cdot \\ p_{n,j} \end{bmatrix}$$

for $j = 1, 2, \ldots, n$.

21 Elementary transformation matrices

In the next three sections, we systematically investigate the simplification of m by n matrices under the relation of equivalence. The first important result, which we obtain in this section, is that two m by n matrices are equivalent if and only if one can be carried into the other by a sequence of elementary transformations. To get this result, we must show that an elementary transformation on a matrix can be accomplished by matrix multiplication, and that the multiplication of a matrix by a nonsingular matrix is equivalent to performing a sequence of elementary transformations on the matrix.

The three types of elementary row transformations that are performed on an m by n matrix A can be accomplished by multiplying the matrix A by certain simple matrices that we will now describe.

Let $I_m^{(i,j)}$ be the m by m matrix obtained from the identity matrix I_m by interchanging the ith and jth rows of I_m. Thus,

$$I_m^{(i,j)} = \begin{array}{c} \\ \\ \\ \\ i \\ \\ \\ \\ j \\ \\ \\ \end{array} \begin{bmatrix} 1 & & & \overset{i}{\vdots} & & & \overset{j}{\vdots} & & \\ & \ddots & & \vdots & & & \vdots & & \\ & & 1 & & & & & & \\ & \cdots & & 0 & & \cdots & 1 & & \\ & & & & 1 & & & & \\ & & & \vdots & & \ddots & \vdots & & \\ & & & & & & 1 & & \\ & \cdots & & 1 & & \cdots & 0 & & \\ & & & & & & & 1 & \\ & & & & & & & & \ddots \\ & & & & & & & & & 1 \end{bmatrix}. \qquad (21\text{-}1)$$

Note that $I_m^{(i,j)}$ can be obtained from I_m by interchanging the ith and jth columns. The matrix $I_m^{(i,j)}$ is called an *elementary transformation matrix of Type I*. It follows from the definition of matrix multiplication that an elementary transformation matrix of Type I has the following property:

(21.1) Let A be an m by n matrix. The matrix $I_m^{(i,j)}A$ is the matrix obtained from A by interchanging the ith and jth rows of A. The matrix $AI_n^{(i,j)}$ is the matrix obtained from A by interchanging the ith and jth columns of A.

The interchange of two columns of a matrix A is called an *elementary column transformation of Type I*. By 21.1, such a transformation can be accomplished on an m by n matrix A by performing this same column transformation on I_n to obtain $I_n^{(i,j)}$, and then postmultiplying A by $I_n^{(i,j)}$.

As a corollary of 21.1, we find that a matrix $I_m^{(i,j)}$ is nonsingular, and that it is its own inverse. Indeed, $I_m^{(i,j)}I_m^{(i,j)}$ is the matrix obtained from $I_m^{(i,j)}$ by interchanging the ith and jth rows of $I_m^{(i,j)}$, yielding the identity matrix I_m.

Let $I_m^{(i,j,c)}$ be the m by m matrix obtained from I_m by multiplying each element of the ith row of I_m by the number c and adding it to the corresponding element of the jth row ($i \neq j$). Then,

$$I_m^{(i,j,c)} = \begin{array}{cc} & \begin{array}{ccccccc} & & i & & j & & \end{array} \\ \begin{array}{c} \\ \\ i \\ \\ j \\ \\ \end{array} & \left[\begin{array}{ccccccc} 1 & & & & & & \\ & \ddots & \vdots & & \vdots & & \\ \cdots & & 1 & & & & \\ & & \vdots & \ddots & & & \\ \cdots & & c & \cdots & 1 & & \\ & & & & & \ddots & \\ & & & & & & 1 \end{array}\right] \end{array}. \tag{21-2}$$

The matrix $I_m^{(i,j,c)}$ can also be described as the matrix obtained from I_m by multiplying each element of the jth column of I_m by the number c and adding it to the corresponding element of the ith column. The matrix $I_m^{(i,j,c)}$ is called an *elementary transformation matrix of Type II*, because of the following result:

(21.2) Let A be an m by n matrix. The matrix $I_m^{(i,j,c)}A$ is the matrix obtained from A by multiplying each element of the ith row of A by the number c and adding the product to the corresponding element of the jth row. The matrix $AI_m^{(i,j,c)}$ is the matrix obtained from A by multiplying each element of the jth column of A by the number c and adding the product to the corresponding element of the ith column.

The proof of 21.2 is an exercise in matrix multiplication. The transformation of a matrix A accomplished by postmultiplying A by an elementary transformation matrix of Type II is called an *elementary column transformation of Type II*. As an example of 21.2, we have

$$I_4^{(1,3,c)}A = \begin{bmatrix} 1 & 0 & 0 & 0 \\ 0 & 1 & 0 & 0 \\ c & 0 & 1 & 0 \\ 0 & 0 & 0 & 1 \end{bmatrix} \begin{bmatrix} a_{1,1} & a_{1,2} & a_{1,3} \\ a_{2,1} & a_{2,2} & a_{2,3} \\ a_{3,1} & a_{3,2} & a_{3,3} \\ a_{4,1} & a_{4,2} & a_{4,3} \end{bmatrix}$$

$$= \begin{bmatrix} a_{1,1} & a_{1,2} & a_{1,3} \\ a_{2,1} & a_{2,2} & a_{2,3} \\ ca_{1,1} + a_{3,1} & ca_{1,2} + a_{3,2} & ca_{1,3} + a_{3,3} \\ a_{4,1} & a_{4,2} & a_{4,3} \end{bmatrix},$$

and

$$
AI_3^{(1,2,c)} = \begin{bmatrix} a_{1,1} & a_{1,2} & a_{1,3} \\ a_{2,1} & a_{2,2} & a_{2,3} \\ a_{3,1} & a_{3,2} & a_{3,3} \\ a_{4,1} & a_{4,2} & a_{4,3} \end{bmatrix} \begin{bmatrix} 1 & 0 & 0 \\ c & 1 & 0 \\ 0 & 0 & 1 \end{bmatrix} = \begin{bmatrix} a_{1,1} + ca_{1,2} & a_{1,2} & a_{1,3} \\ a_{2,1} + ca_{2,2} & a_{2,2} & a_{2,3} \\ a_{3,1} + ca_{3,2} & a_{3,2} & a_{3,3} \\ a_{4,1} + ca_{4,2} & a_{4,2} & a_{4,3} \end{bmatrix}.
$$

The elementary transformation matrices of Type II are nonsingular, and the inverse of $I_m^{(i,j,c)}$ is $I_m^{(i,j,-c)}$, which is a matrix of the same type. By 21.2, $I_m^{(i,j,-c)}I_m^{(i,j,c)}$ is a matrix obtained from $I_m^{(i,j,c)}$ by multiplying each element of the ith row of $I_m^{(i,j,c)}$ by $-c$ and adding the result to the corresponding element of the jth row. Thus, $I_m^{(i,j,-c)}I_m^{(i,j,c)} = I_m$.

Let ${}^{(c)}I_m^{(i)}$ be the matrix obtained from I_m by multiplying each element of the ith row of I_m by the number $c \neq 0$ (or multiplying each element of the ith column of I_m by $c \neq 0$). The matrix ${}^{(c)}I_m^{(i)}$ is an *elementary transformation matrix of Type III*. We have,

$$
{}^{(c)}I_m^{(i)} = \begin{array}{cc} & \begin{array}{ccccccc} & & & i & & & \end{array} \\ i & \begin{bmatrix} 1 & & & & & & \\ & \ddots & & \vdots & & & \\ & & 1 & & & & \\ & \cdots & & c & & & \\ & & & & 1 & & \\ & & & & & \ddots & \\ & & & & & & 1 \end{bmatrix} \end{array}. \tag{21-3}
$$

(21.3) Let A be an m by n matrix. The matrix ${}^{(c)}I_m^{(i)}A$ is the matrix obtained from A by multiplying each element of the ith row of A by c. The matrix $A\ {}^{(c)}I_n^{(i)}$ is the matrix obtained from A by multiplying each element of ith column of A by c.

The proof of 21.3 is left as an exercise (Exercise 21.3).

The multiplication of each element of a column of a matrix A by the same nonzero number c is called an *elementary column transformation of Type III*.

A matrix ${}^{(c)}I_m^{(i)}$ is nonsingular, since it follows from 21.3 that ${}^{(1/c)}I_m^{(i)}\ {}^{(c)}I_m^{(i)} = I_m$.

Summarizing the results 21.1, 21.2, and 21.3, we find that an elementary row or column transformation of any type can be performed on a matrix A

as follows: Perform the transformation on an identity matrix of the proper size, obtaining an elementary transformation matrix. Then, for a row transformation, premultiply A by this elementary transformation matrix; for a column transformation, postmultiply A by this matrix. We have also discovered that each type of elementary transformation matrix is nonsingular and has an inverse that is a matrix of the same type.

As an application of these results, we will give a method for calculating the inverse of a nonsingular matrix. By Theorem 18.3, a matrix P can be transformed into a matrix in echelon form by a sequence of elementary row transformations. Thus, by the discussion of the preceding paragraph, there is a sequence of elementary transformation matrices, which we will denote by $E_1, E_2, \ldots, E_k$, such that $E_kE_{k-1} \cdots E_2E_1P = P^*$, where P^* is in echelon form. If P is an n by n nonsingular matrix, then, by Theorem 18.7, the row rank of P is n. Since P^* is obtained from P by elementary row transformations, the row rank of P^* is n. Moreover, the row rank of the echelon matrix P^* is the associated integer k of the echelon form. Hence $k = n$, and

$$P^* = \begin{bmatrix} 1 & p^*_{1,2} & p^*_{1,3} & \cdots & & p^*_{1,n} \\ 0 & 1 & p^*_{2,3} & \cdots & & p^*_{2,n} \\ \cdot & 0 & \cdot & & & \cdot \\ & & \cdot & \cdot & & \cdot \\ \cdot & & & \cdot & \cdot & \cdot \\ \cdot & & & \cdot & 1 & p^*_{n-1,n} \\ 0 & \cdot & \cdot & \cdot & 0 & 1 \end{bmatrix}$$

has 1 in each diagonal position and 0 in every position below the diagonal. Now it is possible to transform P^* into I_n by a sequence of elementary row transformations. First multiply each element of the second row of P^* by $-p^*_{1,2}$ and add the product to the corresponding element of the first row. This puts 0 in the (1, 2)-position, and the elements $p^{**}_{1,j} = p^*_{1,j} - p^*_{1,2}p^*_{2,j}$ in the $(1, j)$-position for $j = 3, \ldots, n$. Next, multiply each element of the third row of the resulting matrix by $-p^{**}_{1,3}$, and add the product to the corresponding element of the first row; multiply each element of the third row by $-p^*_{2,3}$ and add the product to the corresponding element of the second row. We now have a matrix with 1 on the diagonal in the first three columns and 0 elsewhere in these columns. Clearly, this process can be continued until we arrive at the identity matrix I_n. Thus, there is a sequence of elementary transformation matrices, $E_{k+1}, E_{k+2}, \ldots, E_t$, such that $E_tE_{t-1} \cdots E_{k+2}E_{k+1}P^* = I_n$. Hence,

$$(E_tE_{t-1} \cdots E_{k+1}E_k \cdots E_2E_1)P = I_n. \tag{21-4}$$

Therefore, $P^{-1} = E_t E_{t-1} \cdots E_{k+1} E_k \cdots E_2 E_1$. Now E_1 is the matrix obtained from I_n by performing the first elementary row transformation on I_n, $E_2 E_1$ is the matrix obtained from E_1 by performing the second elementary row transformation on E_1, and so forth. Finally, P^{-1} is the matrix obtained from $E_{t-1} \cdots E_{k+1} E_k \cdots E_2 E_1$ by performing the last elementary row transformation on $E_{t-1} \cdots E_{k+1} E_k \cdots E_2 E_1$. Thus, by this application of 21.1, 21.2, and 21.3, we have proved the following:

(21.4) The inverse of a nonsingular n by n matrix P is obtained by performing the same sequence of elementary row transformations on the identity matrix I_n as that which transforms the matrix P into I_n.

Example 1. Let

$$P = \begin{bmatrix} 0 & 0 & 2 & -2 \\ 0 & 0 & 5 & 3 \\ 3 & -1 & 0 & 0 \\ 1 & 4 & 0 & 0 \end{bmatrix}.$$

The matrix P is transformed into I_4 by the following sequence of elementary row transformations:

$$P \xrightarrow{\text{Type I}} \begin{bmatrix} 1 & 4 & 0 & 0 \\ 0 & 0 & 5 & 3 \\ 3 & -1 & 0 & 0 \\ 0 & 0 & 2 & -2 \end{bmatrix} \xrightarrow{\text{Type II}} \begin{bmatrix} 1 & 4 & 0 & 0 \\ 0 & 0 & 5 & 3 \\ 0 & -13 & 0 & 0 \\ 0 & 0 & 2 & -2 \end{bmatrix} \xrightarrow{\text{Type I}}$$

$$\begin{bmatrix} 1 & 4 & 0 & 0 \\ 0 & -13 & 0 & 0 \\ 0 & 0 & 5 & 3 \\ 0 & 0 & 2 & -2 \end{bmatrix} \xrightarrow{\text{Type III}} \begin{bmatrix} 1 & 4 & 0 & 0 \\ 0 & 1 & 0 & 0 \\ 0 & 0 & 5 & 3 \\ 0 & 0 & 2 & -2 \end{bmatrix} \xrightarrow{\text{Type III}} \begin{bmatrix} 1 & 4 & 0 & 0 \\ 0 & 1 & 0 & 0 \\ 0 & 0 & 1 & 3/5 \\ 0 & 0 & 2 & -2 \end{bmatrix}$$

$$\xrightarrow{\text{Type II}} \begin{bmatrix} 1 & 4 & 0 & 0 \\ 0 & 1 & 0 & 0 \\ 0 & 0 & 1 & 3/5 \\ 0 & 0 & 0 & -16/5 \end{bmatrix} \xrightarrow{\text{Type III}} \begin{bmatrix} 1 & 4 & 0 & 0 \\ 0 & 1 & 0 & 0 \\ 0 & 0 & 1 & 3/5 \\ 0 & 0 & 0 & 1 \end{bmatrix} \xrightarrow{\text{Type II}}$$

$$\begin{bmatrix} 1 & 0 & 0 & 0 \\ 0 & 1 & 0 & 0 \\ 0 & 0 & 1 & 3/5 \\ 0 & 0 & 0 & 1 \end{bmatrix} \xrightarrow{\text{Type II}} \begin{bmatrix} 1 & 0 & 0 & 0 \\ 0 & 1 & 0 & 0 \\ 0 & 0 & 1 & 0 \\ 0 & 0 & 0 & 1 \end{bmatrix}.$$

We now perform these same elementary row transformations on the identity matrix I_4:

$$I_4 \xrightarrow{\text{Type I}} \begin{bmatrix} 0 & 0 & 0 & 1 \\ 0 & 1 & 0 & 0 \\ 0 & 0 & 1 & 0 \\ 1 & 0 & 0 & 0 \end{bmatrix} \xrightarrow{\text{Type II}} \begin{bmatrix} 0 & 0 & 0 & 1 \\ 0 & 1 & 0 & 0 \\ 0 & 0 & 1 & -3 \\ 1 & 0 & 0 & 0 \end{bmatrix} \xrightarrow{\text{Type I}} \begin{bmatrix} 0 & 0 & 0 & 1 \\ 0 & 0 & 1 & -3 \\ 0 & 1 & 0 & 0 \\ 1 & 0 & 0 & 0 \end{bmatrix}$$

$$\xrightarrow{\text{Type III}} \begin{bmatrix} 0 & 0 & 0 & 1 \\ 0 & 0 & -1/13 & 3/13 \\ 0 & 1 & 0 & 0 \\ 1 & 0 & 0 & 0 \end{bmatrix} \xrightarrow{\text{Type III}} \begin{bmatrix} 0 & 0 & 0 & 1 \\ 0 & 0 & -1/13 & 3/13 \\ 0 & 1/5 & 0 & 0 \\ 1 & 0 & 0 & 0 \end{bmatrix} \xrightarrow{\text{Type II}}$$

$$\begin{bmatrix} 0 & 0 & 0 & 1 \\ 0 & 0 & -1/13 & 3/13 \\ 0 & 1/5 & 0 & 0 \\ 1 & -2/5 & 0 & 0 \end{bmatrix} \xrightarrow{\text{Type III}} \begin{bmatrix} 0 & 0 & 0 & 1 \\ 0 & 0 & -1/13 & 3/13 \\ 0 & 1/5 & 0 & 0 \\ -5/16 & 1/8 & 0 & 0 \end{bmatrix} \xrightarrow{\text{Type II}}$$

$$\begin{bmatrix} 0 & 0 & 4/13 & 1/13 \\ 0 & 0 & -1/13 & 3/13 \\ 0 & 1/5 & 0 & 0 \\ -5/16 & 1/8 & 0 & 0 \end{bmatrix} \xrightarrow{\text{Type II}} \begin{bmatrix} 0 & 0 & 4/13 & 1/13 \\ 0 & 0 & -1/13 & 3/13 \\ 3/16 & 1/8 & 0 & 0 \\ -5/16 & 1/8 & 0 & 0 \end{bmatrix}.$$

Thus,

$$P^{-1} = \begin{bmatrix} 0 & 0 & 4/13 & 1/13 \\ 0 & 0 & -1/13 & 3/13 \\ 3/16 & 1/8 & 0 & 0 \\ -5/16 & 1/8 & 0 & 0 \end{bmatrix},$$

which can be checked directly by matrix multiplication. In practice, the work is shortened by performing each elementary transformation on I_4 as it is performed on the matrix P.

This discussion yields the following important theorem and corollary:

(21.5) Theorem. A nonsingular matrix P is a product of elementary transformation matrices.

PROOF. By equation (21-4),

$$\begin{aligned} P &= (E_t E_{t-1} \cdots E_{k+1} E_k \cdots E_2 E_1)^{-1} \\ &= E_1^{-1} E_2^{-1} \cdots E_k^{-1} E_{k+1}^{-1} \cdots E_{t-1}^{-1} E_t^{-1}. \end{aligned}$$

Theorem 21.5 follows from the fact that the inverse of each elementary transformation matrix E_i is again an elementary transformation matrix.

(21.6) Corollary. An m by n matrix A is equivalent to an m by n matrix B if and only if A can be transformed into B by a sequence of elementary row and column transformations.

PROOF. Suppose first that A is equivalent to B. By Definition 20.2, $B = PAQ$, where P is a nonsingular m by m matrix and Q is a nonsingular n by n matrix. By Theorem 21.5, P and Q can be expressed as products of elementary transformation matrices. Thus,

$$B = E_tE_{t-1} \cdots E_1A\bar{E}_1\bar{E}_2 \cdots \bar{E}_s, \tag{21-5}$$

where the E_i and $\bar{E}_j$ are elementary transformation matrices. By 21.1, 21.2, and 21.3, premultiplication by each E_i performs a row transformation and postmultiplication by each $\bar{E}_j$ performs a column transformation. Thus, A is transformed into B by a sequence of elementary transformations.

Conversely, if B is obtained from A by a sequence of elementary row and column transformations, then each of these transformations can be accomplished by multiplication by an elementary transformation matrix. Thus, equation (21-5) holds. Since each E_i and $\bar{E}_j$ is nonsingular, it follows from 17.8 that $P = E_tE_{t-1} \cdots E_1$ and $Q = \bar{E}_1\bar{E}_2 \cdots \bar{E}_s$ are nonsingular. Hence, $B = PAQ$, and A is equivalent to B.

Exercises

21.1 Construct the following elementary transformation matrices: $I_4^{(1,3)}$; $I_5^{(2,4,1/2)}$; ${}^{(\sqrt{2})}I_3^{(2)}$; $I_3^{(1,2)}$; $I_4^{(1,4,10)}$. What is the inverse of each matrix?

21.2 Let

$$A = \begin{bmatrix} 2 & -1 & 0 \\ 7 & 5 & 1 \\ -3 & 4 & 2 \\ 1 & 3 & 1 \end{bmatrix} \quad \text{and} \quad B = \begin{bmatrix} \frac{1}{2} & \frac{2}{3} & -1 & 4 & \frac{3}{2} \\ -5 & 0 & 1 & \frac{1}{2} & 6 \\ \frac{5}{3} & 2 & -3 & 0 & 1 \end{bmatrix}.$$

Find the following products without multiplying the matrices: $I_4^{(1,2)}A$; $A\,{}^{(1/3)}I_3^{(2)}$; ${}^{(1/3)}I_3^{(2)}B$; $BI_5^{(1,3,6)}$; $I_4^{(1,3)}AI_3^{(1,2)}$; $I_3^{(1,2)}B\,{}^{(-1)}I_5^{(3)}$.

21.3 Prove statements 21.1, 21.2, and 21.3.

21.4 Let A and B be the matrices of Exercise 21.2. Find nonsingular matrices P_1 and P_2 such that P_1A and P_2B are in echelon form.

21.5 Find the inverses of the following nonsingular matrices:

$$\begin{bmatrix} 0 & 0 & 0 & 1 \\ 0 & 0 & 2 & 0 \\ 0 & 3 & 0 & 0 \\ 4 & 0 & 0 & 0 \end{bmatrix}; \quad \begin{bmatrix} 2 & -1 & 3 \\ 1 & 4 & 2 \\ 0 & 1 & -2 \end{bmatrix}; \quad \begin{bmatrix} 1 & 0 & 0 & 0 \\ \frac{1}{16} & \frac{1}{3} & 0 & 0 \\ -2 & 0 & 1 & 0 \\ \frac{1}{6} & 0 & 0 & \frac{1}{2} \end{bmatrix}; \quad \begin{bmatrix} 1 & 1 & 1 \\ 1 & 0 & 1 \\ 0 & 0 & 1 \end{bmatrix}.$$

21.6 Express the matrices of Exercise 21.5 as products of elementary transformation matrices.

21.7 Show that the following pairs of matrices are equivalent:

$$\begin{bmatrix} 2 & 2 & 2 & 2 \\ 2 & 2 & 2 & 2 \\ 2 & 2 & 2 & 2 \\ 2 & 2 & 2 & 2 \end{bmatrix} \text{ and } \begin{bmatrix} 1 & 0 & 0 & 0 \\ 0 & 0 & 0 & 0 \\ 0 & 0 & 0 & 0 \\ 0 & 0 & 0 & 0 \end{bmatrix}; \quad \begin{bmatrix} -2 & 3 & 1 \\ 1 & 2 & 4 \\ \frac{1}{2} & \frac{9}{2} & \frac{13}{2} \end{bmatrix} \text{ and } \begin{bmatrix} 1 & 0 & 0 \\ 0 & 1 & 0 \\ 0 & 0 & 0 \end{bmatrix}.$$

***21.8** Show that the transpose of an elementary transformation matrix is an elementary transformation matrix of the same type.

22 Rank of a matrix

The concept of the row rank of a matrix A has been useful in several previous discussions. Now we examine its relation to two additional definitions of *rank*.

(22.1) Definition. Let $\mathcal{V}$ and $\mathcal{W}$ be finite dimensional vector spaces, and let L be a linear transformation of $\mathcal{V}$ into $\mathcal{W}$. The *rank* of L is the dimension of the range space $L(\mathcal{V})$ of L.

(22.2) Definition. Let $A = [a_{i,j}]$ be an m by n matrix. The *column rank of* A is the dimension of the *column space of* A, which is the subspace of $\mathcal{V}_m$ spanned by the vectors $\langle a_{1,j}, a_{2,j}, \ldots, a_{m,j}\rangle$, $j = 1, 2, \ldots, n$, which are the columns of A.

It is not difficult to discover the relation between these two definitions.

(22.3) Theorem. Let L be a linear transformation of an n-dimensional vector space $\mathcal{V}$ into an m-dimensional vector space $\mathcal{W}$. The rank of L is equal to the column rank of any matrix A of L.

PROOF. Suppose that A is the matrix of L with respect to bases $\{\mathbf{U}_1, \mathbf{U}_2, \ldots, \mathbf{U}_n\}$ in $\mathcal{V}$ and $\{\mathbf{W}_1, \mathbf{W}_2, \ldots, \mathbf{W}_m\}$ in $\mathcal{W}$. It follows from the definition of A (see Section 16) that the jth column of A, for $j = 1, 2, \ldots, n$, gives the coordinates $\langle a_{1,j}, a_{2,j}, \ldots, a_{m,j}\rangle$ of $L(\mathbf{U}_j)$ with respect to the basis $\{\mathbf{W}_1, \mathbf{W}_2, \ldots, \mathbf{W}_m\}$. The range space $L(\mathcal{V})$ of L is spanned by the vectors $L(\mathbf{U}_1), L(\mathbf{U}_2), \ldots, L(\mathbf{U}_n)$. Thus, under the isomorphism between $\mathcal{W}$ and the sequence space $\mathcal{V}_m$, the subspace of $\mathcal{V}_m$ spanned by the vectors $\langle a_{1,j}, a_{2,j}, \ldots, a_{m,j}\rangle$, $j = 1, 2, \ldots, n$, is isomorphic to the range space of L. Therefore, these vector spaces have the same dimension. That is, the rank of L is equal to the column rank of A.

(22.4) Corollary. If a matrix B is equivalent to a matrix A, then A and B have the same column rank.

PROOF. If B is equivalent to A, then, by Theorem 20.1, A and B are matrices of the same linear transformation L of an n-dimensional space $\mathcal{V}$ into an m-dimensional space $\mathcal{W}$ with respect to suitable bases in these spaces. By Theorem 22.3, column rank of A = rank of L = column rank of B.

We wish to show next that the column rank of a matrix is equal to the row rank. To do this, we first consider a matrix that is in echelon form.

(22.5) Theorem. Let A be an m by n matrix in echelon form. The column rank of A is equal to the row rank of A.

PROOF. We have already observed that the row rank of a matrix $A = [a_{i,j}]$ in echelon form is the associated integer k of the echelon form. If $i > k$, then $a_{i,j} = 0$ for all j. That is, the columns of A as vectors in $\mathcal{V}_m$ are of the form $\langle a_{1,j}, a_{2,j}, \ldots, a_{k,j}, 0, 0, \ldots, 0\rangle$ for $j = 1, 2, \ldots, n$. Thus, the dimension of the subspace of $\mathcal{V}_m$ spanned by these vectors is at most k. The columns $m_1, m_2, \ldots, m_k$ of A as vectors in $\mathcal{V}_m$ are $\langle 1, 0, \ldots, 0\rangle$, $\langle a_{1,m_2}, 1, 0, \ldots, 0\rangle, \ldots, \langle a_{1,m_k}, a_{2,m_k}, \ldots, a_{k-1,m_k}, 1, 0, \ldots, 0\rangle$. It is easy to verify that these k vectors are linearly independent. Hence, the dimension of the column space of A is at least k. Therefore, this dimension is k, so that the column rank of $A = k =$ row rank of A.

Example 1. The 4 by 7 matrix

$$A = \begin{bmatrix} 0 & 1 & -7 & \frac{1}{2} & 2 & -3 & 6 \\ 0 & 0 & 0 & 1 & -5 & 4 & \frac{1}{3} \\ 0 & 0 & 0 & 0 & 0 & 1 & -1 \\ 0 & 0 & 0 & 0 & 0 & 0 & 0 \end{bmatrix}$$

is in echelon form with $k = 3$, $m_1 = 2$, $m_2 = 4$, $m_3 = 6$. The vectors $\langle 0, 1, -7, -\frac{1}{2}, 2, -3, 6\rangle$, $\langle 0, 0, 0, 1, -5, 4, \frac{1}{3}\rangle$, $\langle 0, 0, 0, 0, 0, 1, -1\rangle$ are a basis of the row space of A. Thus, the row rank of A is 3. The vectors $\langle 1, 0, 0, 0\rangle$, $\langle \frac{1}{2}, 1, 0, 0\rangle$, $\langle -3, 4, 1, 0\rangle$ are a basis of the column space of A, so that the column rank of A is 3.

(22.6) Corollary. The column rank of an m by n matrix A is equal to the row rank of A.

PROOF. Carry the matrix A into echelon form A^* by a sequence of elementary row transformations. Then row rank of A = row rank of A^*. There is a nonsingular matrix P such that $A^* = PA$, where P is the product of the elementary transformation matrices corresponding to the elementary row transformations performed on A. Then $A^* = PA = PAI_n$ is equivalent to A. By Corollary 22.4, column rank of A = column rank of A^*. Since A^* is in echelon form, it follows from Theorem 22.5 that column rank of A^* = row rank of A^*. Hence, row rank of A = row rank of A^* = column rank of A^* = column rank of A.

Since the row rank of any matrix A is the same as its column rank, we will refer to this number simply as the *rank of A*. By Theorem 22.3, the rank of A is the same as the rank of the linear transformation L defined by A with respect to chosen bases in two finite dimensional vector spaces, $\mathcal{V}$ and $\mathcal{W}$. By Corollary 22.4, equivalent matrices have the same rank. Earlier results that involved the row rank of a matrix can now be stated simply in terms of rank. For example, an n by n matrix A is nonsingular if and only if the rank of A is n (Theorem 18.7).

Exercises

22.1 Let L be a linear transformation of $\mathcal{V}$ into $\mathcal{W}$, and let M be a linear transformation of $\mathcal{W}$ into $\mathcal{P}$. Prove that rank of $ML \leq$ rank of M and rank of $ML \leq$ rank of L.

***22.2** Let A be an m by n matrix and B be an n by p matrix. Use Exercise 22.1 to prove that the rank of AB does not exceed the rank of either A or B.

22.3 Let A be an m by n matrix. Prove that A and A' have the same rank.

22.4 Find the rank of the following matrices:

$$\begin{bmatrix} -1 & 2 \\ 3 & 1 \\ 4 & 6 \\ 2 & 9 \end{bmatrix}; \quad \begin{bmatrix} -2 & 1 & 0 & 3 \\ 1 & 5 & -1 & 6 \\ -1 & 15 & -3 & 18 \end{bmatrix}; \quad \begin{bmatrix} 3 & 3 & 3 & 3 & 3 \\ 2 & 2 & 2 & 2 & 2 \\ 1 & 1 & 1 & 1 & 1 \\ 2 & 2 & 2 & 2 & 2 \\ 3 & 3 & 3 & 3 & 3 \end{bmatrix}; \quad [2 \ \ -1 \ \ 3 \ \ 7 \ \ 6].$$

23 Canonical form of a matrix under equivalence

In this section we solve the problem of simplifying a linear transformation L of an n-dimensional space $\mathcal{V}$ into an m-dimensional space $\mathcal{W}$ by obtaining the so-called "rational canonical form" for an m by n matrix under equivalence.

Let D_r be the m by n matrix (for any m and n) that has 1 in the first r positions on the diagonal and zeros elsewhere. It is clear that $r \geq 0$ and that r is less than or equal to the smaller of the two dimensions m or n. For example, if $m = 3$, $n = 4$,

$$D_0 = \begin{bmatrix} 0 & 0 & 0 & 0 \\ 0 & 0 & 0 & 0 \\ 0 & 0 & 0 & 0 \end{bmatrix}, \quad D_1 = \begin{bmatrix} 1 & 0 & 0 & 0 \\ 0 & 0 & 0 & 0 \\ 0 & 0 & 0 & 0 \end{bmatrix}, \quad D_2 = \begin{bmatrix} 1 & 0 & 0 & 0 \\ 0 & 1 & 0 & 0 \\ 0 & 0 & 0 & 0 \end{bmatrix},$$

$$D_3 = \begin{bmatrix} 1 & 0 & 0 & 0 \\ 0 & 1 & 0 & 0 \\ 0 & 0 & 1 & 0 \end{bmatrix}.$$

We already know that an m by n matrix A can be carried into echelon form A^* by elementary row transformations. The following example shows how a matrix A^* in echelon form can be carried into a D_r matrix by elementary column transformations.

Example 1. Let

$$A^* = \begin{bmatrix} 0 & 1 & \frac{2}{3} & -5 & 0 \\ 0 & 0 & 0 & 1 & 4 \\ 0 & 0 & 0 & 0 & 0 \\ 0 & 0 & 0 & 0 & 0 \end{bmatrix}.$$

Then A^* is in echelon form with $k = 2$, $m_1 = 2$, $m_2 = 4$. Perform the following sequence of elementary column transformations on A^*. (1) Multiply each element of the second column by $-\frac{2}{3}$ and add the product to the corresponding element of the third column:

$$A^* \xrightarrow{\text{Type II}} \begin{bmatrix} 0 & 1 & 0 & -5 & 0 \\ 0 & 0 & 0 & 1 & 4 \\ 0 & 0 & 0 & 0 & 0 \\ 0 & 0 & 0 & 0 & 0 \end{bmatrix}.$$

(2) Multiply each element of the second column by 5 and add the product to the fourth column:

$$\begin{bmatrix} 0 & 1 & 0 & -5 & 0 \\ 0 & 0 & 0 & 1 & 4 \\ 0 & 0 & 0 & 0 & 0 \\ 0 & 0 & 0 & 0 & 0 \end{bmatrix} \xrightarrow{\text{Type II}} \begin{bmatrix} 0 & 1 & 0 & 0 & 0 \\ 0 & 0 & 0 & 1 & 4 \\ 0 & 0 & 0 & 0 & 0 \\ 0 & 0 & 0 & 0 & 0 \end{bmatrix}.$$

(3) Multiply each element of the fourth column by -4 and add the product to the fifth column:

$$\begin{bmatrix} 0 & 1 & 0 & 0 & 0 \\ 0 & 0 & 0 & 1 & 4 \\ 0 & 0 & 0 & 0 & 0 \\ 0 & 0 & 0 & 0 & 0 \end{bmatrix} \xrightarrow{\text{Type II}} \begin{bmatrix} 0 & 1 & 0 & 0 & 0 \\ 0 & 0 & 0 & 1 & 0 \\ 0 & 0 & 0 & 0 & 0 \\ 0 & 0 & 0 & 0 & 0 \end{bmatrix}.$$

(4) Interchange column one and column two:

$$\begin{bmatrix} 0 & 1 & 0 & 0 & 0 \\ 0 & 0 & 0 & 1 & 0 \\ 0 & 0 & 0 & 0 & 0 \\ 0 & 0 & 0 & 0 & 0 \end{bmatrix} \xrightarrow{\text{Type I}} \begin{bmatrix} 1 & 0 & 0 & 0 & 0 \\ 0 & 0 & 0 & 1 & 0 \\ 0 & 0 & 0 & 0 & 0 \\ 0 & 0 & 0 & 0 & 0 \end{bmatrix}.$$

(5) Interchange column two and column four:

$$\begin{bmatrix} 1 & 0 & 0 & 0 & 0 \\ 0 & 0 & 0 & 1 & 0 \\ 0 & 0 & 0 & 0 & 0 \\ 0 & 0 & 0 & 0 & 0 \end{bmatrix} \xrightarrow{\text{Type I}} \begin{bmatrix} 1 & 0 & 0 & 0 & 0 \\ 0 & 1 & 0 & 0 & 0 \\ 0 & 0 & 0 & 0 & 0 \\ 0 & 0 & 0 & 0 & 0 \end{bmatrix} = D_2.$$

The method employed in Example 1 can be used to carry any matrix A^* in echelon form into a D_r matrix. The nonzero elements other than the leading 1's in each row can be replaced by 0's by elementary column transformations of Type II. Then the columns can be rearranged by Type I elementary column transformations to put the 1's on the diagonal. By 21.1 and 21.2, these column transformations can be accomplished by postmultiplying A^* by elementary transformation matrices, and the product of these elementary transformation matrices is a nonsingular matrix Q. Hence, $A^*Q = D_r$. The matrix Q is obtained by performing the same column transformations on the identity matrix I_n as are performed on A^*. In Example 1,

$$Q = \begin{bmatrix} 0 & 0 & 0 & 1 & 0 \\ 1 & 5 & -\frac{2}{3} & 0 & -20 \\ 0 & 0 & 1 & 0 & 0 \\ 0 & 1 & 0 & 0 & -4 \\ 0 & 0 & 0 & 0 & 1 \end{bmatrix}.$$

Our results enable us to characterize the relation of equivalence of rectangular matrices in terms of the concept of rank.

(23.1) Theorem. An m by n matrix A is equivalent to a D_r matrix, where r is the rank of A.

PROOF. The matrix A can be carried to echelon form A^* by elementary row transformations. Hence, there is a nonsingular matrix P such that $PA = A^*$. By the remarks above, there exists a nonsingular matrix Q such that $A^*Q = D_r$. Therefore, $PAQ = A^*Q = D_r$, so that A is equivalent to D_r. The rank of a matrix in the form D_r is obviously r. By Corollary 22.4, the rank of A is equal to rank of D_r, which is r.

In practice, the recipe of Theorem 23.1 for carrying a matrix to the diagonal form D_r can be varied as is indicated in the following example.

Example 2. Let

$$A = \begin{bmatrix} -3 & 1/2 & 0 & 2 \\ 6 & -4 & 1 & 7 \\ 2/5 & 5 & 9 & 0 \end{bmatrix}.$$

Then,

$$A \xrightarrow[\text{Type I}]{\text{Row}} \begin{bmatrix} 6 & -4 & 1 & 7 \\ -3 & 1/2 & 0 & 2 \\ 2/5 & 5 & 9 & 0 \end{bmatrix} \xrightarrow[\text{Type I}]{\text{Column}} \begin{bmatrix} 1 & -4 & 6 & 7 \\ 0 & 1/2 & -3 & 2 \\ 9 & 5 & 2/5 & 0 \end{bmatrix} \xrightarrow[\text{Type II}]{\text{Row}}$$

$$\begin{bmatrix} 1 & -4 & 6 & 7 \\ 0 & 1/2 & -3 & 2 \\ 0 & 41 & -268/5 & -63 \end{bmatrix} \xrightarrow[\text{Type II}]{\text{Column}} \begin{bmatrix} 1 & 0 & 6 & 7 \\ 0 & 1/2 & -3 & 2 \\ 0 & 41 & -268/5 & -63 \end{bmatrix} \xrightarrow[\text{Type II}]{\text{Column}}$$

$$\begin{bmatrix} 1 & 0 & 0 & 7 \\ 0 & 1/2 & -3 & 2 \\ 0 & 41 & -268/5 & -63 \end{bmatrix} \xrightarrow[\text{Type II}]{\text{Column}} \begin{bmatrix} 1 & 0 & 0 & 0 \\ 0 & 1/2 & -3 & 2 \\ 0 & 41 & -268/5 & -63 \end{bmatrix} \xrightarrow[\text{Type III}]{\text{Row}}$$

$$\begin{bmatrix} 1 & 0 & 0 & 0 \\ 0 & 1 & -6 & 4 \\ 0 & 41 & -268/5 & -63 \end{bmatrix} \xrightarrow[\text{Type II}]{\text{Row}} \begin{bmatrix} 1 & 0 & 0 & 0 \\ 0 & 1 & -6 & 4 \\ 0 & 0 & 962/5 & -227 \end{bmatrix} \xrightarrow[\text{Type II}]{\text{Column}}$$

$$\begin{bmatrix} 1 & 0 & 0 & 0 \\ 0 & 1 & 0 & 4 \\ 0 & 0 & 962/5 & -227 \end{bmatrix} \xrightarrow[\text{Type II}]{\text{Column}} \begin{bmatrix} 1 & 0 & 0 & 0 \\ 0 & 1 & 0 & 0 \\ 0 & 0 & 962/5 & -227 \end{bmatrix} \xrightarrow[\text{Type III}]{\text{Row}}$$

$$\begin{bmatrix} 1 & 0 & 0 & 0 \\ 0 & 1 & 0 & 0 \\ 0 & 0 & 1 & -1135/962 \end{bmatrix} \xrightarrow[\text{Type II}]{\text{Column}} \begin{bmatrix} 1 & 0 & 0 & 0 \\ 0 & 1 & 0 & 0 \\ 0 & 0 & 1 & 0 \end{bmatrix} = D_3.$$

The nonsingular matrices P and Q such that $PAQ = D_3$ are found by performing the row transformations on I_3 and the column transformations on I_4, respectively. In this example,

$$P = \begin{bmatrix} 0 & 1 & 0 \\ 2 & 0 & 0 \\ -205/481 & -45/962 & 5/962 \end{bmatrix} \quad \text{and} \quad Q = \begin{bmatrix} 0 & 0 & 1 & 1135/962 \\ 0 & 1 & 6 & 1481/481 \\ 1 & 4 & 18 & -848/481 \\ 0 & 0 & 0 & 1 \end{bmatrix}.$$

The matrices P and Q such that $PAQ = D_r$ are not unique, since a matrix A can be carried into a D_r matrix by different sequences of elementary transformations. However, it is a consequence of the following theorem that each matrix A is equivalent to exactly one diagonal matrix D_r.

(23.2) Theorem. Let A and B be m by n matrices. Then A and B are equivalent if and only if the rank of A = rank of B.

PROOF. If A and B are equivalent, then the rank of A = rank of B, by Corollary 22.4. Conversely, suppose that the rank of A = rank of $B = r$. By Theorem 23.1, there exist nonsingular matrices P, P_1, Q, Q_1, such that $PAQ = D_r = P_1BQ_1$. Therefore, $(P_1^{-1}P)A(QQ_1^{-1}) = B$, where $P_1^{-1}P$ and QQ_1^{-1} are nonsingular matrices. Hence A and B are equivalent.

The matrix D_r to which a matrix A is equivalent is called the *rational canonical form* for A under the relation of equivalence. It is "rational" because the elements of D_r are rational functions of the elements of A. That is, only the rational operations of addition, subtraction, multiplication and division are performed on the elements of A to obtain D_r. Also, the matrices P and Q, such that $PAQ = D_r$, have elements which are rational functions of A. For example, if the elements of A are all rational numbers, then the elements of P and Q are rational numbers. The matrix D_r is called "canonical," since it is the unique matrix of this form to which A is equivalent.

Example 3. Let the matrix A of Example 2 be the matrix of a linear transformation L of $\mathcal{V}_4$ into $\mathcal{V}_3$ with respect to the bases $E^{(4)}$ and $E^{(3)}$. Define new bases in $\mathcal{V}_4$ and $\mathcal{V}_3$ by means of the nonsingular matrices Q' and $(P^{-1})'$, where P and Q are the matrices determined in Example 2 such that $PAQ = D_3$. Using the method 21.4,

$$P^{-1} = \begin{bmatrix} 0 & \frac{1}{2} & 0 \\ 1 & 0 & 0 \\ 9 & 41 & \frac{962}{5} \end{bmatrix}.$$

Then,

$$\begin{aligned}
\bar{\mathbf{U}}_1 &= & & & & 1 \cdot \mathbf{E}_3^{(4)} & &= \langle 0, 0, 1, 0\rangle \\
\bar{\mathbf{U}}_2 &= & & 1 \cdot \mathbf{E}_2^{(4)} + & & 4 \cdot \mathbf{E}_3^{(4)} & &= \langle 0, 1, 4, 0\rangle \\
\bar{\mathbf{U}}_3 &= 1 \cdot \mathbf{E}_1^{(4)} + & & 6 \cdot \mathbf{E}_2^{(4)} + & & 18 \cdot \mathbf{E}_3^{(4)} & &= \langle 1, 6, 18, 0\rangle \\
\bar{\mathbf{U}}_4 &= \left(\frac{1135}{962}\right) \cdot \mathbf{E}_1^{(4)} + \left(\frac{1481}{481}\right) \cdot \mathbf{E}_2^{(4)} + \left(-\frac{848}{481}\right) \cdot \mathbf{E}_3^{(4)} + 1 \cdot \mathbf{E}_4^{(4)} \\
&= \left\langle \frac{1135}{962}, \frac{1481}{481}, -\frac{848}{481}, 1\right\rangle;
\end{aligned}$$

$$\begin{aligned}
\bar{\mathbf{W}}_1 &= & 1 \cdot \mathbf{E}_2^{(3)} + 9 \cdot \mathbf{E}_3^{(3)} &= \langle 0, 1, 9\rangle \\
\bar{\mathbf{W}}_2 &= \tfrac{1}{2} \cdot \mathbf{E}_1^{(3)} & + 41 \cdot \mathbf{E}_3^{(3)} &= \langle \tfrac{1}{2}, 0, 41\rangle \\
\bar{\mathbf{W}}_3 &= & \left(\frac{962}{5}\right) \cdot \mathbf{E}_3^{(3)} &= \left\langle 0, 0, \frac{962}{5}\right\rangle.
\end{aligned}$$

With respect to these new bases, the matrix of L is D_3. Therefore L is given by

$$\begin{bmatrix} \bar{s}_1 \\ \bar{s}_2 \\ \bar{s}_3 \end{bmatrix} = \begin{bmatrix} 1 & 0 & 0 & 0 \\ 0 & 1 & 0 & 0 \\ 0 & 0 & 1 & 0 \end{bmatrix} \begin{bmatrix} \bar{r}_1 \\ \bar{r}_2 \\ \bar{r}_3 \\ \bar{r}_4 \end{bmatrix} = \begin{bmatrix} \bar{r}_1 \\ \bar{r}_2 \\ \bar{r}_3 \end{bmatrix}.$$

That is, if $\mathbf{V} \in \mathcal{V}_4$ has coordinates $\langle \bar{r}_1, \bar{r}_2, \bar{r}_3, \bar{r}_4 \rangle$ with respect to the new basis in $\mathcal{V}_4$, then $L(\mathbf{V})$ has coordinates $\langle \bar{r}_1, \bar{r}_2, \bar{r}_3 \rangle$ with respect to the new basis in $\mathcal{V}_3$. It is clear that the range space $L(\mathcal{V}_4)$ of L is $\mathcal{V}_3$, and that the null space $L^{-1}(\{\mathbf{0}\})$ of L is the subspace of $\mathcal{V}_4$ spanned by the single vector $\bar{\mathbf{U}}_4$.

Exercises

23.1 Carry the following matrices to rational canonical form D_r by elementary row and column transformations. Find the matrices P and Q such that $PAQ = D_r$ in each case:

$$\begin{bmatrix} 2 & -2 & 2 & 5 & 1 \\ 1 & 1 & 1 & 3 & -1 \\ 3 & 5 & 4 & 2 & 4 \end{bmatrix}; \qquad \begin{bmatrix} 3 & 2 & 1 & 0 & 0 \\ 0 & 1 & 2 & 0 & 0 \\ 1 & 4 & 7 & 2 & 3 \\ 5 & 3 & -1 & 1 & 2 \\ 6 & 1 & -2 & 3 & 6 \end{bmatrix};$$

$$\begin{bmatrix} -1 & 2 \\ 0 & 5 \\ 3 & 4 \\ 6 & 2 \end{bmatrix}; \qquad \begin{bmatrix} \sqrt{2} & \sqrt{2} & \sqrt{2} & \sqrt{2} \\ \sqrt{6} & \sqrt{6} & \sqrt{6} & \sqrt{6} \\ \sqrt{30} & \sqrt{30} & \sqrt{30} & \sqrt{30} \end{bmatrix}.$$

23.2 How many equivalence classes are there for the relation of equivalence on the set ${}_m\mathfrak{A}_n$ of all m by n matrices?

23.3 As in Example 3, let each m by n matrix of Exercise 23.1 be the matrix of a linear transformation L from $\mathcal{V}_n$ into $\mathcal{V}_m$ with respect to the bases $E^{(n)}$ and $E^{(m)}$. Define new bases in $\mathcal{V}_n$ and $\mathcal{V}_m$ so that L has matrix D_r with respect to these new bases. Determine the null space and the range space of L in each case.

CHAPTER SIX

Determinants

24 Definition of a determinant

The determinant of a square matrix has important applications in many branches of mathematics. In elementary algebra, for example, determinants are utilized in the solution of n linear equations in n unknowns. In this chapter, we define the determinant of an n by n matrix A, derive the principal properties of determinants, and indicate some applications. Then, in Chapter Seven, we will use several of the properties of determinants in the study of the similarity of matrices.

Let $j_1, j_2, \ldots, j_n$ be an ordering of the positive integers $1, 2, \ldots, n$. An *inversion* occurs in this ordering whenever a greater integer precedes a smaller one. The *number of inversions* of $j_1, j_2, \ldots, j_n$ is the sum $k = \sum_{s=1}^{n-1} k_s$, where k_s is the number of integers greater than s that precede s in the given ordering. For example, if $n = 6$, then in the ordering 3, 2, 6, 1, 5, 4, we have $k_1 = 3$, $k_2 = 1$, $k_3 = 0$, $k_4 = 2$, $k_5 = 1$, and $k = 7$.

(24.1) Definition. The *determinant* of an n by n matrix $A = [a_{i,j}]$ is the number

$$|A| = \sum (-1)^k a_{1,j_1} a_{2,j_2} \cdots a_{n,j_n},$$

where in each term the column (second) subscripts $j_1, j_2, \ldots, j_n$ are some ordering of $1, 2, \ldots, n$, and the sum is taken over all possible orderings of the column subscripts. For each term, the exponent k of $(-1)^k$ is the number of inversions of the column subscripts $j_1, j_2, \ldots, j_n$.

Besides the notation $|A|$ for the determinant of $A = [a_{i,j}]$, we also write

$$|a_{i,j}| \quad \text{and} \quad \begin{vmatrix} a_{1,1} & a_{1,2} & \cdots & a_{1,n} \\ a_{2,1} & a_{2,2} & \cdots & a_{2,n} \\ \vdots & \vdots & & \vdots \\ a_{n,1} & a_{n,2} & \cdots & a_{n,n} \end{vmatrix}.$$

Example 1. If $n = 2$, then

$$A = \begin{bmatrix} a_{1,1} & a_{1,2} \\ a_{2,1} & a_{2,2} \end{bmatrix},$$

and the possible orderings of the column subscripts are 1, 2 and 2, 1. The first ordering has no inversions and the second ordering has one inversion. Therefore, by Definition 24.1,

$$\begin{vmatrix} a_{1,1} & a_{1,2} \\ a_{2,1} & a_{2,2} \end{vmatrix} = (-1)^0 a_{1,1}a_{2,2} + (-1)^1 a_{1,2}a_{2,1} = a_{1,1}a_{2,2} - a_{1,2}a_{2,1}.$$

If $n = 3$,

$$A = \begin{bmatrix} a_{1,1} & a_{1,2} & a_{1,3} \\ a_{2,1} & a_{2,2} & a_{2,3} \\ a_{3,1} & a_{3,2} & a_{3,3} \end{bmatrix},$$

and there are six possible orderings for the column subscripts: 1, 2, 3; 1, 3, 2; 2, 1, 3; 2, 3, 1; 3, 1, 2; and 3, 2, 1. By Definition 24.1,

$$\begin{aligned} \begin{vmatrix} a_{1,1} & a_{1,2} & a_{1,3} \\ a_{2,1} & a_{2,2} & a_{2,3} \\ a_{3,1} & a_{3,2} & a_{3,3} \end{vmatrix} &= (-1)^0 a_{1,1}a_{2,2}a_{3,3} + (-1)^1 a_{1,1}a_{2,3}a_{3,2} + (-1)^1 a_{1,2}a_{2,1}a_{3,3} \\ &\quad + (-1)^2 a_{1,2}a_{2,3}a_{3,1} + (-1)^2 a_{1,3}a_{2,1}a_{3,2} + (-1)^3 a_{1,3}a_{2,2}a_{3,1} \\ &= a_{1,1}a_{2,2}a_{3,3} + a_{1,2}a_{2,3}a_{3,1} + a_{1,3}a_{2,1}a_{3,2} - a_{1,3}a_{2,2}a_{3,1} \\ &\quad - a_{1,1}a_{2,3}a_{3,2} - a_{1,2}a_{2,1}a_{3,3}. \end{aligned}$$

In the sum $\Sigma\,(-1)^k a_{1,j_1}a_{2,j_2} \cdots a_{n,j_n}$ of Definition 24.1, the row (first) subscripts of each term are in natural order $1, 2, \ldots, n$ and the column (second) subscripts are these same numbers in some order. Therefore, each term is a signed product of n elements of $A = [a_{i,j}]$, with exactly one element from each row and one element from each column. Every product of n elements of A with exactly one element from each row and column can be written with the row subscripts in natural order. Since the sum is taken over all possible orderings of the column subscripts, the determinant $|A|$ is the sum of all products of n elements of A, with one element from each row and column, where the sign of each term is determined by the number of inversions of the column subscripts when the row subscripts are in natural order. There are $n(n-1)(n-2)\ldots(2)(1) = n!$ possible orderings for the column subscripts. Therefore, there are $n!$ terms in the sum.

For each square matrix A with real numbers as elements, $|A|$ is a real number. Thus, the determinant is a function that maps a real square matrix into a real number. Moreover, $|A|$ is an *integral function* of the elements $a_{i,j}$ of A since the evaluation of $|A|$ involves only the integral operations of addition, subtraction, and multiplication. Thus, if the elements of A are integers, $|A|$ is an integer, and if the elements of A are rational numbers, $|A|$ is a rational number. Although we have restricted our attention to matrices with real number elements, it is evident that Definition 24.1 would apply to matrices with elements in any algebraic system in which the operations of addition, subtraction, and multiplication can be performed, subject to the usual algebraic rules. For example, the elements of A can be polynomials in a variable x, in which case $|A|$ is a polynomial in x.

In order to establish a result that can be used in deriving the properties of determinants, we first note the following fact.

(24.2) Let l be the number of inversions of the ordering $i_1, i_2, \ldots, i_n$ of $1, 2, \ldots, n$. The ordering $i_1, i_2, \ldots, i_n$ can be carried into the natural ordering $1, 2, \ldots, n$ by l interchanges of adjacent integers.

PROOF. The number of inversions l is equal to $\sum_{s=1}^{n-1} l_s$, where l_s is the number of integers greater than s that precede s in the ordering $i_1, i_2, \ldots, i_n$. Since l_1 numbers precede 1, it follows that 1 can be put in first position by l_1 adjacent interchanges. Moving 1 to first position does not change l_s for $s \geq 2$. Hence, the number of inversions of the new ordering is $\sum_{s=2}^{n-1} l_s$. Now 2 can be moved into second position by l_2 adjacent interchanges, producing a new ordering with $\sum_{s=3}^{n-1} l_s$ inversions. This process can be continued until the ordering $1, 2, \ldots, n$ is obtained by $l = \sum_{s-1}^{n-1} l_s$ adjacent interchanges.

Consider the sum $S = \Sigma (-1)^k a_{i_1,j_1} a_{i_2,j_2} \cdots a_{i_n,j_n}$, which is described exactly as the sum appearing in Definition 24.1, except that the row subscripts are in a fixed order $i_1, i_2, \ldots, i_n$ which is not necessarily the natural order $1, 2, \ldots, n$. That is, the row subscripts are in the same order $i_1, i_2, \ldots, i_n$ in each term of S. There is a simple relation between S and $|A|$:

(24.3) Theorem.

$$S = \sum (-1)^k a_{i_1,j_1} a_{i_2,j_2} \cdots a_{i_n,j_n} = (-1)^l |A|,$$

where l is the number of inversions of the fixed ordering $i_1, i_2, \ldots, i_n$.

PROOF. Except possibly for differences in sign, the terms of S are the $n!$ distinct terms of $|A|$, since every product of n elements of $A = [a_{i,j}]$ with one element from each row and one from each column appears exactly once as a term of S. Thus, it is sufficient to show that each term of S is $(-1)^l$ times the term of $|A|$ that is the product of the same n elements. Let $(-1)^k a_{i_1,j_1}a_{i_2,j_2} \cdots a_{i_n,j_n}$ be a term of S. Rearranging the factors $a_{i,j}$ in this term, we have

$$(-1)^k a_{i_1,j_1}a_{i_2,j_2} \cdots a_{i_n,j_n} = (-1)^k a_{1,m_1}a_{2,m_2} \cdots a_{n,m_n},$$

where the latter product is a term of $|A|$, except possibly for sign. The corresponding term of $|A|$ is $(-1)^m a_{1,m_1}a_{2,m_2} \cdots a_{n,m_n}$, where m is the number of inversions of the ordering $m_1, m_2, \ldots, m_n$. Therefore, the proof is complete if $(-1)^k = (-1)^l(-1)^m$.

By 24.2, the factors of the product $a_{i_1,j_1}a_{i_2,j_2} \cdots a_{i_n,j_n}$ can be arranged so that $a_{i_1,j_1}a_{i_2,j_2} \cdots a_{i_n,j_n} = a_{1,m_1}a_{2,m_2} \cdots a_{n,m_n}$ by l successive interchanges of adjacent factors. Each time two adjacent factors $a_{i,j}a_{s,t}$ are interchanged, the number of inversions of the column subscripts is either increased by one (if $t > j$) or decreased by one (if $t < j$). Thus, starting with the ordering $j_1, j_2, \ldots, j_n$ which has k inversions, we change the number of inversions by one l times and arrive at the ordering $m_1, m_2, \ldots, m_n$ with m inversions. Therefore, if l is even, then k and m have the same parity (i.e., k and m are both even or both odd), and if l is odd, then k and m have opposite parity (i.e., one is even and the other is odd). In every case, $(-1)^k = (-1)^l(-1)^m$, and, as indicated above, the proof is complete.

Example 2. Let $S = \Sigma\,(-1)^k a_{3,j_1}a_{1,j_2}a_{2,j_3}$ be the sum taken over all orderings of the column subscripts j_1, j_2, j_3, where, in each term, k is the number of inversions of j_1, j_2, j_3. The number of inversions of the fixed orderings of the row subscripts 3, 1, 2 is $l = 2$. Then, by Theorem 24.3, $S = (-1)^2|A| = |A|$, where

$$A = \begin{bmatrix} a_{1,1} & a_{1,2} & a_{1,3} \\ a_{2,1} & a_{2,2} & a_{2,3} \\ a_{3,1} & a_{3,2} & a_{3,3} \end{bmatrix}.$$

On the other hand, if S is computed directly, we find

$$\begin{aligned} S &= (-1)^0 a_{3,1}a_{1,2}a_{2,3} + (-1)^1 a_{3,1}a_{1,3}a_{2,2} + (-1)^1 a_{3,2}a_{1,1}a_{2,3} \\ &\quad + (-1)^2 a_{3,2}a_{1,3}a_{2,1} + (-1)^2 a_{3,3}a_{1,1}a_{2,2} + (-1)^3 a_{3,3}a_{1,2}a_{2,1} \\ &= a_{1,1}a_{2,2}a_{3,3} + a_{1,2}a_{2,3}a_{3,1} + a_{1,3}a_{2,1}a_{3,2} - a_{1,3}a_{2,2}a_{3,1} - a_{1,1}a_{2,3}a_{3,2} \\ &\quad - a_{1,2}a_{2,1}a_{3,3} = |A|. \end{aligned}$$

The determinant of a square matrix A can also be expressed as a sum on the row subscripts.

(24.4) **Theorem.** Let $T = \Sigma\ (-1)^l\ a_{i_1,1}\ a_{i_2,2} \cdots a_{i_n,n}$, where in each term the row subscripts $i_1, i_2, \ldots, i_n$ are some ordering of $1, 2, \ldots, n$, and the sum is taken over all possible orderings of the row subscripts. For each term, the exponent l of $(-1)^l$ is the number of inversions of $i_1, i_2, \ldots, i_n$. Then T is the determinant of the n by n matrix $A = [a_{i,j}]$.

The proof of Theorem 24.4 is similar to that of Theorem 24.3 and is left as an exercise (Exercise 24.6).

Exercises

24.1 Count the number of inversions in the following orderings of 1, 2, 3, 4, 5, 6, 7: 7, 3, 5, 1, 6, 4, 2; 5, 1, 2, 4, 3, 7, 6; 3, 4, 7, 6, 5, 1, 2.

24.2 Find the signs of the terms $a_{1,5}a_{2,6}a_{3,3}a_{4,1}a_{5,4}a_{6,2}$ and $a_{1,6}a_{2,3}a_{3,2}a_{4,5}a_{5,4}a_{6,1}$ in the expansion of the determinant of the 6 by 6 matrix $A = [a_{i,j}]$.

24.3 Let A be a square triangular matrix; that is, each element below the diagonal is 0. Prove that $|A|$ is equal to the product of the diagonal elements. In particular, the determinant of a square diagonal matrix is equal to the product of the diagonal elements, and $|I_n| = 1$.

24.4 Prove that $|r \cdot A| = r^n|A|$.

24.5 Find the values of the following determinants:

$$\begin{vmatrix} x+1 & x^2+x+1 & x \\ x^2-1 & x+2 & 3 \\ x-4 & 0 & x^2 \end{vmatrix}; \quad \begin{vmatrix} -3 & 1 & 7 \\ 0 & 2 & 6 \\ -4 & 5 & 1 \end{vmatrix}; \quad \begin{vmatrix} 1 & 0 & 0 & 0 & 0 \\ 0 & 1 & 0 & 0 & 0 \\ 0 & 0 & 1 & 0 & 0 \\ 0 & -5 & 0 & 1 & 0 \\ 0 & 0 & 0 & 0 & 1 \end{vmatrix};$$

$$\begin{vmatrix} \frac{1}{2} & 0 & 0 & 0 \\ 4 & \frac{1}{3} & 0 & 0 \\ -1 & 2 & \frac{1}{5} & 0 \\ 7 & 8 & 10 & \frac{1}{7} \end{vmatrix}; \quad \begin{vmatrix} 0 & 0 & 0 & \sqrt{2} \\ 0 & 0 & \sqrt{3} & 0 \\ 0 & \sqrt{5} & 0 & 0 \\ \sqrt{7} & 0 & 0 & 0 \end{vmatrix}.$$

24.6 Prove Theorem 24.4.

24.7 Prove that if $t > s$, there are $(t - 1 - s + 1) + (t - 1 - s) = 2t - 2s - 1$ inversions in the ordering $1, 2, \ldots, s-1, t, s+1, \ldots, t-1, s, t+1, \ldots, n$.

25 Properties of determinants

Throughout this section, $A = [a_{i,j}]$ is an n by n matrix.

(25.1) Theorem. $|A'| = |A|$.

PROOF. The matrix A' is the transpose of A (see Exercise 17.16 for the definition of the transpose of a matrix). Thus, $A' = [b_{i,j}]$, where $b_{i,j} = a_{j,i}$ for all i, j. By Definition 24.1,

$$|A'| = \sum (-1)^k b_{1,j_1} b_{2,j_2} \cdots b_{n,j_n} = \sum (-1)^k a_{j_1,1} a_{j_2,2} \cdots a_{j_n,n},$$

where each sum is taken over all possible orderings of $j_1, j_2, \ldots, j_n$ and, in each term, k is the number of inversions of $j_1, j_2, \ldots, j_n$. By Theorem 24.4, the second sum is equal to $|A|$, so that $|A'| = |A|$.

The property given in Theorem 25.1 allows us to replace "row" by "column" in the statement of the remaining properties of determinants.

(25.2) Theorem. If B is the matrix obtained from A by interchanging two rows (columns), then $|B| = -|A|$.

PROOF. Suppose that the rows s and t of A are interchanged to obtain B. Then $B = [b_{i,j}]$, where for all j, $b_{i,j} = a_{i,j}$ if $i \neq s$ or $i \neq t$, and $b_{s,j} = a_{t,j}$, $b_{t,j} = a_{s,j}$. We may assume that $s < t$. Then, by Definition 24.1,

$$\begin{aligned} |B| &= \sum (-1)^k b_{1,j_1} b_{2,j_2} \cdots b_{s,j_s} \cdots b_{t,j_t} \cdots b_{n,j_n} \\ &= \sum (-1)^k a_{1,j_1} a_{2,j_2} \cdots a_{t,j_s} \cdots a_{s,j_t} \cdots a_{n,j_n}. \end{aligned}$$

The row subscripts of the second sum are in the fixed order $1, 2, \ldots, s-1, t, s+1, \ldots, t-1, s, t+1, \ldots, n$, which has $(t-1-s+1) + (t-1-s) = 2t-2s-1$ inversions since $t > s$ (see Exercise 24.7). Therefore, by Theorem 24.3, the second sum is equal to $(-1)^{2t-2s-1}|A| = -|A|$. Hence, $|B| = -|A|$.

If B is the matrix obtained from A by interchanging two columns of A, then B' is obtained from A' by interchanging two rows of A'. Therefore, $|B'| = -|A'|$ by what we have just proved. Hence, by Theorem 25.1,

$$|B| = |B'| = -|A'| = -|A|.$$

The last part of the proof of Theorem 25.2 illustrates how it follows from Theorem 25.1 that each "row" result for determinants yields a corresponding "column" result. In the remaining theorems, we will omit the proof for columns.

(25.3) Theorem. If two rows (columns) of A are identical, then $|A| = 0$.

PROOF. Let B be the matrix obtained from A by interchanging the identical rows of A. Then $B = A$, and hence $|B| = |A|$. However, by Theorem 25.2, $|B| = -|A|$. Therefore, $|A| = -|A|$, $2|A| = 0$, and $|A| = 0$.

(25.4) Theorem. If B is the matrix obtained from A by multiplying every element of a row (column) of A by the number r, then $|B| = r|A|$.

PROOF. Suppose that every element of row S of A is multiplied by r to obtain the matrix B. Then $B = [b_{i,j}]$, where for all j, $b_{i,j} = a_{i,j}$ if $i \neq s$ and $b_{s,j} = ra_{s,j}$. By Definition 24.1,

$$\begin{aligned} B &= \sum (-1)^k b_{1,j_1} b_{2,j_2} \cdots b_{s,j_s} \cdots b_{n,j_n} \\ &= \sum (-1)^k a_{1,j_1} a_{2,j_2} \cdots r a_{s,j_s} \cdots a_{n,j_n} \\ &= r \left(\sum (-1)^k a_{1,j_1} a_{2,j_2} \cdots a_{s,j_s} \cdots a_{n,j_n} \right) = r|A|. \end{aligned}$$

Theorem 25.4 can be used to simplify the expansion of a determinant by removing common factors from rows and columns.

Example 1.

$$\begin{aligned} \begin{vmatrix} 18 & -2 & 7 & 5 \\ -2 & 4 & 1 & -1 \\ 6 & -12 & -3 & 3 \\ 0 & 20 & -1 & 10 \end{vmatrix} &= 2 \begin{vmatrix} 9 & -2 & 7 & 5 \\ -1 & 4 & 1 & -1 \\ 3 & -12 & -3 & 3 \\ 0 & 20 & -1 & 10 \end{vmatrix} = 4 \begin{vmatrix} 9 & -1 & 7 & 5 \\ -1 & 2 & 1 & -1 \\ 3 & -6 & -3 & 3 \\ 0 & 10 & -1 & 10 \end{vmatrix} \\ &= 12 \begin{vmatrix} 9 & -1 & 7 & 5 \\ -1 & 2 & 1 & -1 \\ 1 & -2 & -1 & 1 \\ 0 & 10 & -1 & 10 \end{vmatrix} = -12 \begin{vmatrix} 9 & -1 & 7 & 5 \\ 1 & -2 & -1 & 1 \\ 1 & -2 & -1 & 1 \\ 0 & 10 & -1 & 10 \end{vmatrix} \\ &= 0, \end{aligned}$$

by Theorems 25.3 and 25.4.

(25.5) Theorem. If B is a matrix obtained from A by multiplying each element of a row (column) of A by a number r and adding the product to the corresponding element of another row (column), then $|B| = |A|$.

PROOF. Suppose that B is obtained from A by multiplying each element of row s of A by r and adding these elements to corresponding ones in row t ($s \neq t$). Then $B = [b_{i,j}]$, where for all j, $b_{i,j} = a_{i,j}$ if $i \neq t$, and $b_{t,j} = a_{t,j} + ra_{s,j}$. Therefore,

$$\begin{aligned}
|B| &= \sum (-1)^k b_{1,j_1} b_{2,j_2} \cdots b_{t,j_t} \cdots b_{n,j_n} \\
&= \sum (-1)^k a_{1,j_1} a_{2,j_2} \cdots (a_{t,j_t} + ra_{s,j_t}) \cdots a_{n,j_n} \\
&= \sum (-1)^k a_{1,j_1} a_{2,j_2} \cdots a_{t,j_t} \cdots a_{n,j_n} \\
&\qquad + \sum (-1)^k a_{1,j_1} a_{2,j_2} \cdots ra_{s,j_t} \cdots a_{n,j_n} \\
&= |A| + r \sum (-1)^k a_{1,j_1} a_{2,j_2} \cdots a_{s,j_t} \cdots a_{n,j_n} \\
&= |A| + 0 = |A|
\end{aligned}$$

by Theorem 25.3, since the last sum is the expansion of the determinant of a matrix with two identical rows. For example, if $s < t$, this matrix is

$$\begin{array}{r} \\ \\ \\ \\ s\text{—} \\ \\ \\ \\ t\text{—} \\ \\ \\ \\ \\ \end{array}
\begin{bmatrix}
a_{1,1} & a_{1,2} & \cdots & a_{1,n} \\
\cdot & \cdot & & \cdot \\
\cdot & \cdot & & \cdot \\
\cdot & \cdot & & \cdot \\
a_{s,1} & a_{s,2} & \cdots & a_{s,n} \\
\cdot & \cdot & & \cdot \\
\cdot & \cdot & & \cdot \\
\cdot & \cdot & & \cdot \\
a_{s,1} & a_{s,2} & \cdots & a_{s,n} \\
\cdot & \cdot & & \cdot \\
\cdot & \cdot & & \cdot \\
\cdot & \cdot & & \cdot \\
a_{n,1} & a_{n,2} & \cdots & a_{n,n}
\end{bmatrix}.$$

Example 2. Theorems 25.2, 25.4, and 25.5, and the fact that the determinant of a triangular matrix is the product of the diagonal elements (see Exercise 24.3) can be used to find the value of a determinant.

$$\begin{vmatrix} 2 & -\frac{1}{2} & 4 \\ -7 & 3 & 0 \\ 1 & 6 & -5 \end{vmatrix} = - \begin{vmatrix} 1 & 6 & -5 \\ -7 & 3 & 0 \\ 2 & -\frac{1}{2} & 4 \end{vmatrix} = - \begin{vmatrix} 1 & 6 & -5 \\ 0 & 45 & -35 \\ 2 & -\frac{1}{2} & 4 \end{vmatrix}$$

$$= - \begin{vmatrix} 1 & 6 & -5 \\ 0 & 45 & -35 \\ 0 & -\frac{25}{2} & 14 \end{vmatrix} = -45 \begin{vmatrix} 1 & 6 & -5 \\ 0 & 1 & -\frac{7}{9} \\ 0 & -\frac{25}{2} & 14 \end{vmatrix}$$

$$= -45 \begin{vmatrix} 1 & 6 & -5 \\ 0 & 1 & -\frac{7}{9} \\ 0 & 0 & \frac{77}{18} \end{vmatrix} = (-45)(\tfrac{77}{18}) = -\tfrac{385}{2}.$$

(25.6) Theorem. Let $A = [a_{i,j}]$, $B = [b_{i,j}]$, and $C = [c_{i,j}]$ be n by n matrices, where for all j, $a_{i,j} = b_{i,j} = c_{i,j}$ if $i \neq s$ and $c_{s,j} = a_{s,j} + b_{s,j}$. Then $|C| = |A| + |B|$.

In Theorem 25.6, the matrices A, B, and C have identical rows except for row s. Row s of A may differ from row s of B, and each element of row s of C is the sum of the corresponding elements in row s of A and B. The proof, which is an easy exercise in the use of Definition 24.1, is left as Exercise 25.3. As in the case of the other properties of determinants, there is a corresponding property for columns.

Example 3.

$$\begin{vmatrix} x+1 & x^3+3 \\ x^2+2 & x^4+4 \end{vmatrix} = \begin{vmatrix} x & x^3+3 \\ x^2 & x^4+4 \end{vmatrix} + \begin{vmatrix} 1 & x^3+3 \\ 2 & x^4+4 \end{vmatrix}$$

$$= \begin{vmatrix} x & x^3 \\ x^2 & x^4 \end{vmatrix} + \begin{vmatrix} x & 3 \\ x^2 & 4 \end{vmatrix} + \begin{vmatrix} 1 & x^3 \\ 2 & x^4 \end{vmatrix} + \begin{vmatrix} 1 & 3 \\ 2 & 4 \end{vmatrix}$$

$$= (x^5 - x^5) + (4x - 3x^2) + (x^4 - 2x^3) + (4 - 6)$$

$$= x^4 - 2x^3 - 3x^2 + 4x - 2.$$

Theorems 25.2, 25.4, and 25.5 state how the determinant of an n by n matrix A is affected if an elementary transformation is performed on A. By Theorem 25.2, $|I_n^{(i,j)}A| = -|A| = |AI_n^{(i,j)}|$, where $I_n^{(i,j)}$ is an elementary transformation matrix of Type I. If $I_n^{(i,j,c)}$ is an elementary transformation matrix of Type II, then, by Theorem 25.5, $|I_n^{(i,j,c)}A| = |A| = |AI_n^{(i,j,c)}|$. By Theorem 25.4, $|{}^{(r)}I_n^{(i)}A| = r|A| = |A\,{}^{(r)}I_n^{(i)}|$, where ${}^{(r)}I_n^{(i)}$ is an elementary transformation matrix of Type III. In particular, since $|I_n| = 1$,

$$|I_n^{(i,j)}| = |I_n^{(i,j)}I_n| = -|I_n| = -1,$$

$$|I_n^{(i,j,c)}| = |I_n^{(i,j,c)}I_n| = |I_n| = 1, \quad \text{and} \quad |{}^{(r)}I_n^{(i)}| = |{}^{(r)}I_n^{(i)}I_n| = r|I_n| = r.$$

(25.7) Theorem. An n by n matrix A is nonsingular if and only if $|A| \neq 0$.

PROOF. By the results of Section 23, A can be carried into canonical form D_k, where k is the rank of A, by a sequence of elementary transformations. As a consequence of the remarks above, $|D_k|$ is a nonzero constant multiple of $|A|$. That is, $|D_k| = r|A|$, where $r \neq 0$. By Theorem 18.7, A is nonsingular if and only if $k = n$. Moreover, $|D_k| \neq 0$ if and only if $k = n$ (see Exercise 24.3). Thus, A is nonsingular if and only if $|D_k| \neq 0$. Since $r \neq 0$, it follows from $|D_k| = r|A|$that $|D_k| \neq 0$ if and only if $|A| \neq 0$. Therefore, A is nonsingular if and only if $|A| \neq 0$.

The following theorem gives the important "product rule" for determinants.

(25.8) Theorem. Let $A = [a_{i,j}]$ and $B = [b_{i,j}]$ be n by n matrices. Then $|AB| = |A||B|$.

PROOF. First consider the special case where A is an elementary transformation matrix. If $A = I_n^{(i,j)}$, then

$$|I_n^{(i,j)}B| = -|B| \quad \text{and} \quad |I_n^{(i,j)}||B| = (-1)|B| = -|B|.$$

If $A = I_n^{(i,j,c)}$, then

$$|I_n^{(i,j,c)}B| = |B| \quad \text{and} \quad |I_n^{(i,j,c)}||B| = (1)|B| = |B|.$$

Finally if $A = {}^{(r)}I_n^{(i)}$, then

$$|{}^{(r)}I_n^{(i)}B| = r|B| \quad \text{and} \quad |{}^{(r)}I_n^{(i)}||B| = r|B|.$$

Thus, in every case, $|AB| = |A||B|$. Next suppose the A is any nonsingular matrix. Then, by Theorem 21.5, $A = E_1E_2 \cdots E_k$ is a product of elementary transformation matrices. By the first part of the proof,

$$|A| = |E_1E_2E_3 \cdots E_k| = |E_1|\,|E_2E_3 \cdots E_k| = |E_1|\,|E_2|\,|E_3 \cdots E_k|$$
$$= \cdots = |E_1|\,|E_2|\,|E_3| \cdots |E_k|,$$

and

$$|AB| = |E_1E_2 \cdots E_kB| = |E_1|\,|E_2 \cdots E_kB|$$
$$= |E_1|\,|E_2| \cdots |E_k|\,|B| = |A|\,|B|.$$

If A is singular, then, by Theorem 25.7, $|A| = 0$. Hence, $|A|\,|B| = 0$. Moreover, since rank of $A = k < n$, it follows that rank of $AB \leq k < n$ (see Exercise 22.2). By Theorem 18.7, AB is singular, and, by Theorem 25.7, $|AB| = 0$. Therefore, $|AB| = 0 = |A|\,|B|$, which completes the proof.

(25.9) **Corollary.** If P is a nonsingular n by n matrix, then $|P^{-1}| = 1/|P|$.

PROOF. Since $P^{-1}P = I_n$, it follows from Theorem 25.8 that $|P^{-1}|\,|P| = |P^{-1}P| = |I_n| = 1$. Hence, $|P^{-1}| = 1/|P|$.

Exercises

25.1 Evaluate the following determinants:

$$\begin{vmatrix} -2 & 1 & 3 & 7 \\ 4 & -5 & 6 & 0 \\ 2 & 4 & 6 & 8 \\ -1 & 0 & 9 & 2 \end{vmatrix}; \quad \begin{vmatrix} -\frac{1}{2} & \frac{3}{2} & 2 & \frac{1}{2} & 3 \\ -\frac{1}{4} & 6 & -3 & 2 & 1 \\ -1 & \frac{5}{2} & 7 & 3 & \frac{2}{3} \\ 0 & 21 & -16 & 7 & -2 \\ 4 & 3 & -6 & 5 & 1 \end{vmatrix}; \quad \begin{vmatrix} x+y & y+z & z+w \\ y+z & z+w & x+y \\ z+w & x+y & y+z \end{vmatrix}.$$

25.2 For

$$A = \begin{bmatrix} 1 & 2 & 4 & 8 \\ 1 & 3 & 9 & 27 \\ 1 & 4 & 16 & 64 \\ 1 & 5 & 25 & 125 \end{bmatrix},$$

evaluate $|A^2|$; $|5 \cdot A|$; $|AA'|$; $|\frac{1}{2} \cdot A^{-1}|$; $|A^3A'A^{-1}|$.

25.3 Prove Theorem 25.6.

25.4 Let A and B be n by n matrices. Prove that $|AB| = |BA|$.

***25.5** Prove that if every element of a row (column) of a square matrix A is 0, then $|A| = 0$.

25.6 Let A be a nonsingular matrix such that $A^{-1} = A'$. Prove that $|A| = \pm 1$.

26 Expansion of a determinant

The labor involved in finding the value of a determinant of an n by n matrix A directly from Definition 24.1 is prohibitive if $n > 3$. For example, if $n = 4$, $\Sigma\,(-1)^k a_{1,j_1}a_{2,j_2}a_{3,j_3}a_{4,j_4}$ has 24 terms. Therefore, methods of evaluating a determinant have been devised. Using the properties of determinants, a method for evaluating a determinant was suggested in Example 2 of Section 25. In this section, we derive another procedure for computing a determinant.

Let $A = [a_{i,j}]$ be an n by n matrix. If the row and column containing an element $a_{i,j}$ is deleted from A, then an $(n-1)$ by $(n-1)$ matrix is obtained. The determinant of this $(n-1)$ by $(n-1)$ matrix is called the *minor of the element* $a_{i,j}$, and is denoted by $\Delta_{i,j}$. By Definition 24.1,

$$\Delta_{i,j} = \sum (-1)^l a_{1,j_1} a_{2,j_2} \cdots a_{i-1,j_{i-1}} a_{i+1,j_{i+1}} \cdots a_{n,j_n},$$

where the sum is taken over all possible orderings $j_1, j_2, \ldots, j_{i-1}, j_{i+1}, \ldots, j_n$ of $1, 2, \ldots, j-1, j+1, \ldots, n$, and, for each term, l is the number of inversions of $j_1, j_2, \ldots, j_{i-1}, j_{i+1}, \ldots, j_n$. The following theorem gives the rule for expanding a determinant according to the elements of any row or column.

(26.1) Theorem. For any i, $|A| = \sum_{j=1}^{n} a_{i,j}(-1)^{i+j}\Delta_{i,j}$; and for any j,

$$|A| = \sum_{i=1}^{n} a_{i,j}(-1)^{i+j}\Delta_{i,j}.$$

PROOF. By Theorem 25.1, the second identity, which is the *column expansion*, follows from the first identity, which is the *row expansion*. We first consider the special case, where $i = 1$, and prove

$$|A| = \sum_{j=1}^{n} a_{1,j}(-1)^{1+j}\Delta_{1,j}. \tag{26-1}$$

By Definition 24.1,

$$|A| = \sum (-1)^k a_{1,j_1} a_{2,j_2} \cdots a_{n,j_n} = \sum_{j_1=1}^{n} a_{1,j_1} \left(\sum{}' (-1)^k a_{2,j_2} a_{3,j_3} \cdots a_{n,j_n}\right),$$

where, for each value of j_1, the sum $\Sigma' (-1)^k a_{2,j_2} a_{3,j_3} \cdots a_{n,j_n}$ is taken over all orderings $j_2, j_3, \ldots, j_n$ of $1, 2, \ldots, j_1 - 1, j_1 + 1, \ldots, j_n$, and, for each term, k is the number of inversions of $j_1, j_2, j_3, \ldots, j_n$. For a fixed value of j_1, there are $j_1 - 1$ inversions contributed to the total k, because j_1 is in the first position of the ordering $j_1, j_2, j_3, \ldots, j_n$. Hence, there are $k - (j_1 - 1)$ inversions in the ordering $j_2, j_3, \ldots, j_n$. Thus, for each j_1,

$$\Delta_{1,j_1} = \sum{}' (-1)^{k-j_1+1} a_{2,j_2} a_{3,j_3} \cdots a_{n,j_n},$$

and

$$\begin{aligned}(-1)^{1+j_1}\Delta_{1,j_1} &= \sum{}' (-1)^{k+2} a_{2,j_2} a_{3,j_3} \cdots a_{n,j_n} \\ &= \sum{}' (-1)^{k} a_{2,j_2} a_{3,j_3} \cdots a_{n,j_n}.\end{aligned}$$

Therefore,

$$|A| = \sum_{j_1=1}^{n} a_{1,j_1}(-1)^{1+j_1}\Delta_{1,j_1},$$

which is the required identity (26-1).

Consider a matrix B whose first row is the ith row of A and whose remaining rows are the rows of A except for the ith row, in the order 1, 2, 3, . . . , $i-1, i+1$, . . . , n. The matrix B can be obtained from A by $i-1$ successive interchanges of two rows. By Theorem 25.2, $|B| = (-1)^{i-1}|A|$. The minors of the elements of the first row of B are the minors of the elements of the ith row of A. Therefore, by (26-1),

$$|B| = \sum_{j=1}^{n} a_{i,j}(-1)^{1+j}\Delta_{i,j},$$

and

$$|A| = (-1)^{2(i-1)}|A| = (-1)^{i-1}|B| = \sum_{j=1}^{n} a_{i,j}(-1)^{i+j}\Delta_{i,j}.$$

Example 1.

$$\begin{vmatrix} 2 & -1 & 3 & 5 \\ 4 & 0 & 1 & 0 \\ 9 & -7 & 4 & 2 \\ 11 & -6 & 2 & 0 \end{vmatrix} = 4(-1)^{2+1}\begin{vmatrix} -1 & 3 & 5 \\ -7 & 4 & 2 \\ -6 & 2 & 0 \end{vmatrix} + 0(-1)^{2+2}\begin{vmatrix} 2 & 3 & 5 \\ 9 & 4 & 2 \\ 11 & 2 & 0 \end{vmatrix}$$

$$+ 1(-1)^{2+3}\begin{vmatrix} 2 & -1 & 5 \\ 9 & -7 & 2 \\ 11 & -6 & 0 \end{vmatrix} + 0(-1)^{2+4}\begin{vmatrix} 2 & -1 & 3 \\ 9 & -7 & 4 \\ 11 & -6 & 2 \end{vmatrix}$$

$$= (-4)\begin{vmatrix} -1 & 3 & 5 \\ -7 & 4 & 2 \\ -6 & 2 & 0 \end{vmatrix} + (-1)\begin{vmatrix} 2 & -1 & 5 \\ 9 & -7 & 2 \\ 11 & -6 & 0 \end{vmatrix}.$$

$$\begin{vmatrix} -1 & 3 & 5 \\ -7 & 4 & 2 \\ -6 & 2 & 0 \end{vmatrix} = (-6)(-1)^{3+1}\begin{vmatrix} 3 & 5 \\ 4 & 2 \end{vmatrix} + 2(-1)^{3+2}\begin{vmatrix} -1 & 5 \\ -7 & 2 \end{vmatrix} + 0(-1)^{3+3}\begin{vmatrix} -1 & 3 \\ -7 & 4 \end{vmatrix}$$

$$= (-6)(6 - 20) + (-2)(-2 + 35) = 18.$$

$$\begin{vmatrix} 2 & -1 & 5 \\ 9 & -7 & 2 \\ 11 & -6 & 0 \end{vmatrix} = 11(-1)^{3+1}\begin{vmatrix} -1 & 5 \\ -7 & 2 \end{vmatrix} + (-6)(-1)^{3+2}\begin{vmatrix} 2 & 5 \\ 9 & 2 \end{vmatrix} + 0(-1)^{3+3}\begin{vmatrix} 2 & -1 \\ 9 & -7 \end{vmatrix}$$

$$= (11)(-2 + 35) + (6)(4 - 45) = 117.$$

Hence the value of the determinant is $(-4)(18) + (-1)(117) = -189$. The amount of computation can be reduced by using Theorems 25.5 and 25.4. For example,

$$\begin{vmatrix} 2 & -1 & 3 & 5 \\ 4 & 0 & 1 & 0 \\ 9 & -7 & 4 & 2 \\ 11 & -6 & 2 & 0 \end{vmatrix} = \begin{vmatrix} -10 & -1 & 3 & 5 \\ 0 & 0 & 1 & 0 \\ -7 & -7 & 4 & 2 \\ 3 & -6 & 2 & 0 \end{vmatrix} = (-1)^{2+3} \begin{vmatrix} -10 & -1 & 5 \\ -7 & -7 & 2 \\ 3 & -6 & 0 \end{vmatrix}$$

$$= (-3) \begin{vmatrix} -10 & -1 & 5 \\ -7 & -7 & 2 \\ 1 & -2 & 0 \end{vmatrix} = (-3) \begin{vmatrix} -10 & -21 & 5 \\ -7 & -21 & 2 \\ 1 & 0 & 0 \end{vmatrix}$$

$$= (-3)(-21) \begin{vmatrix} -10 & 1 & 5 \\ -7 & 1 & 2 \\ 1 & 0 & 0 \end{vmatrix} = (-3)(-21)(-1)^{3+1} \begin{vmatrix} 1 & 5 \\ 1 & 2 \end{vmatrix}$$

$$= (-3)(-21)(2 - 5) = -189.$$

The minor $\Delta_{i,j}$ of an element $a_{i,j}$ of a square matrix A with the sign $(-1)^{i+j}$ attached is called the *cofactor* of $a_{i,j}$, and is denoted by $A_{i,j}$. Thus, $A_{i,j} = (-1)^{i+j}\Delta_{i,j}$. With this notation, the row and column expansions of $|A|$ given in Theorem 26.1 can be written

$$|A| = \sum_{j=1}^{n} a_{i,j}A_{i,j} \quad \text{and} \quad |A| = \sum_{i=1}^{n} a_{i,j}A_{i,j}.$$

A useful identity is obtained if the elements of a given row (column) of A are multiplied by the cofactors of another row (column):

(26.2) Theorem. If $s \neq k$, then $\sum_{j=1}^{n} a_{s,j}A_{k,j} = 0$, and if $t \neq k$, then

$$\sum_{i=1}^{n} a_{i,t}A_{i,k} = 0.$$

PROOF. Let $B = [b_{i,j}]$, where, for all j and all $i \neq k$, $b_{i,j} = a_{i,j}$ and $b_{k,j} = a_{s,j}$ for $s \neq k$. Then row k of B is identical with row s of B. Moreover, $B_{k,j} = A_{k,j}$ for all j, since, except for row k, the rows of B are the same as the rows of A. Therefore, by Theorems 26.1 and 25.3,

$$\sum_{j=1}^{n} a_{s,j}A_{k,j} = \sum_{j=1}^{n} b_{k,j}B_{k,j} = |B| = 0.$$

The second identity follows similarly from the second identity of Theorem 26.1.

Exercises

26.1 Let

$$A = \begin{bmatrix} -2 & 1 & 0 & 3 \\ 4 & 7 & 6 & 2 \\ -10 & 1 & 1 & 4 \\ 3 & 2 & 1 & -5 \end{bmatrix}.$$

Compute the minors of elements 0, 6, and −10. Also compute the cofactors of these elements.

26.2 Use Theorem 26.1 to find the values of the determinants given in Exercises 24.5 and 25.1.

26.3 Prove, in detail, that the second identity of Theorem 26.1 follows from the first identity and Theorem 25.1.

27 Some applications of determinants

In Section 26, we defined a minor of an element in a square matrix. More generally, if $A = [a_{i,j}]$ is an m by n matrix, then a *minor of A* is the determinant of a square k by k submatrix of A ($k \leq m$, $k \leq n$) obtained from A by choosing any k rows and any k columns of A. Such a minor is called a *k-rowed minor of A*.

Example 1. If

$$A = \begin{bmatrix} -\frac{2}{3} & \sqrt{5} & 1 & 0 \\ -\sqrt{3} & \frac{1}{2} & 4 & 7 \\ 3 & 1 & -1 & 2 \end{bmatrix},$$

then the three-rowed minors of A are

$$\begin{vmatrix} -\frac{2}{3} & \sqrt{5} & 1 \\ -\sqrt{3} & \frac{1}{2} & 4 \\ 3 & 1 & -1 \end{vmatrix}, \quad \begin{vmatrix} -\frac{2}{3} & \sqrt{5} & 0 \\ -\sqrt{3} & \frac{1}{2} & 7 \\ 3 & 1 & 2 \end{vmatrix}, \quad \begin{vmatrix} -\frac{2}{3} & 1 & 0 \\ -\sqrt{3} & 4 & 7 \\ 3 & -1 & 2 \end{vmatrix}, \text{ and } \begin{vmatrix} \sqrt{5} & 1 & 0 \\ \frac{1}{2} & 4 & 7 \\ 1 & -1 & 2 \end{vmatrix}.$$

There are 18 two-rowed minors of A, and the one-rowed minors are just the elements of A.

(27.1) Theorem. An m by n matrix $A = [a_{i,j}]$ has rank k if and only if A has a nonzero k-rowed minor and every s-rowed minor with $s > k$ is zero.

PROOF. Suppose that t is the greatest positive integer such that A has a nonzero t-rowed minor and every s-rowed minor with $s > t$ is zero. Let

k be the rank of A. If we show $t = k$, then both parts of the theorem follow. Let B be a t by t submatrix of A such that $|B| \neq 0$, and let C be the t by n submatrix of A that contains the same t rows as B. Since $|B| \neq 0$, B has rank t by Theorems 25.7 and 18.7. Therefore,

$$\begin{aligned} t &= \text{rank of } B = \text{column rank of } B \leq \text{column rank of } C \\ &= \text{row rank of } C \leq \text{row rank of } A = \text{rank of } A = k. \end{aligned}$$

Hence $t \leq k$. Now let D be any $(t + 1)$ by n submatrix of A. The column rank of D must be less than $t + 1$, for otherwise D would contain $t + 1$ linearly independent columns (as vectors in $\mathcal{V}_{t+1}$). Then if E is the $(t + 1)$ by $(t + 1)$ submatrix of D formed from these $t + 1$ columns, it follows that $t + 1 = \text{column rank of } E = \text{rank of } E$. Hence, E is nonsingular, and $|E| \neq 0$. But since E is a submatrix of A, this implies that A has a $(t + 1)$ by $(t + 1)$ nonzero minor, which is a contradiction. Therefore, row rank of $D = \text{column rank of } D < t + 1$. Since D was any $(t + 1)$ by n submatrix of A, it follows that any $t + 1$ rows of A are linearly dependent. Thus, the row space of A has dimension less than or equal to t. Consequently,

$$k = \text{rank of } A = \text{row rank of } A \leq t.$$

We have proved that $t \leq k$ and $k \leq t$. Hence, $t = k$.

Sometimes the rank of a matrix is defined by the statement of Theorem 27.1, in which case it is referred to as the *determinantal rank*. Thus, for every m by n matrix A, row rank of A = column rank of A = rank of A = determinantal rank of A. In Example 1, rank of $A = 3$, since

$$\begin{vmatrix} -\frac{2}{3} & 1 & 0 \\ -\sqrt{3} & 4 & 7 \\ 3 & -1 & 2 \end{vmatrix} = 11 + 2\sqrt{3}.$$

As a second application of determinants, we derive another method for finding the inverse of a nonsingular matrix that is of more theoretical than practical interest. Let $A = [a_{i,j}]$ be an n by n matrix. The *adjoint* of A is the n by n matrix that has the cofactor $A_{j,i}$ of $a_{j,i}$ in the (i, j)-position for all i, j. Thus, if we denote the adjoint of A by A^{adj}, then A^{adj} is the transpose of the matrix $[A_{i,j}]$. That is, $A^{\text{adj}} = [A_{i,j}]'$.

(27.2) Theorem. For any n by n matrix $A = [a_{i,j}]$, $AA^{\text{adj}} = A^{\text{adj}}A = |A| \cdot I_n$.

PROOF. By the definition of matrix multiplication, the element in the ith row, jth column of AA^{adj} is $\sum_{k=1}^{n} a_{i,k}A_{j,k}$ (since $A_{j,k}$ is in the (k, j)-position of A^{adj}). If $j = i$, then $\sum_{k=1}^{n} a_{i,k}A_{j,k} = |A|$ by Theorem 26.1, and if $j \neq i$, then $\sum_{k=1}^{n} a_{i,k}A_{j,k} = 0$ by Theorem 26.2. Hence, each diagonal element of AA^{adj} is $|A|$, and the elements not on the diagonal are zero. Therefore, $AA^{\text{adj}} = |A| \cdot I_n$. The identity $A^{\text{adj}}A = |A| \cdot I_n$ is proved similarly.

(27.3) **Corollary.** If A is a nonsingular n by n matrix, then $A^{-1} = (1/|A|) \cdot A^{\text{adj}}$.

PROOF.

$$\begin{aligned}[(1/|A|) \cdot A^{\text{adj}}]A &= (1/|A|) \cdot (A^{\text{adj}}A) \\ &= (1/|A|) \cdot (|A| \cdot I_n) = [(1/|A|)|A|] \cdot I_n = I_n.\end{aligned}$$

Computationally, the method 21.4 for finding the inverse of a nonsingular matrix is preferable to the formula given in Corollary 27.3. For example, if $n = 4$, to compute $(1/|A|) \cdot A^{\text{adj}}$ requires the evaluation of $|A|$ and the 16 3 by 3 cofactors $A_{i,j}$.

If $A = [a_{i,j}]$ is a nonsingular n by n matrix, then the system of n linear equations in n unknowns, which can be written as the single matrix equation $AX = B$, has a unique solution $X = A^{-1}B$ (Theorem 18.8). Using the form of A^{-1} given in Corollary 27.3,

$$\begin{bmatrix} x_1 \\ x_2 \\ \cdot \\ \cdot \\ \cdot \\ x_n \end{bmatrix} = \frac{1}{|A|} \cdot A^{\text{adj}} \begin{bmatrix} b_1 \\ b_2 \\ \cdot \\ \cdot \\ \cdot \\ b_n \end{bmatrix} = \frac{1}{|A|} \cdot [A_{i,j}]' \begin{bmatrix} b_1 \\ b_2 \\ \cdot \\ \cdot \\ \cdot \\ b_n \end{bmatrix}$$

$$= \frac{1}{|A|} \cdot \begin{bmatrix} \sum_{k=1}^{n} A_{k,1}b_k \\ \sum_{k=1}^{n} A_{k,2}b_k \\ \cdot \\ \cdot \\ \cdot \\ \sum_{k=1}^{n} A_{k,n}b_k \end{bmatrix} = \begin{bmatrix} \sum_{k=1}^{n} A_{k,1}b_k/|A| \\ \sum_{k=1}^{n} A_{k,2}b_k/|A| \\ \cdot \\ \cdot \\ \cdot \\ \sum_{k=1}^{n} A_{k,n}b_k/|A| \end{bmatrix}.$$

Hence $x_i = \sum_{k=1}^{n} A_{k,i}b_k/|A|$ for $i = 1, 2, \ldots, n$. Note that $\sum_{k=1}^{n} A_{k,i}b_k = \sum_{k=1}^{n} b_k A_{k,i}$ is the expansion of the determinant

$$\begin{vmatrix} a_{1,1} & a_{1,2} & \cdots & a_{1,i-1} & b_1 & a_{1,i+1} & \cdots & a_{1,n} \\ a_{2,1} & a_{2,2} & \cdots & a_{2,i-1} & b_2 & a_{2,i+1} & \cdots & a_{2,n} \\ \cdot & \cdot & & \cdot & \cdot & \cdot & & \cdot \\ \cdot & \cdot & & \cdot & \cdot & \cdot & & \cdot \\ \cdot & \cdot & & \cdot & \cdot & \cdot & & \cdot \\ a_{n,1} & a_{n,2} & \cdots & a_{n,i-1} & b_n & a_{n,i+1} & \cdots & a_{n,n} \end{vmatrix}.$$

This solution of the system $AX = B$, where A is nonsingular, is known as *Cramer's rule*.

Exercises

27.1 List the two-rowed minors of the matrix A of Example 1.

27.2 Evaluate the three-rowed minors of the matrix

$$A = \begin{bmatrix} 1 & 1 & 1 & 1 & 1 \\ 2 & -1 & 2 & -1 & 2 \\ 0 & 1 & 0 & 1 & 0 \\ 0 & 0 & 1 & 0 & 0 \end{bmatrix}.$$

27.3 Let A be an m by n matrix such that every s-rowed minor of A is zero ($s < m$, $s < n$). Prove that if $t > s$, then every t-rowed minor of A is zero.

27.4 Find the adjoints of the following matrices:

$$\begin{bmatrix} 3 & -1 & 2 \\ 0 & 1 & -5 \\ 6 & 7 & 4 \end{bmatrix}; \quad \begin{bmatrix} 0 & 0 & 1 & 0 \\ 0 & 1 & -2 & 0 \\ 0 & 0 & 0 & 1 \\ 1 & 0 & 0 & 0 \end{bmatrix}; \quad \begin{bmatrix} 1 & 1 & 1 & 1 \\ 2 & 2 & 2 & 2 \\ 3 & 3 & 3 & 3 \\ 4 & 4 & 4 & 4 \end{bmatrix}.$$

27.5 Let A be an n by n matrix ($n \geq 2$). Prove that $A^{\text{adj}} = \mathbf{O}$ if and only if rank of $A < n - 1$.

***27.6** Prove that $|A^{\text{adj}}| = |A|^{n-1}$ for any n by n matrix $A (n \geq 2)$.

27.7 Solve the following systems of linear equations by Cramer's rule:

(a)
$$\begin{aligned} x_1 + x_2 + x_3 + x_4 &= 1 \\ x_1 - 4x_2 + 6x_3 + x_4 &= 3 \\ 4x_1 + 2x_2 + 6x_3 - 2x_4 &= 4 \\ 6x_1 - 5x_2 + 5x_3 + 3x_4 &= 7; \end{aligned}$$

(b)
$$\begin{aligned} 2x_1 - 3x_2 + x_3 &= 0 \\ x_1 - 5x_2 - x_3 &= 1 \\ 4x_1 + 2x_2 + 3x_3 &= 5; \end{aligned}$$

(c)
$$\begin{aligned} x_1 - 3x_2 + 2x_3 &= 0 \\ 2x_1 - x_2 + x_3 &= 0 \\ 6x_1 + 3x_2 - 5x_3 &= 0. \end{aligned}$$

27.8 Find the inverses of the nonsingular matrices given in Exercise 27.4 by the method of Corollary 27.3.

***27.9** Prove that a homogeneous system of n linear equations in n unknowns, $AX = \mathbf{O}$, has a nontrivial solution if and only if $|A| = 0$.

CHAPTER SEVEN

Similarity of Matrices

28 Characteristic values

In Section 20 we studied the effect of a change of basis on the matrix of a linear transformation L of a finite dimensional vector space $\mathcal{V}$ into itself. We found that if P is the nonsingular matrix describing the change of basis in $\mathcal{V}$ [see equations (19-1)], then the matrices A and B of L with respect to the two bases of $\mathcal{V}$ were related by the equation $B = Q^{-1}AQ$, where $Q = P'$. In this situation, the matrices A and B were said to be similar (see Definition 20.4). In this chapter, our main interest is to characterize the linear transformations of a vector space $\mathcal{V}$ into itself that have a diagonal matrix with respect to a suitable basis in $\mathcal{V}$. This problem is equivalent to that of characterizing the n by n matrices that are similar to a diagonal matrix. It is particularly easy to describe the properties of a linear transformation of $\mathcal{V}$ into itself that has a diagonal matrix with respect to some basis of $\mathcal{V}$.

Throughout this chapter, $\mathcal{V}$ is an n-dimensional real vector space and L is a linear transformation of $\mathcal{V}$ into itself. Certain vectors in $\mathcal{V}$ play a central role in the discussion of similarity, namely, those which are sent into a scalar multiple of themselves by L.

(28.1) Definition. A real number r such that $L(\mathbf{V}) = r \cdot \mathbf{V}$ for some nonzero vector $\mathbf{V} \in \mathcal{V}$ is called a *characteristic value* of L. A nonzero vector $\mathbf{V}$ satisfying $L(\mathbf{V}) = r \cdot \mathbf{V}$ is called a *characteristic vector* of L (belonging to the characteristic value r).

Example 1. Let L be the linear transformation of $\mathcal{V}_3$ that has the matrix

$$A = \begin{bmatrix} 2 & 4 & 1 \\ 1 & -2 & -1 \\ 0 & 0 & 0 \end{bmatrix}$$

with respect to the basis $\{\mathbf{E}_1^{(3)}, \mathbf{E}_2^{(3)}, \mathbf{E}_3^{(3)}\}$. Then r is a characteristic value of L if and only if there is a nonzero vector $\langle x_1, x_2, x_3\rangle \in \mathcal{V}_3$ such that

$$A\begin{bmatrix} x_1 \\ x_2 \\ x_3 \end{bmatrix} = r \cdot \begin{bmatrix} x_1 \\ x_2 \\ x_3 \end{bmatrix} = (r \cdot I_3)\begin{bmatrix} x_1 \\ x_2 \\ x_3 \end{bmatrix},$$

which can be written in the form

$$(A - r \cdot I_3)\begin{bmatrix} x_1 \\ x_2 \\ x_3 \end{bmatrix} = \begin{bmatrix} 0 \\ 0 \\ 0 \end{bmatrix}. \tag{28-1}$$

Thus, the problem of finding the characteristic values of L is reduced to that of finding the nontrivial solutions of a homogeneous system of linear equations. By Corollary 18.6, this system has a nontrivial solution if and only if the rank of $A - r \cdot I_3$ is less than 3, that is, if and only if $|A - r \cdot I_3| = 0$. We have,

$$|A - r \cdot I_3| = \begin{vmatrix} 2-r & 4 & 1 \\ 1 & -2-r & -1 \\ 0 & 0 & -r \end{vmatrix} = -r\begin{vmatrix} 2-r & 4 \\ 1 & -2-r \end{vmatrix}$$

$$= -r(-4 + r^2 - 4) = -r(r^2 - 8) = 0.$$

Thus, the characteristic values of L are 0, $2\sqrt{2}$, and $-2\sqrt{2}$. Corresponding to the characteristic value $r = 0$, the system (28-1) becomes

$$\begin{bmatrix} 2 & 4 & 1 \\ 1 & -2 & -1 \\ 0 & 0 & 0 \end{bmatrix}\begin{bmatrix} x_1 \\ x_2 \\ x_3 \end{bmatrix} = \begin{bmatrix} 0 \\ 0 \\ 0 \end{bmatrix}.$$

Solving this system by the methods of Chapter Three, $\langle x_1, x_2, x_3\rangle = \langle s/4, -3s/8, s\rangle$, where s is any real number. Thus for every $s \neq 0$, $\langle s/4, -3s/8, s\rangle$ is a characteristic vector of L that belongs to the characteristic value $r = 0$. That is, $L(\langle s/4, -3s/8, s\rangle) = 0 \cdot \langle s/4, -3s/8, s\rangle = \langle 0, 0, 0\rangle$. The task of finding the characteristic vectors belonging to the characteristic values $2\sqrt{2}$ and $-2\sqrt{2}$ is left as an exercise (Exercise 28.2).

The example above serves to illustrate the following theorem.

(28.2) Theorem. Let L be a linear transformation of $\mathcal{V}$, and let $\{\mathbf{U}_1, \mathbf{U}_2, \ldots, \mathbf{U}_n\}$ be any basis of $\mathcal{V}$. Let A be the matrix of L with respect to this basis. A real number r is a characteristic value of L if and only if r is a real root of the equation $|A - x \cdot I_n| = 0$. The characteristic vectors of L that belong to a characteristic value r of L are those nonzero vectors $\mathbf{V} \in \mathcal{V}$ with coordinates $\langle x_1, x_2, \ldots, x_n\rangle$ with respect to the basis $\{\mathbf{U}_1, \mathbf{U}_2, \ldots, \mathbf{U}_n\}$, which satisfy

$$(A - r \cdot I_n)\begin{bmatrix} x_1 \\ x_2 \\ \cdot \\ \cdot \\ \cdot \\ x_n \end{bmatrix} = \begin{bmatrix} 0 \\ 0 \\ \cdot \\ \cdot \\ \cdot \\ 0 \end{bmatrix}.$$

The proof of Theorem 28.2 follows step-by-step the argument given in Example 1 and is left as an exercise (Exercise 28.5). In Example 1, $|A - x \cdot I_n| = 0$ is the equation $x^3 - 8x = x(x^2 - 8) = 0$, which has three distinct real roots. However, this is not generally the case. The equation $|A - x \cdot I_n| = 0$ is always a polynomial equation of degree n with real coefficients. Such an equation has n roots (not necessarily distinct), but some of them may be complex numbers. For example, if

$$A = \begin{bmatrix} 2 & -5 & 1 \\ 1 & -2 & -1 \\ 0 & 0 & 0 \end{bmatrix},$$

then

$$|A - x \cdot I_3| = \begin{vmatrix} 2 - x & -5 & 1 \\ 1 & -2 - x & -1 \\ 0 & 0 & -x \end{vmatrix}$$

$$= -x(-4 + x^2 + 5) = -x(x^2 + 1).$$

In this case, the roots of the equation $-x(x^2 + 1) = 0$ are 0, i, and $-i$. A linear transformation L of $\mathcal{V}_3$ with matrix A has 0 as its only characteristic value according to Theorem 28.2.

(28.3) Definition. Let A be a real n by n matrix. The determinant $|A - x \cdot I_n|$, which is a polynomial of degree n in x, is called the *characteristic polynomial* of A. The equation $|A - x \cdot I_n| = 0$ is called the *characteristic equation* of A. The n (possibly complex) roots of this equation are called the *characteristic roots* of A.

Thus, the characteristic values of a linear transformation L are the real characteristic roots of any matrix A of L.

(28.4) Theorem. Similar matrices have the same characteristic polynomial (and hence the same characteristic roots).

PROOF. If $B = P^{-1}AP$, then

$$B - x \cdot I_n = P^{-1}AP - x \cdot P^{-1}P = P^{-1}AP - P^{-1}(x \cdot I_n)P = P^{-1}(A - x \cdot I_n)P.$$

Thus,

$$|B - x \cdot I_n| = |P^{-1}(A - x \cdot I_n)P| = |P^{-1}|\,|A - x \cdot I_n|\,|P| = |A - x \cdot I_n|,$$

by Theorem 25.8 and Corollary 25.9.

It should be noted that matrices with the same characteristic polynomial are not necessarily similar. The n by n triangular matrix

$$A = \begin{bmatrix} 1 & a_{1,2} & a_{1,3} & \cdots & & a_{1,n} \\ 0 & 1 & a_{2,3} & \cdots & & a_{2,n} \\ 0 & 0 & 1 & \cdots & & a_{3,n} \\ 0 & 0 & 0 & \cdot & & \cdot \\ \cdot & \cdot & \cdot & & \cdot & \cdot \\ \cdot & \cdot & \cdot & & & \cdot \\ \cdot & \cdot & \cdot & & \cdot & a_{n-1,n} \\ 0 & 0 & 0 & \cdots & 0 & 1 \end{bmatrix}$$

has characteristic polynomial $(1 - x)^n$, which is also the characteristic polynomial of I_n. Suppose that some $a_{i,j} \neq 0$ so that $A \neq I_n$. Then A and I_n are not similar since I_n is similar only to itself. Indeed, $P^{-1}I_nP = P^{-1}P = I_n$ for any nonsingular P.

Exercises

28.1 Let L be the linear transformation of $\mathcal{V}_4$ into itself that has matrix

$$A = \begin{bmatrix} 2 & -3 & 4 & 1 \\ 0 & 3 & 1 & 2 \\ 0 & 0 & 1 & 5 \\ 0 & 0 & -2 & 3 \end{bmatrix}$$

with respect to the basis $E^{(4)}$. Find the characteristic values and characteristic vectors of L.

28.2 In Example 1, find the characteristic vectors that belong to the characteristic values $2\sqrt{2}$ and $-2\sqrt{2}$.

***28.3** Prove that the set of all characteristic vectors of a linear transformation L of $\mathcal{V}$ that belong to the same characteristic value r form a subspace of $\mathcal{V}$.

28.4 Prove that a linear transformation L of $\mathcal{V}$ is nonsingular if and only if 0 is not a characteristic value of L.

28.5 Prove Theorem 28.2.

28.6 Prove that if the n by n matrices A and B are similar, then $|A| = |B|$.

28.7 Find the characteristic roots of the following matrices:

$$\begin{bmatrix} \frac{1}{2} & 2 \\ -\frac{1}{3} & 5 \end{bmatrix}; \qquad \begin{bmatrix} 0 & 0 & 1 & 0 \\ 0 & 0 & 0 & 1 \\ 0 & 1 & 0 & 0 \\ 1 & 0 & 0 & 0 \end{bmatrix}; \qquad \begin{bmatrix} 1 & 2 & 3 \\ 0 & 1 & 2 \\ 0 & -2 & 1 \end{bmatrix}.$$

29 Matrices similar to diagonal matrices

In this section we find the necessary and sufficient condition for a real n by n matrix A to be similar to a real diagonal matrix.

(29.1) Theorem. Let A be a real n by n matrix, and let L be the linear transformation of $\mathcal{V}$ that has matrix A with respect to some basis of $\mathcal{V}$. The matrix A is similar to a diagonal matrix

$$D = \begin{bmatrix} r_1 & 0 & \cdots & 0 \\ 0 & r_2 & & \cdot \\ \cdot & & \cdot & \cdot \\ \cdot & & \cdot & \cdot \\ \cdot & & \cdot & 0 \\ 0 & \cdots & 0 & r_n \end{bmatrix}, \qquad (29\text{-}1)$$

where $r_1, r_2, \ldots, r_n$ are real numbers, if and only if there is a basis of $\mathcal{V}$ consisting of characteristic vectors of L.

PROOF. By Theorem 20.3, A is similar to D if and only if there is a basis $\{\mathbf{W}_1, \mathbf{W}_2, \ldots, \mathbf{W}_n\}$ of $\mathcal{V}$ such that L has matrix D with respect to this basis. For any basis $\{\mathbf{W}_1, \mathbf{W}_2, \ldots, \mathbf{W}_n\}$, the coordinates of $L(\mathbf{W}_i)$ are the elements in the ith column of the matrix of L with respect to this basis. Thus, L has matrix D if and only if $L(\mathbf{W}_i) = r_i \cdot \mathbf{W}_i$ for $i = 1, 2, \ldots, n$. However $L(\mathbf{W}_i) = r_i \cdot \mathbf{W}_i$ if and only if the vector $\mathbf{W}_i$ in the basis $\{\mathbf{W}_1, \mathbf{W}_2, \ldots, \mathbf{W}_n\}$ is a characteristic vector of L.

Suppose that the condition of Theorem 29.1 is satisfied. That is, $\mathcal{V}$ has a basis $\{\mathbf{W}_1, \mathbf{W}_2, \ldots, \mathbf{W}_n\}$ consisting of characteristic vectors of L. Let A be the matrix of L with respect to a basis $\{\mathbf{U}_1, \mathbf{U}_2, \ldots, \mathbf{U}_n\}$ of $\mathcal{V}$. By the proof of Theorem 29.1, L has a diagonal matrix D with respect to the basis $\{\mathbf{W}_1, \mathbf{W}_2, \ldots, \mathbf{W}_n\}$. Let $P = [p_{i,j}]$ be the matrix of the change of basis from the **U**-basis to the **W**-basis. Then, for $i = 1, 2, \ldots, n$, the row $\langle p_{i,1}, p_{i,2}, \ldots, p_{i,n}\rangle$ of P gives the coordinates of $\mathbf{W}_i$ with respect to the **U**-basis [see equations (19-1)]. Moreover, by the results of Section 20, $D = (P')^{-1}AP'$. Setting $Q = P'$, we have $D = Q^{-1}AQ$, where the columns of Q are the coordinates of the characteristic vectors $\mathbf{W}_i$ with respect to the **U**-basis. Thus, we have a method for constructing a nonsingular matrix Q such that $Q^{-1}AQ$ is a diagonal matrix, given a basis of characteristic vectors of L. Conversely, as a consequence of Exercise 29.1, if Q is any nonsingular matrix such that $Q^{-1}AQ = D$, where D is a diagonal matrix, then the columns of Q must be the coordinates of n characteristic vectors of L which form a basis of $\mathcal{V}$.

Example 1. Let

$$A = \begin{bmatrix} 2 & -2 & 2 & 1 \\ -1 & 3 & 0 & 3 \\ 0 & 0 & 4 & -2 \\ 0 & 0 & 2 & -1 \end{bmatrix}.$$

Let L be the linear transformation of $\mathcal{V}_4$ that has matrix A with respect to the basis $E^{(4)}$. The characteristic equation of A is

$$\begin{vmatrix} 2-x & -2 & 2 & 1 \\ -1 & 3-x & 0 & 3 \\ 0 & 0 & 4-x & -2 \\ 0 & 0 & 2 & -1-x \end{vmatrix} = x(x-3)(x-4)(x-1) = 0.$$

Thus, the characteristic roots of A are 0, 3, 4, and 1, and these are characteristic values of L. Corresponding to these characteristic values, we have the following systems of homogeneous equations, which we solve for the characteristic vectors of L:

$$\begin{bmatrix} 2 & -2 & 2 & 1 \\ -1 & 3 & 0 & 3 \\ 0 & 0 & 4 & -2 \\ 0 & 0 & 2 & -1 \end{bmatrix}\begin{bmatrix} x_1 \\ x_2 \\ x_3 \\ x_4 \end{bmatrix} = \begin{bmatrix} 0 \\ 0 \\ 0 \\ 0 \end{bmatrix}, \quad \begin{bmatrix} -1 & -2 & 2 & 1 \\ -1 & 0 & 0 & 3 \\ 0 & 0 & 1 & -2 \\ 0 & 0 & 2 & -4 \end{bmatrix}\begin{bmatrix} x_1 \\ x_2 \\ x_3 \\ x_4 \end{bmatrix} = \begin{bmatrix} 0 \\ 0 \\ 0 \\ 0 \end{bmatrix},$$

$$\begin{bmatrix} -2 & -2 & 2 & 1 \\ -1 & -1 & 0 & 3 \\ 0 & 0 & 0 & -2 \\ 0 & 0 & 2 & -5 \end{bmatrix}\begin{bmatrix} x_1 \\ x_2 \\ x_3 \\ x_4 \end{bmatrix} = \begin{bmatrix} 0 \\ 0 \\ 0 \\ 0 \end{bmatrix}, \quad \begin{bmatrix} 1 & -2 & 2 & 1 \\ -1 & 2 & 0 & 3 \\ 0 & 0 & 3 & -2 \\ 0 & 0 & 2 & -2 \end{bmatrix}\begin{bmatrix} x_1 \\ x_2 \\ x_3 \\ x_4 \end{bmatrix} = \begin{bmatrix} 0 \\ 0 \\ 0 \\ 0 \end{bmatrix}.$$

The solutions are $\langle -3s, -2s, s/2, s\rangle$, $\langle 3s, s, 2s, s\rangle$, $\langle -s, s, 0, 0\rangle$ and $\langle 2s, s, 0, 0\rangle$, where s is any real number. Choosing $s = 1$ in each case, we obtain the vectors $\langle -3, -2, \tfrac{1}{2}, 1\rangle$, $\langle 3, 1, 2, 1\rangle$, $\langle -1, 1, 0, 0\rangle$ and $\langle 2, 1, 0, 0\rangle$. Since

$$\begin{vmatrix} -3 & -2 & \frac{1}{2} & 1 \\ 3 & 1 & 2 & 1 \\ -1 & 1 & 0 & 0 \\ 2 & 1 & 0 & 0 \end{vmatrix} = \tfrac{9}{2} \neq 0,$$

it follows from Corollary 19.2 that these characteristic vectors of L form a basis of $\mathcal{V}_4$. By Theorem 29.1, A is similar to a diagonal matrix D. Also, by the remarks above, the matrix

$$Q = \begin{bmatrix} -3 & 3 & -1 & 2 \\ -2 & 1 & 1 & 1 \\ \frac{1}{2} & 2 & 0 & 0 \\ 1 & 1 & 0 & 0 \end{bmatrix}$$

is a nonsingular matrix such that $Q^{-1}AQ = D$. Moreover,

$$D = \begin{bmatrix} 0 & 0 & 0 & 0 \\ 0 & 3 & 0 & 0 \\ 0 & 0 & 4 & 0 \\ 0 & 0 & 0 & 1 \end{bmatrix},$$

where the diagonal elements of D are the characteristic roots of A. Since D is the matrix of L with respect to the basis $\{\langle -3, -2, \frac{1}{2}, 1\rangle, \langle 3, 1, 2, 1\rangle, \langle -1, 1, 0, 0\rangle, \langle 2, 1, 0, 0\rangle\}$, it is apparent that the null space of L is spanned by the vector $\langle -3, -2, \frac{1}{2}, 1\rangle$ and that the range space of L is spanned by the vectors $\langle 3, 1, 2, 1\rangle$, $\langle -1, 1, 0, 0\rangle$, and $\langle 2, 1, 0, 0\rangle$.

The final statement in Example 1 illustrates the following theorem.

(29.2) Theorem. If A is similar to a diagonal matrix D, then the diagonal elements of D are the characteristic roots of A.

PROOF. If A is similar to a diagonal matrix D [given by (29-1)], then, by Theorem 28.4,

$$|A - x \cdot I_n| = |D - x \cdot I_n| = \begin{vmatrix} r_1 - x & 0 & \cdots & 0 \\ 0 & r_2 - x & & \cdot \\ \cdot & & \cdot & \cdot \\ \cdot & & & \cdot \\ \cdot & & \cdot & 0 \\ 0 & \cdots & 0 & r_n - x \end{vmatrix}$$

$$= (r_1 - x)(r_2 - x) \cdots (r_n - x).$$

Therefore, $r_1, r_2, \ldots, r_n$ are the characteristic roots of A.

In Example 1, the matrix A has four distinct real characteristic roots, and we found that $\mathcal{V}_4$ has a basis consisting of characteristic vectors of the associated linear transformation L. This is an example of the following theorem.

(29.3) Theorem. If a (real) n by n matrix A has n real distinct characteristic roots, then A is similar to a (real) diagonal matrix.

PROOF. Let L be a linear transformation of $\mathcal{V}$ that has matrix A with respect to a basis $\{\mathbf{U}_1, \mathbf{U}_2, \ldots, \mathbf{U}_n\}$ of $\mathcal{V}$, and denote the characteristic roots of A by $r_1, r_2, \ldots, r_n$. Let $\mathbf{W}_i$ be a characteristic vector of L belonging to r_i for $i = 1, 2, \ldots, n$. By Theorem 29.1, it is sufficient to show that $\{\mathbf{W}_1, \mathbf{W}_2, \ldots, \mathbf{W}_n\}$ is a basis of $\mathcal{V}$, which is the case if $\{\mathbf{W}_1, \mathbf{W}_2, \ldots, \mathbf{W}_n\}$ is a linearly independent set. Assume that this set is linearly dependent. Each $\mathbf{W}_i \neq 0$, since $\mathbf{W}_i$ is a characteristic vector. By Theorem 8.2, there is an integer k, where $2 \leq k \leq n$, such that $\{\mathbf{W}_1, \mathbf{W}_2, \ldots, \mathbf{W}_{k-1}\}$ is a linearly independent set and

$$\mathbf{W}_k = c_1 \cdot \mathbf{W}_1 + c_2 \cdot \mathbf{W}_2 + \cdots + c_{k-1} \cdot \mathbf{W}_{k-1}, \tag{29-2}$$

where at least one $c_i \neq 0$. Let $\langle w_{1,i}, w_{2,i}, \ldots, w_{n,i}\rangle$ for $i = 1, 2, \ldots, k$ be the coordinates of $\mathbf{W}_i$ with respect to the basis $\{\mathbf{U}_1, \mathbf{U}_2, \ldots, \mathbf{U}_n\}$. Then equation (29-2) can be written as a matrix equation:

$$\begin{bmatrix} w_{1,k} \\ w_{2,k} \\ \cdot \\ \cdot \\ \cdot \\ w_{n,k} \end{bmatrix} = c_1 \cdot \begin{bmatrix} w_{1,1} \\ w_{2,1} \\ \cdot \\ \cdot \\ \cdot \\ w_{n,1} \end{bmatrix} + c_2 \cdot \begin{bmatrix} w_{1,2} \\ w_{2,2} \\ \cdot \\ \cdot \\ \cdot \\ w_{n,2} \end{bmatrix} + \cdots + c_{k-1} \cdot \begin{bmatrix} w_{1,k-1} \\ w_{2,k-1} \\ \cdot \\ \cdot \\ \cdot \\ w_{n,k-1} \end{bmatrix}. \tag{29-3}$$

Multiply equation (29-3) by the matrix A, recalling that

$$A \begin{bmatrix} w_{1,i} \\ w_{2,i} \\ \cdot \\ \cdot \\ \cdot \\ w_{n,i} \end{bmatrix} = r_i \cdot \begin{bmatrix} w_{1,i} \\ w_{2,i} \\ \cdot \\ \cdot \\ \cdot \\ w_{n,i} \end{bmatrix},$$

for $i = 1, 2, \ldots, k$. This is the case since each $\mathbf{W}_i$ is a characteristic vector. We obtain

$$r_k \cdot \mathbf{W}_k = (c_1 r_1) \cdot \mathbf{W}_1 + (c_2 r_2) \cdot \mathbf{W}_2 + \cdots + (c_{k-1} r_{k-1}) \cdot \mathbf{W}_{k-1}. \tag{29-4}$$

From equation (29-2), we have

$$r_k \cdot \mathbf{W}_k = (c_1 r_k) \cdot \mathbf{W}_1 + (c_2 r_k) \cdot \mathbf{W}_2 + \cdots + (c_{k-1} r_k) \cdot \mathbf{W}_{k-1}. \quad (29\text{-}5)$$

Subtracting equation (29-5) from (29-4),

$$\mathbf{0} = c_1(r_1 - r_k) \cdot \mathbf{W}_1 + c_2(r_2 - r_k) \cdot \mathbf{W}_2 + \cdots + c_{k-1}(r_{k-1} - r_k) \cdot \mathbf{W}_{k-1}. \quad (29\text{-}6)$$

Since $r_k \neq r_i$ for $i = 1, 2, \ldots, k - 1$ and at least one $c_i \neq 0$, it follows that one of the coefficients in equation (29-6) is not zero. But this contradicts the fact that $\{\mathbf{W}_1, \mathbf{W}_2, \ldots, \mathbf{W}_{k-1}\}$ is a linearly independent set. Hence, the assumption that the set $\{\mathbf{W}_1, \mathbf{W}_2, \ldots, \mathbf{W}_n\}$ is linearly dependent is false, which completes the proof of the theorem.

We have found the condition for a real n by n matrix A to be similar to a diagonal matrix (Theorem 29.1), and we have shown that this condition is satisfied if A has n real distinct characteristic roots (Theorem 29.3). Moreover, by Theorem 29.2, if not all of the characteristic roots of A are real, then A is not similar to a (real) diagonal matrix. In this case, it follows from Theorem 29.1 that the characteristic vectors of a linear transformation defined by A do not span $\mathcal{V}$. If all of the characteristic roots of A are real, but not distinct, then A may or may not be similar to a diagonal matrix, as shown in the following examples.

Example 2. Let $A = I_n$. Then

$$|A - x \cdot I_n| = \begin{vmatrix} 1 - x & 0 & \cdots & 0 \\ 0 & 1 - x & & \cdot \\ \cdot & & \cdot & \cdot \\ \cdot & & \cdot & \cdot \\ \cdot & & \cdot & 0 \\ 0 & \cdots & 0 & 1 - x \end{vmatrix}$$

$$= (1 - x)(1 - x) \cdots (1 - x).$$

Hence, the characteristic roots are $r_1 = r_2 = \cdots = r_n = 1$. However, A is similar to a diagonal matrix, since A is the diagonal matrix I_n. The linear transformation L of $\mathcal{V}$ defined by $A = I_n$ (with respect to any basis of $\mathcal{V}$) is the identity transformation, and any basis of $\mathcal{V}$ is a basis consisting of characteristic vectors of L.

Example 3. Let

$$A = \begin{bmatrix} 1 & -4 & 3 \\ 0 & 1 & 6 \\ 0 & 0 & 2 \end{bmatrix}.$$

Then

$$|A - x \cdot I_3| = \begin{vmatrix} 1-x & -4 & 3 \\ 0 & 1-x & 6 \\ 0 & 0 & 2-x \end{vmatrix} = (1-x)(1-x)(2-x).$$

The characteristic roots of A are $r_1 = r_2 = 1$, $r_3 = 2$. Let $\mathcal{V} = \mathcal{V}_3$, and let L be the linear transformation with matrix A with respect to the basis $E^{(3)}$. The characteristic vectors of L that belong to the characteristic value $r_1 = r_2 = 1$ are the vectors $\langle x_1, x_2, x_3\rangle$, where

$$\begin{bmatrix} 0 & -4 & 3 \\ 0 & 0 & 6 \\ 0 & 0 & 1 \end{bmatrix}\begin{bmatrix} x_1 \\ x_2 \\ x_3 \end{bmatrix} = \begin{bmatrix} 0 \\ 0 \\ 0 \end{bmatrix}.$$

Thus, $\langle x_1, x_2, x_3\rangle = \langle s, 0, 0\rangle = s \cdot \langle 1, 0, 0\rangle$, where s is any real number. The characteristic vectors $\langle x_1, x_2, x_3\rangle$ that belong to $r_3 = 2$ satisfy

$$\begin{bmatrix} -1 & -4 & 3 \\ 0 & -1 & 6 \\ 0 & 0 & 0 \end{bmatrix}\begin{bmatrix} x_1 \\ x_2 \\ x_3 \end{bmatrix} = \begin{bmatrix} 0 \\ 0 \\ 0 \end{bmatrix}.$$

Thus, for r_3, $\langle x_1, x_2, x_3\rangle = \langle -21s, 6s, s\rangle = s \cdot \langle -21, 6, 1\rangle$, where s is any real number. Therefore, the subspace of $\mathcal{V}$ spanned by the characteristic vectors of L is spanned by $\{\langle 1, 0, 0\rangle, \langle -21, 6, 1\rangle\}$. This subspace has dimension two. Hence, $\mathcal{V}$ does not have a basis consisting of characteristic vectors, so that, by Theorem 29.1, A is not similar to a diagonal matrix.

Exercises

***29.1** Let L be a linear transformation of $\mathcal{V}$ that has matrix A with respect to a basis $\{\mathbf{U}_1, \mathbf{U}_2, \ldots, \mathbf{U}_n\}$ of $\mathcal{V}$. Suppose that Q is a nonsingular matrix such that $Q^{-1}AQ$ is a diagonal matrix. Prove that the columns of Q are the coordinates with respect to $\{\mathbf{U}_1, \mathbf{U}_2, \ldots, \mathbf{U}_n\}$ of n characteristic vectors of L that form a basis of $\mathcal{V}$.

29.2 In Example 1, find Q^{-1} and compute the product $Q^{-1}AQ$.

29.3 Which of the following matrices are similar to diagonal matrices?

$$\begin{bmatrix} 2 & -1 & 0 & 0 \\ -2 & 3 & 0 & 0 \\ 2 & 0 & 4 & 2 \\ 1 & 3 & -2 & -1 \end{bmatrix}; \begin{bmatrix} -2 & 0 & 1 \\ 0 & 1 & -7 \\ 0 & 1 & 0 \end{bmatrix}; \begin{bmatrix} 0 & 0 & 0 & 1 \\ 0 & 0 & 1 & 0 \\ 0 & 1 & 0 & 0 \\ 1 & 0 & 0 & 0 \end{bmatrix}; \begin{bmatrix} 3 & -1 & -1 & -2 \\ 1 & 1 & -1 & -1 \\ 1 & 0 & 0 & -1 \\ 0 & -1 & 1 & 1 \end{bmatrix}.$$

29.4 For those matrices A of Exercise 29.3 that are similar to a diagonal matrix D, find a nonsingular matrix Q such that $Q^{-1}AQ = D$.

29.5 Prove that if A is similar to a diagonal matrix, then A' is similar to a diagonal matrix.

*29.6 Prove that if A is similar to a diagonal matrix, then A^n (where n is a positive integer) is similar to a diagonal matrix, and the characteristic roots of A^n are the nth powers of the characteristic roots of A.

30 Orthogonal linear transformations and orthogonal matrices

In Section 13 we discussed the rotations T_φ of $\mathcal{E}_2$ into $\mathcal{E}_2$, where $\mathcal{E}_2$ is the two-dimensional Euclidean vector space consisting of all geometrical vectors in a plane. Relative to a rectangular Cartesian coordinate system in $\mathcal{E}_2$, a vector $\mathbf{V} \in \mathcal{E}_2$ with coordinates $\langle x, y\rangle$ is sent into a vector $T_\varphi(\mathbf{V})$ with coordinates $\langle x \cos \varphi - y \sin \varphi, x \sin \varphi + y \cos \varphi\rangle$. Let $\mathbf{W} \in \mathcal{E}_2$ have coordinates $\langle s, t\rangle$. Then, by Theorem 3.4,

$$\begin{aligned} T_\varphi(\mathbf{V}) \circ T_\varphi(\mathbf{W}) &= (x \cos \varphi - y \sin \varphi)(s \cos \varphi - t \sin \varphi) \\ &\quad + (x \sin \varphi + y \cos \varphi)(s \sin \varphi + t \cos \varphi) \\ &= xs + yt = \mathbf{V} \circ \mathbf{W}. \end{aligned}$$

Thus, the inner product of two vectors in $\mathcal{E}_2$ is left unchanged when each vector is mapped by the linear transformation T_φ. This fact implies that the length of a vector, $(\mathbf{V} \circ \mathbf{V})^{1/2}$, is unchanged. Moreover, since $\cos \theta = (\mathbf{V} \circ \mathbf{W})/(\mathbf{V} \circ \mathbf{V})^{1/2}(\mathbf{W} \circ \mathbf{W})^{1/2}$, where θ is the angle between $\mathbf{V}$ and $\mathbf{W}$, the angle between two vectors is preserved by T_φ.

We now define a class of linear transformations of a Euclidean vector space $\mathcal{E}$ into itself that has the properties exhibited by the rotations T_φ of $\mathcal{E}_2$.

(30.1) Definition. Let $\mathcal{E}$ be a Euclidean vector space. A linear transformation L of $\mathcal{E}$ into itself such that $\mathcal{I}(\mathbf{V}, \mathbf{V}) = \mathcal{I}(L(\mathbf{V}), L(\mathbf{V}))$ for all $\mathbf{V} \in \mathcal{E}$ is called an *orthogonal transformation* of $\mathcal{E}$.

Thus, an orthogonal transformation of $\mathcal{E}$ preserves the length $[\mathcal{I}(\mathbf{V}, \mathbf{V})]^{1/2}$ of each vector $\mathbf{V} \in \mathcal{E}$. It is not difficult to show that an orthogonal transformation leaves the inner product $\mathcal{I}(\mathbf{V}, \mathbf{W})$ of two vectors unchanged (see Exercise 30.1). Therefore, if the angle θ between two vectors in $\mathcal{E}$ is defined by $\cos \theta = \mathcal{I}(\mathbf{V}, \mathbf{W})/[\mathcal{I}(\mathbf{V}, \mathbf{V})]^{1/2}[\mathcal{I}(\mathbf{W}, \mathbf{W})]^{1/2}$, an orthogonal transformation also preserves angles.

(30.2) Theorem. Let L be an orthogonal transformation of a Euclidean vector space $\mathcal{E}$ of dimension n. Let $A = [a_{i,j}]$ be the matrix of L with respect to an orthonormal basis $\{\mathbf{U}_1, \mathbf{U}_2, \ldots, \mathbf{U}_n\}$ of $\mathcal{E}$. Then A is nonsingular, and $A^{-1} = A'$.

PROOF. For $j = 1, 2, \ldots, n$, the jth column of A gives the coordinates $\langle a_{1,j}, a_{2,j}, \ldots, a_{n,j}\rangle$ of $L(\mathbf{U}_j)$ with respect to the given basis. Therefore, for $i = 1, 2, \ldots, n$, the ith row of A' gives the coordinates $\langle a_{1,i}, a_{2,i}, \ldots, a_{n,i}\rangle$ of $L(\mathbf{U}_i)$. Since $\{\mathbf{U}_1, \mathbf{U}_2, \ldots, \mathbf{U}_n\}$ is an orthonormal basis of $\mathcal{E}$, it follows from Theorem 9.6 that

$$\mathcal{g}(L(\mathbf{U}_i), L(\mathbf{U}_j)) = \sum_{k=1}^{n} a_{k,i}a_{k,j}.$$

By the definition of matrix multiplication, this is the element in the (i, j)-position of $A'A$ for all i, j. Since L is an orthogonal transformation, $\mathcal{g}(\mathbf{U}_i, \mathbf{U}_j) = \mathcal{g}(L(\mathbf{U}_i), L(\mathbf{U}_j))$. Moreover, $\mathcal{g}(\mathbf{U}_i, \mathbf{U}_j) = 0$ if $i \neq j$, and $\mathcal{g}(\mathbf{U}_i, \mathbf{U}_i) = 1$, again using the fact that $\{\mathbf{U}_1, \mathbf{U}_2, \ldots, \mathbf{U}_n\}$ is an orthonormal basis. Hence, the matrix $A'A$ has 1 in each diagonal position and 0 elsewhere. That is, $A'A = I_n$. This proves that A is nonsingular, and $A^{-1} = A'$.

(30.3) Definition. A (real) nonsingular n by n matrix A such that $A^{-1} = A'$ is called an *orthogonal matrix.*

By Theorem 30.2, the matrix of an orthogonal transformation L of a Euclidean vector space $\mathcal{E}$ with respect to an orthonormal basis is an orthogonal matrix. In particular, L is a nonsingular linear transformation.

Example 1. Let L be an orthogonal transformation of $\mathcal{E}_2$, and let

$$A = \begin{bmatrix} a_{1,1} & a_{1,2} \\ a_{2,1} & a_{2,2} \end{bmatrix}$$

be the matrix of L with respect to the orthonormal basis $\{\mathbf{I}, \mathbf{J}\}$, which determines a rectangular Cartesian coordinate system of $\mathcal{E}_2$. Then A is an orthogonal matrix. Since $A^{-1} = A'$, it follows that $AA' = I_2$. Using the properties of determinants given by Theorems 25.8 and 25.1, this matrix equation yields

$$1 = |I_2| = |AA'| = |A|\,|A'| = |A|\,|A| = |A|^2.$$

Therefore, $|A| = \pm 1$. Thus, we have

$$\begin{bmatrix} a_{1,1} & a_{1,2} \\ a_{2,1} & a_{2,2} \end{bmatrix}\begin{bmatrix} a_{1,1} & a_{2,1} \\ a_{1,2} & a_{2,2} \end{bmatrix} = \begin{bmatrix} 1 & 0 \\ 0 & 1 \end{bmatrix}, \quad \text{and} \quad \begin{vmatrix} a_{1,1} & a_{1,2} \\ a_{2,1} & a_{2,2} \end{vmatrix} = \pm 1.$$

Consequently, the elements of the matrix A are subject to the following conditions:

$$a_{1,1}^2 + a_{1,2}^2 = 1, \qquad a_{1,1}a_{2,1} + a_{1,2}a_{2,2} = 0,$$

$$a_{2,1}^2 + a_{2,2}^2 = 1, \quad \text{and} \quad a_{1,1}a_{2,2} - a_{2,1}a_{1,2} = \pm 1.$$

Suppose first that $|A| = a_{1,1}a_{2,2} - a_{2,1}a_{1,2} = 1$. Then

$$a_{1,1}a_{2,1}^2 + a_{1,2}a_{2,2}a_{2,1} = 0$$

$$a_{1,1}a_{2,2}^2 - a_{2,1}a_{1,2}a_{2,2} = a_{2,2},$$

and adding, we obtain $a_{1,1}(a_{2,1}^2 + a_{2,2}^2) = a_{1,1} = a_{2,2}$. The equation $a_{1,1}a_{2,1} + a_{1,2}a_{2,2} = 0$, now becomes $a_{1,1}(a_{2,1} + a_{1,2}) = 0$. Therefore, either $a_{1,1} = 0$ or $a_{1,2} = -a_{2,1}$. If $a_{1,1} = 0$, then the original equations yield $a_{1,2} = -a_{2,1} = \pm 1$. Thus, in every case,

$$A = \begin{bmatrix} u & -v \\ v & u \end{bmatrix},$$

where $u^2 + v^2 = 1$. We now observe that there is an angle φ such that $u = \cos\varphi$ and $v = \sin\varphi$. Therefore, when $|A| = 1$, the matrix of the orthogonal transformation L is the matrix of the rotation T_φ. That is, L is a rotation of $\mathcal{E}_2$.

If $|A| = -1$, an analysis similar to the one above shows that

$$A = \begin{bmatrix} u & v \\ v & -u \end{bmatrix},$$

where $u^2 + v^2 = 1$. Again, there is an angle φ such that $u = \cos\varphi$ and $v = \sin\varphi$. Thus, a vector $\mathbf{V} \in \mathcal{E}_2$ with coordinates $\langle x, y\rangle$ is sent into $L(\mathbf{V})$ with coordinates $\langle x', y'\rangle$, where

$$\begin{bmatrix} \cos\varphi & \sin\varphi \\ \sin\varphi & -\cos\varphi \end{bmatrix} \begin{bmatrix} x \\ y \end{bmatrix} = \begin{bmatrix} x' \\ y' \end{bmatrix}.$$

It is left as an exercise (Exercise 30.9) to show that in this case L is a *reflection* of $\mathcal{E}_2$ through the line that makes an angle $\varphi/2$ with the X-axis at the origin of the coordinate system (see Figure 29).

FIGURE 29

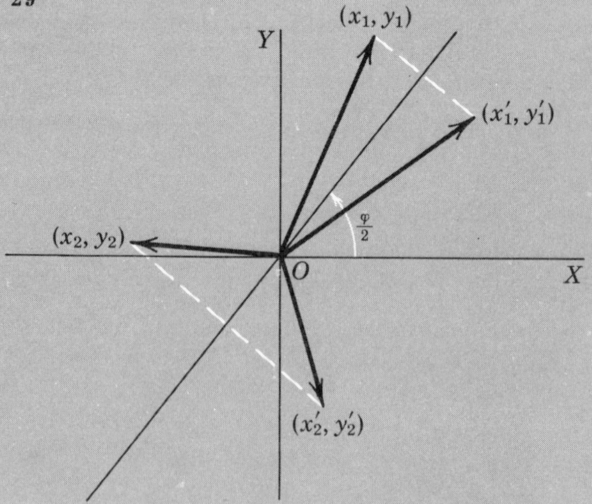

Suppose that $\{\mathbf{U}_1, \mathbf{U}_2, \ldots, \mathbf{U}_n\}$ is an orthonormal basis of $\mathcal{E}$ and that $\{\mathbf{W}_1, \mathbf{W}_2, \ldots, \mathbf{W}_n\}$ is any set of n vectors in $\mathcal{E}$. Then

$$\begin{aligned} \mathbf{W}_1 &= p_{1,1} \cdot \mathbf{U}_1 + p_{1,2} \cdot \mathbf{U}_2 + \cdots + p_{1,n} \cdot \mathbf{U}_n \\ \mathbf{W}_2 &= p_{2,1} \cdot \mathbf{U}_1 + p_{2,2} \cdot \mathbf{U}_2 + \cdots + p_{2,n} \cdot \mathbf{U}_n \\ &\cdots \\ \mathbf{W}_n &= p_{n,1} \cdot \mathbf{U}_1 + p_{n,2} \cdot \mathbf{U}_2 + \cdots + p_{n,n} \cdot \mathbf{U}_n. \end{aligned} \tag{30-1}$$

Since $\{\mathbf{U}_1, \mathbf{U}_2, \ldots, \mathbf{U}_n\}$ is an orthonormal basis, it follows from Theorem 9.6 that

$$\mathcal{G}(\mathbf{W}_i, \mathbf{W}_j) = \sum_{k=1}^{n} p_{i,k}p_{j,k} \tag{30-2}$$

for all i, j. The equations (30-2) imply that $\{\mathbf{W}_1, \mathbf{W}_2, \ldots, \mathbf{W}_n\}$ is an orthonormal basis of $\mathcal{E}$ if and only if the matrix $P = [p_{i,j}]$ is an orthogonal matrix. The details of this argument are left for the reader to supply (Exercise 30.6). Thus, the matrix of a change of basis from one orthonormal basis to another orthonormal basis in a Euclidean vector space is an orthogonal matrix. If the discussion of Section 20, on the relation between two matrices that are the matrices of the same linear transformation of a vector space $\mathcal{V}$ into itself, is applied to the present situation, we obtain the following theorem.

(30.3) Theorem. Let A and B be n by n matrices, and let $\mathcal{E}$ be an n-dimensional Euclidean vector space. Then A and B are matrices of the same linear transformation L of $\mathcal{E}$ into itself (with respect to suitable orthonormal bases in $\mathcal{E}$) if and only if there exists an orthogonal matrix Q such that $B = Q^{-1}AQ$.

Theorem 30.3 suggests the next definition.

(30.4) Definition. Let A and B be n by n matrices. The matrix B is *orthogonally equivalent* to the matrix A if there exists an orthogonal matrix Q such that $B = Q^{-1}AQ$.

Orthogonal equivalence is an equivalence relation on the set $\mathfrak{A}_n$ of all real n by n matrices. From Definition 30.4 it is immediately obvious that orthogonal equivalence is a special case of similarity.

We conclude this section with a result on the reduction of an n by n matrix under orthogonal equivalence that will be useful in the simplification of quadratic forms in Chapter Eight.

(30.5) Theorem. Let A be an n by n matrix such that all of the characteristic roots $r_1, r_2, \ldots, r_n$ of A are real. There exists an orthogonal matrix Q such that

$$Q^{-1}AQ = \begin{bmatrix} r_1 & b^*_{1,2} & b^*_{1,3} & \cdots & & b^*_{1,n} \\ 0 & r_2 & b^*_{2,3} & \cdots & & b^*_{2,n} \\ \cdot & 0 & r_3 & & & \cdot \\ \cdot & \cdot & 0 & \cdot & & \cdot \\ & \cdot & \cdot & \cdot & & \\ \cdot & \cdot & \cdot & & \cdot & \cdot \\ & & \cdot & & & \\ & & & & & b^*_{n-1,n} \\ 0 & 0 & 0 & \cdots & 0 & r_n \end{bmatrix} \tag{30-3}$$

PROOF. The proof is by induction on n. If $n = 1$, then $A = [a_{1,1}]$, $r_1 = a_{1,1}$ is the characteristic root of A, and $I_1AI_1 = I_1^{-1}AI_1 = [r_1]$, where $I_1 = [1]$ is an orthogonal matrix. Therefore let $n > 1$, and assume that the theorem is true for $(n-1)$ by $(n-1)$ matrices. Let L be the linear transformation of an n-dimensional Euclidean vector space $\mathcal{E}$ into itself that has matrix A with respect to an orthonormal basis $\{\mathbf{U}_1, \mathbf{U}_2, \ldots, \mathbf{U}_n\}$ of $\mathcal{E}$. Then $r_1, r_2, \ldots, r_n$ are characteristic values of L. Let $\mathbf{W}_1$ be a characteristic vector of L that belongs to the characteristic value r_1. Since $\mathbf{W}_1 \neq \mathbf{0}$, there is a basis of $\mathcal{E}$ that contains $\mathbf{W}_1$. By the Gram-Schmidt orthogonalization process (Theorem 9.5), there is an orthonormal basis $\{\overline{\mathbf{W}}_1, \overline{\mathbf{W}}_2, \ldots, \overline{\mathbf{W}}_n\}$ of $\mathcal{E}$ such that $\overline{\mathbf{W}}_1 = (1/|\mathbf{W}_1|) \cdot \mathbf{W}_1$. Since

$$L(\overline{\mathbf{W}}_1) = \frac{1}{|\mathbf{W}_1|} \cdot L(\mathbf{W}_1) = \frac{1}{|\mathbf{W}_1|} \cdot (r_1 \cdot \mathbf{W}_1) = r_1 \cdot \left(\frac{1}{|\mathbf{W}_1|} \cdot \mathbf{W}_1\right) = r_1 \cdot \overline{\mathbf{W}}_1,$$

it follows that $\overline{\mathbf{W}}_1$ is a characteristic vector of L that belongs to r_1. The matrix $P = [p_{i,j}]$ of the change of basis from the $\mathbf{U}$-basis to the $\overline{\mathbf{W}}$-basis is an orthogonal matrix, and the coordinates of $\overline{\mathbf{W}}_1$ with respect to the $\mathbf{U}$-basis are $\langle p_{1,1}, p_{1,2}, \ldots, p_{1,n}\rangle$. Therefore, we have

$$A \begin{bmatrix} p_{1,1} \\ p_{1,2} \\ \cdot \\ \cdot \\ \cdot \\ p_{1,n} \end{bmatrix} = r_1 \cdot \begin{bmatrix} p_{1,1} \\ p_{1,2} \\ \cdot \\ \cdot \\ \cdot \\ p_{1,n} \end{bmatrix}, \quad \text{and} \quad P \begin{bmatrix} p_{1,1} \\ p_{1,2} \\ \cdot \\ \cdot \\ \cdot \\ p_{1,n} \end{bmatrix} = \begin{bmatrix} 1 \\ 0 \\ \cdot \\ \cdot \\ \cdot \\ 0 \end{bmatrix}.$$

The latter equation can be written

$$\begin{bmatrix} p_{1,1} \\ p_{1,2} \\ \cdot \\ \cdot \\ \cdot \\ p_{1,n} \end{bmatrix} = P^{-1} \begin{bmatrix} 1 \\ 0 \\ \cdot \\ \cdot \\ \cdot \\ 0 \end{bmatrix}.$$

Hence,

$$A \left(P^{-1} \begin{bmatrix} 1 \\ 0 \\ \cdot \\ \cdot \\ \cdot \\ 0 \end{bmatrix} \right) = A \begin{bmatrix} p_{1,1} \\ p_{1,2} \\ \cdot \\ \cdot \\ \cdot \\ p_{1,n} \end{bmatrix} = r_1 \cdot \begin{bmatrix} p_{1,1} \\ p_{1,2} \\ \cdot \\ \cdot \\ \cdot \\ p_{1,n} \end{bmatrix} = r_1 \cdot \left(P^{-1} \begin{bmatrix} 1 \\ 0 \\ \cdot \\ \cdot \\ \cdot \\ 0 \end{bmatrix} \right)$$

$$= P^{-1} \left(r_1 \cdot \begin{bmatrix} 1 \\ 0 \\ \cdot \\ \cdot \\ \cdot \\ 0 \end{bmatrix} \right) = P^{-1} \begin{bmatrix} r_1 \\ 0 \\ \cdot \\ \cdot \\ \cdot \\ 0 \end{bmatrix}.$$

Consequently,

$$PAP^{-1} \begin{bmatrix} 1 \\ 0 \\ \cdot \\ \cdot \\ \cdot \\ 0 \end{bmatrix} = \begin{bmatrix} r_1 \\ 0 \\ \cdot \\ \cdot \\ \cdot \\ 0 \end{bmatrix},$$

which implies that the first column of PAP^{-1} is

$$\begin{bmatrix} r_1 \\ 0 \\ \cdot \\ \cdot \\ \cdot \\ 0 \end{bmatrix}.$$

Let $Q_1 = P^{-1}$. Then Q_1 is an orthogonal matrix (see Exercise 30.5) such that

$$Q_1^{-1}AQ_1 = \begin{bmatrix} r_1 & b_{1,2} & \cdots & b_{1,n} \\ 0 & b_{2,2} & \cdots & b_{2,n} \\ \cdot & \cdot & & \cdot \\ \cdot & \cdot & & \cdot \\ \cdot & \cdot & & \cdot \\ 0 & b_{n,2} & \cdots & b_{n,n} \end{bmatrix}.$$

Let B be the $(n-1)$ by $(n-1)$ matrix

$$\begin{bmatrix} b_{2,2} & \cdots & b_{2,n} \\ \cdot & & \cdot \\ \cdot & & \cdot \\ \cdot & & \cdot \\ b_{n,2} & \cdots & b_{n,n} \end{bmatrix}.$$

Then $|A - x \cdot I_n| = |Q_1^{-1}AQ_1 - x \cdot I_n| = (r_1 - x)|B - x \cdot I_{n-1}|$. Thus, the characteristic roots of B are $r_2, r_3, \ldots, r_n$. By the induction assumption, there is an $(n-1)$ by $(n-1)$ orthogonal matrix Q_2 such that

$$Q_2^{-1}BQ_2 = \begin{bmatrix} r_2 & b^*_{2,3} & \cdots & b^*_{2,n} \\ 0 & r_3 & & \\ \cdot & 0 & \cdot & \cdot \\ \cdot & & & \cdot \\ \cdot & \cdot & \cdot & \cdot \\ & \cdot & & \\ & \cdot & \cdot & b^*_{n-1,n} \\ 0 & 0 & \cdots & r_n \end{bmatrix}.$$

Then the matrix

$$Q_3 = \begin{bmatrix} 1 & 0 & \cdots & 0 \\ 0 & & & \\ \cdot & & & \\ \cdot & & Q_2 & \\ \cdot & & & \\ 0 & & & \end{bmatrix}$$

is an n by n orthogonal matrix such that

$$Q_3^{-1}Q_1^{-1}AQ_1Q_3 = \begin{bmatrix} r_1 & b_{1,2}^* & b_{1,3}^* & \cdots & & b_{1,n}^* \\ 0 & r_2 & b_{2,3}^* & \cdots & & b_{2,n}^* \\ \cdot & 0 & r_3 & & & \cdot \\ \cdot & \cdot & 0 & \cdot & & \cdot \\ \cdot & & \cdot & & \cdot & \cdot \\ & \cdot & \cdot & & & \\ & \cdot & \cdot & & & \\ & & & & \cdot & b_{n-1,n}^* \\ 0 & 0 & 0 & \cdots & 0 & r_n \end{bmatrix}.$$

The matrix $Q = Q_1Q_3$, being the product of orthogonal matrices, is orthogonal. Hence $Q^{-1}AQ$ has the triangular form (30-3).

Exercises

***30.1** Prove that if L is an orthogonal transformation of a Euclidean vector space $\mathcal{E}$, then $\mathcal{g}(\mathbf{V}, \mathbf{W}) = \mathcal{g}(L(\mathbf{V}), L(\mathbf{W}))$ for all vectors $\mathbf{V}$, $\mathbf{W} \in \mathcal{E}$. Use the fact that $\mathcal{g}(\mathbf{V} - \mathbf{W}, \mathbf{V} - \mathbf{W}) = \mathcal{g}(L(\mathbf{V} - \mathbf{W}), L(\mathbf{V} - \mathbf{W}))$ and expand this identity.

30.2 Let L be the linear transformation of $\mathcal{E}_3$ given by the equations

$$x' = x \cos \varphi - y \sin \varphi$$

$$y' = x \sin \varphi + y \cos \varphi$$

$$z' = z$$

with respect to a rectangular Cartesian coordinate system. Prove that L is an orthogonal transformation of $\mathcal{E}_3$.

***30.3** Let L and M be orthogonal transformations of a Euclidean vector space $\mathcal{E}$. Prove that LM is an orthogonal transformation of $\mathcal{E}$.

***30.4** Let A be an orthogonal matrix, and let L be a linear transformation of a Euclidean vector space $\mathcal{E}$ that has matrix A with respect to an orthonormal basis of $\mathcal{E}$. Prove that L is an orthogonal transformation of $\mathcal{E}$. *Hint:* Express the inner product of two vectors in $\mathcal{E}$ as a matrix product.

***30.5** Let A be an orthogonal matrix. Prove (a) $|A| = \pm 1$; (b) A' is orthogonal; (c) A^{-1} is orthogonal; and (d) $Q^{-1}AQ$ is orthogonal, for any orthogonal matrix Q.

30.6 Let $\{\mathbf{U}_1, \mathbf{U}_2, \ldots, \mathbf{U}_n\}$ be an orthonormal basis of a Euclidean vector space $\mathcal{E}$. Let $\{\mathbf{W}_1, \mathbf{W}_2, \ldots, \mathbf{W}_n\}$ be a set of n vectors in $\mathcal{E}$ given by equations (30-1). Prove that $\{\mathbf{W}_1, \mathbf{W}_2, \ldots, \mathbf{W}_n\}$ is an orthonormal basis of $\mathcal{E}$ if and only if the matrix $P = [p_{i,j}]$ is an orthogonal matrix.

30.7 Prove that orthogonal equivalence is an equivalence relation on the set $\mathfrak{A}_n$ of all real n by n matrices.

30.8 For each of the following matrices A, find an orthogonal matrix Q such that $Q^{-1}AQ$ is in triangular form (30-3).

$$\begin{bmatrix} 1 & 0 & 1 \\ -1 & -\tfrac{1}{2} & -\tfrac{1}{2} \\ -1 & -\tfrac{3}{2} & -\tfrac{3}{2} \end{bmatrix}; \qquad \begin{bmatrix} 1 & \tfrac{2}{3} \\ 2 & \tfrac{4}{3} \end{bmatrix}; \qquad \begin{bmatrix} 0 & 0 & -1 \\ 0 & 4 & -6 \\ -2 & 0 & 1 \end{bmatrix}.$$

30.9 For the problem stated in Example 1, give the details of the computation which shows that

$$A = \begin{bmatrix} \cos\varphi & \sin\varphi \\ \sin\varphi & -\cos\varphi \end{bmatrix}$$

in the case where $|A| = -1$. Show that the orthogonal transformation L with matrix A is a reflection of $\mathcal{E}_2$.

CHAPTER EIGHT

Quadratic Forms

31 Bilinear and quadratic mappings

We recall that if $\mathcal{E}$ is a Euclidean vector space, the inner product $\mathcal{I}(\mathbf{U}, \mathbf{W})$, for $\mathbf{U}, \mathbf{W} \in \mathcal{E}$, is a mapping of ordered pairs of vectors $\langle \mathbf{U}, \mathbf{W} \rangle$ into the real numbers that is bilinear, symmetric, and positive definite (see Definition 9.2). We now generalize this concept by retaining only the bilinearity condition of Definition 9.2.

(31.1) Definition. Let $\mathcal{V}$ be an n-dimensional vector space. A mapping $\mathcal{B}$ from ordered pairs of vectors in $\mathcal{V}$ to the real numbers is called a *bilinear mapping* if $\mathcal{B}$ satisfies

$$\begin{aligned}\mathcal{B}(r_1 \cdot \mathbf{U}_1 + r_2 \cdot \mathbf{U}_2, s_1 \cdot \mathbf{W}_1 + s_2 \cdot \mathbf{W}_2) &= r_1 s_1 \mathcal{B}(\mathbf{U}_1, \mathbf{W}_1) + r_1 s_2 \mathcal{B}(\mathbf{U}_1, \mathbf{W}_2) \\ &\quad + r_2 s_1 \mathcal{B}(\mathbf{U}_2, \mathbf{W}_1) + r_2 s_2 \mathcal{B}(\mathbf{U}_2, \mathbf{W}_2),\end{aligned}$$

for all vectors $\mathbf{U}_1, \mathbf{U}_2, \mathbf{W}_1, \mathbf{W}_2$ in $\mathcal{V}$ and all real numbers r_1, r_2, s_1, s_2.

Let $\{\mathbf{U}_1, \mathbf{U}_2, \ldots, \mathbf{U}_n\}$ be a basis of $\mathcal{V}$, and let $\mathbf{U} = r_1 \cdot \mathbf{U}_1 + r_2 \cdot \mathbf{U}_2 + \cdots + r_n \cdot \mathbf{U}_n$, $\mathbf{W} = s_1 \cdot \mathbf{U}_1 + s_2 \cdot \mathbf{U}_2 + \cdots + s_n \cdot \mathbf{U}_n$. Then, if $\mathcal{B}$ is a bilinear mapping, it follows from Definition 31.1 that

$$\begin{aligned}\mathcal{B}(\mathbf{U}, \mathbf{W}) &= \mathcal{B}(r_1 \cdot \mathbf{U}_1 + r_2 \cdot \mathbf{U}_2 + \cdots + r_n \cdot \mathbf{U}_n, \\ &\qquad s_1 \cdot \mathbf{U}_1 + s_2 \cdot \mathbf{U}_2 + \cdots + s_n \cdot \mathbf{U}_n) \qquad (31\text{-}1) \\ &= \sum_{i,j=1}^{n} r_i s_j \mathcal{B}(\mathbf{U}_i, \mathbf{U}_j) = \sum_{i,j=1}^{n} r_i \mathcal{B}(\mathbf{U}_i, \mathbf{U}_j) s_j.\end{aligned}$$

Let $A = [a_{i,j}]$ be an n by n matrix such that $a_{i,j} = \mathcal{B}(\mathbf{U}_i, \mathbf{U}_j)$ for all i, j. Then by the definition of matrix multiplication, equation (31-1) can be written

$$\mathcal{B}(\mathbf{U}, \mathbf{W}) = \sum_{i,j=1}^{n} r_i a_{i,j} s_j = [r_1 \quad r_2 \quad . \; . \; . \quad r_n] A \begin{bmatrix} s_1 \\ s_2 \\ \cdot \\ \cdot \\ \cdot \\ s_n \end{bmatrix}. \qquad (31\text{-}2)$$

The matrix A is called the *matrix of* $\mathcal{B}$ with respect to the basis $\{\mathbf{U}_1, \mathbf{U}_2, \ldots, \mathbf{U}_n\}$. Strictly speaking, the right-hand side of equation (31-2) is the 1 by 1 matrix $[\mathcal{B}(\mathbf{U}, \mathbf{W})]$, which we have identified with the real number $\mathcal{B}(\mathbf{U}, \mathbf{W})$, its only element. In the expression for a bilinear mapping, this identification is convenient and causes no confusion.

If, throughout the discussion above, we take $\mathbf{W} = \mathbf{U}$, then the bilinear mapping $\mathcal{B}$ is restricted to pairs $\langle \mathbf{U}, \mathbf{U} \rangle$ of vectors $\mathbf{U} \in \mathcal{V}$. By (31-2) we have

$$\mathcal{B}(\mathbf{U}, \mathbf{U}) = \sum_{i,j=1}^{n} r_i a_{i,j} r_j = [r_1 \quad r_2 \quad . \; . \; . \quad r_n] A \begin{bmatrix} r_1 \\ r_2 \\ \cdot \\ \cdot \\ \cdot \\ r_n \end{bmatrix}. \qquad (31\text{-}3)$$

Such a restricted bilinear mapping is called a *quadratic mapping* of $\mathcal{V}$. Although each bilinear mapping $\mathcal{B}$ determines a unique quadratic mapping, different bilinear mappings may yield the same quadratic mapping. It follows from this observation that the matrix of a quadratic mapping is not unique (see Example 1).

Conversely, if $A = [a_{i,j}]$ is any n by n matrix, then equation (31-2) can be used to define a bilinear mapping $\mathcal{B}$, where $\langle r_1, r_2, \ldots, r_n \rangle$ and $\langle s_1, s_2, \ldots, s_n \rangle$ are the coordinates of $\mathbf{U}$ and $\mathbf{W}$, respectively, relative to a given basis $\{\mathbf{U}_1, \mathbf{U}_2, \ldots, \mathbf{U}_n\}$ of $\mathcal{V}$. Similarly, equation (31-3) can be used to define a quadratic mapping of $\mathcal{V}$.

Example 1. Let

$$A = [a_{i,j}] = \begin{bmatrix} 7 & 5 & -1 \\ 2 & 0 & 3 \\ 1 & -2 & 4 \end{bmatrix}$$

define a bilinear mapping $\mathcal{B}$ of ordered pairs of vectors in $\mathcal{V}_3$ with respect to the basis $E^{(3)}$. Then, for $\mathbf{U} = \langle r_1, r_2, r_3 \rangle$ and $\mathbf{W} = \langle s_1, s_2, s_3 \rangle$ in $\mathcal{V}_3$, we have

$$\mathcal{B}(\mathbf{U}, \mathbf{W}) = [r_1 \quad r_2 \quad r_3]\begin{bmatrix} 7 & 5 & -1 \\ 2 & 0 & 3 \\ 1 & -2 & 4 \end{bmatrix}\begin{bmatrix} s_1 \\ s_2 \\ s_3 \end{bmatrix}$$

$$= [7r_1 + 2r_2 + r_3 \quad 5r_1 - 2r_3 \quad -r_1 + 3r_2 + 4r_3]\begin{bmatrix} s_1 \\ s_2 \\ s_3 \end{bmatrix}$$

$$= 7r_1s_1 + 2r_2s_1 + r_3s_1 + 5r_1s_2 - 2r_3s_2 - r_1s_3 + 3r_2s_3 + 4r_3s_3.$$

If $\mathbf{U} = \langle 1, -6, 2\rangle$ and $\mathbf{W} = \langle -3, 5, 7\rangle$, then $\mathcal{B}(\mathbf{U}, \mathbf{W}) = -63$ and $\mathcal{B}(\mathbf{W}, \mathbf{U}) = 262$. Therefore, $\mathcal{B}$ is not symmetric. Also $\mathcal{B}(\mathbf{U}, \mathbf{U}) = -31$, so that $\mathcal{B}$ is not positive definite.

The corresponding quadratic mapping of $\mathcal{V}_3$ is given by

$$\mathcal{B}(\mathbf{U}, \mathbf{U}) = [r_1 \quad r_2 \quad r_3]\begin{bmatrix} 7 & 5 & -1 \\ 2 & 0 & 3 \\ 1 & -2 & 4 \end{bmatrix}\begin{bmatrix} r_1 \\ r_2 \\ r_3 \end{bmatrix}$$

$$= 7r_1^2 + 2r_2r_1 + r_3r_1 + 5r_1r_2 - 2r_3r_2 - r_1r_3 + 3r_2r_3 + 4r_3^2$$

$$= 7r_1^2 + 7r_1r_2 + r_2r_3 + 4r_3^2.$$

Note that this quadratic mapping can also be expressed by the matrix

$$\begin{bmatrix} 7 & 7 & 0 \\ 0 & 0 & 1 \\ 0 & 0 & 4 \end{bmatrix},$$

which defines a bilinear mapping $\mathcal{C}$ different from $\mathcal{B}$.

There is a second interpretation of bilinear and quadratic mappings that is important in applications. Let

$$\sum_{i,j=1}^{n} x_ia_{i,j}y_j = x_1a_{1,1}y_1 + x_1a_{1,2}y_2 + \cdots + x_1a_{1,n}y_n$$
$$+ x_2a_{2,1}y_1 + \cdots + x_na_{n,n}y_n$$

be a quadratic polynomial in $2n$ variables $x_1, x_2, \ldots, x_n$ and $y_1, y_2, \ldots, y_n$ with real coefficients $a_{i,j}$. Such a polynomial is called a *bilinear form.* If real numbers $r_1, r_2, \ldots, r_n$ and $s_1, s_2, \ldots, s_n$ are substituted for the variables $x_1, x_2, \ldots, x_n$ and $y_1, y_2, \ldots, y_n$, respectively, then $\sum_{i,j=1}^{n} r_ia_{i,j}s_j$ is a *value of the bilinear form.* Note that the value of a bilinear form is given by the same expression as $\mathcal{B}(\mathbf{U}, \mathbf{W})$ in equation (31-2). Therefore, each bilinear form defines a bilinear mapping. If $y_1 = x_1, y_2 = x_2, \ldots, y_n = x_n$, then $\sum_{i,j=1}^{n} x_ia_{i,j}y_j = \sum_{i,j=1}^{n} x_ia_{i,j}x_j$ is a quadratic polynomial in the n variables $x_1, x_2,$

$\ldots, x_n$, which is called a *quadratic form*. A *value of the quadratic form* is obtained by substituting real numbers $r_1, r_2, \ldots, r_n$ for the variables $x_1, x_2, \ldots, x_n$. A value of a quadratic form $\sum_{i,j=1}^{n} r_i a_{i,j} r_j$ is given by the same expression as $\mathcal{B}(\mathbf{U}, \mathbf{U})$ in equation (31-3), so that each quadratic form defines a quadratic mapping of $\mathcal{V}$.

Example 2. The bilinear and quadratic forms related to the bilinear mapping of Example 1 have the expressions

$$\sum_{i,j=1}^{3} x_i a_{i,j} y_j = 7x_1y_1 + 2x_2y_1 + x_3y_1 + 5x_1y_2 - 2x_3y_2 - x_1y_3 + 3x_2y_3 + 4x_3y_3$$

$$\sum_{i,j=1}^{3} x_i a_{i,j} x_j = 7x_1^2 + 7x_1x_2 + x_2x_3 + 4x_3^2.$$

Quadratic forms occur in analytic geometry in the equations of central conics in a plane and central quadric surfaces in three-dimensional space. For example, $ax^2 + bxy + cy^2 = k$ is the equation of a conic with center at the origin of a rectangular Cartesian coordinate system in a plane. This equation can be regarded as the equation of all vectors $\mathbf{U} \in \mathcal{E}_2$ that have coordinates $\langle r_1, r_2 \rangle$ for which the value of the quadratic form $ax^2 + bxy + cy^2$ is the number k. Such vectors are represented by directed line segments $\overrightarrow{OP}$ with initial point at the origin O and terminal point P on the conic (Figure 30). Similarly, $ax^2 + bxy + cy^2 + dxz + eyz + fz^2 = k$ is the equation of a quadric surface with its center at the origin in three-dimensional space. Quadratic forms also have important applications in other fields, including statistics, differential geometry, and mechanics.

FIGURE 30

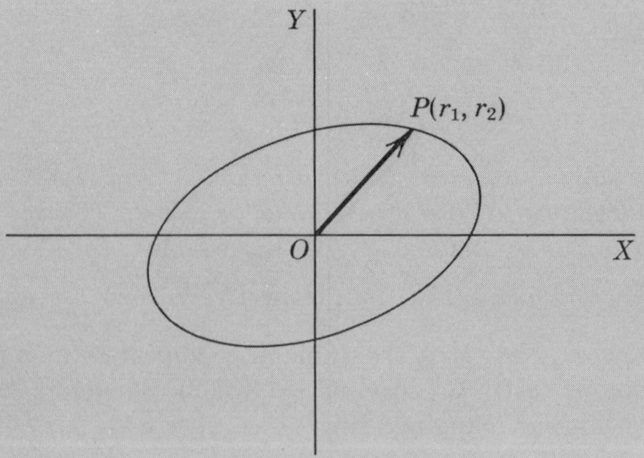

Suppose that $\{\mathbf{W}_1, \mathbf{W}_2, \ldots, \mathbf{W}_n\}$ is a second basis of $\mathcal{V}$ and that $P = [p_{i,j}]$ is the matrix of the change of basis from the basis $\{\mathbf{U}_1, \mathbf{U}_2, \ldots, \mathbf{U}_n\}$ to this new basis. Then

$$[r_1 \quad r_2 \quad \ldots \quad r_n] = [\bar{r}_1 \quad \bar{r}_2 \quad \ldots \quad \bar{r}_n]P, \quad \text{and} \quad \begin{bmatrix} s_1 \\ s_2 \\ \cdot \\ \cdot \\ \cdot \\ s_n \end{bmatrix} = P' \begin{bmatrix} \bar{s}_1 \\ \bar{s}_2 \\ \cdot \\ \cdot \\ \cdot \\ \bar{s}_n \end{bmatrix},$$

where $\langle \bar{r}_1, \bar{r}_2, \ldots, \bar{r}_n \rangle$ and $\langle \bar{s}_1, \bar{s}_2, \ldots, \bar{s}_n \rangle$ are the coordinates of $\mathbf{U}$ and $\mathbf{W}$, respectively, with respect to the second basis [see equations (19-3) and (19-4)]. Substituting in equation (31-2), we obtain

$$\mathcal{B}(\mathbf{U}, \mathbf{W}) = [\bar{r}_1 \quad \bar{r}_2 \quad \ldots \quad \bar{r}_n]PAP' \begin{bmatrix} \bar{s}_1 \\ \bar{s}_2 \\ \cdot \\ \cdot \\ \cdot \\ \bar{s}_n \end{bmatrix}. \tag{31-4}$$

Thus, the matrix of $\mathcal{B}$ with respect to the basis $\{\mathbf{W}_1, \mathbf{W}_2, \ldots, \mathbf{W}_n\}$ is PAP'. If, in particular, $\mathcal{V}$ is a Euclidean vector space and the two given bases are orthonormal, then P is an orthogonal matrix. In this case, $PAP' = Q^{-1}AQ$, where $Q = P' = P^{-1}$. That is, the two matrices of $\mathcal{B}$ are orthogonally equivalent.

(31.2) **Definition.** Let A and B be n by n matrices. The matrix B is *congruent* to the matrix A if there exists a nonsingular n by n matrix P such that $B = PAP'$.

Congruence is an equivalence relation on the set $\mathfrak{A}_n$ of all real n by n matrices. Orthogonal equivalence, which is a special case of similarity, is also a special case of congruence. For if $B = Q^{-1}AQ$, where Q is orthogonal, then $B = PAP'$, where $P = Q^{-1} = Q'$.

These results show that a discussion of the simplification of the expressions for bilinear and quadratic mappings by a change of basis in $\mathcal{V}$ will be concerned with the reduction of matrices under the relations of congruence and orthogonal equivalence. If we limit our discussion to symmetric bilinear and quadratic mappings, it is sufficient to study the effect of these relations on a special class of n by n matrices.

In the expression (31-3) for a quadratic mapping, the terms $r_i a_{i,j} r_j$ and $r_j a_{j,i} r_i$ with $i \neq j$ occur in pairs. The value of the mapping for each vector $\mathbf{U} \in \mathcal{V}$ is unchanged if, for each such pair, we write

$$r_i a_{i,j} r_j + r_j a_{j,i} r_i = r_i \left(\frac{a_{i,j} + a_{j,i}}{2} \right) r_j + r_j \left(\frac{a_{i,j} + a_{j,i}}{2} \right) r_i.$$

Consequently, if $B = [b_{i,j}]$ is an n by n matrix such that $b_{i,j} = b_{j,i} = (a_{i,j} + a_{j,i})/2$ for all pairs i, j, then

$$\mathcal{B}(\mathbf{U}, \mathbf{U}) = \sum_{i,j=1}^{n} r_i b_{i,j} r_j = [r_1 \quad r_2 \quad . \; . \; . \quad r_n] B \begin{bmatrix} r_1 \\ r_2 \\ \cdot \\ \cdot \\ \cdot \\ r_n \end{bmatrix}.$$

An n by n matrix $B = [b_{i,j}]$ such that $b_{i,j} = b_{j,i}$ for $i = 1, 2, \ldots, n$ and $j = 1, 2, \ldots, n$ is called a *symmetric matrix*. Thus, each quadratic mapping and the related quadratic form can be expressed in terms of a symmetric matrix.

Example 3. The quadratic form of Example 2 can be written

$$\begin{aligned} \sum_{i,j=1}^{3} x_i a_{i,j} x_j &= 7x_1^2 + 7x_1x_2 + x_2x_3 + 4x_3^2 \\ &= 7x_1^2 + \tfrac{7}{2}x_1x_2 + \tfrac{7}{2}x_2x_1 + \tfrac{1}{2}x_2x_3 + \tfrac{1}{2}x_3x_2 + 4x_3^2 \\ &= [x_1 \quad x_2 \quad x_3] \begin{bmatrix} 7 & \tfrac{7}{2} & 0 \\ \tfrac{7}{2} & 0 & \tfrac{1}{2} \\ 0 & \tfrac{1}{2} & 4 \end{bmatrix} \begin{bmatrix} x_1 \\ x_2 \\ x_3 \end{bmatrix} = [x_1 \quad x_2 \quad x_3] B \begin{bmatrix} x_1 \\ x_2 \\ x_3 \end{bmatrix}, \end{aligned}$$

where B is a symmetric matrix.

Clearly, an n by n matrix B is symmetric if and only if $B' = B$. If B is symmetric and P is any n by n matrix, then PBP' is again symmetric. Indeed, $(PBP')' = (P')'B'P' = PBP'$. Each quadratic mapping of $\mathcal{V}$ can be written with a symmetric matrix B. A change of basis in $\mathcal{V}$ replaces B by the symmetric matrix PBP', which is congruent to B. Thus, our discussion of the simplification of the expression for a quadratic mapping amounts to a study of the relation of congruence on the set of real symmetric matrices.

Exercises

31.1 Let $A = [a_{i,j}]$ be an n by n matrix. Prove that a mapping $\mathcal{B}$ of ordered pairs of vectors in a vector space $\mathcal{V}$ of dimension n, defined by equation (31-2), is a bilinear mapping.

***31.2** Let $\mathcal{B}$ be a bilinear mapping with matrix A with respect to some basis of $\mathcal{V}$. Prove that $\mathcal{B}$ is a symmetric mapping, that is, $\mathcal{B}(\mathbf{U}, \mathbf{W}) = \mathcal{B}(\mathbf{W}, \mathbf{U})$ for all $\mathbf{U}, \mathbf{W} \in \mathcal{V}$, if and only if A is a symmetric matrix.

31.3 Let $\mathcal{B}$ be a bilinear mapping with matrix A with respect to some basis of $\mathcal{V}$. Let L be the linear transformation of $\mathcal{V}$ with matrix A with respect to this basis. If $\mathbf{U}$ has coordinates $\langle r_1, r_2, \ldots, r_n\rangle$ and $L(\mathbf{W})$ has coordinates $\langle \bar{s}_1, \bar{s}_2, \ldots, \bar{s}_n\rangle$, show that $\mathcal{B}(\mathbf{U}, \mathbf{W}) = r_1\bar{s}_1 + r_2\bar{s}_2 + \cdots + r_n\bar{s}_n$.

31.4 Write out the quadratic forms with the following matrices:

$$\begin{bmatrix} -3 & 2 & 1 \\ 6 & 0 & 2 \\ -1 & 2 & 4 \end{bmatrix}; \qquad \begin{bmatrix} -3 & 8 & 0 \\ 0 & 0 & 4 \\ 0 & 0 & 4 \end{bmatrix}; \qquad \begin{bmatrix} -3 & 4 & 0 \\ 4 & 0 & 2 \\ 0 & 2 & 4 \end{bmatrix}.$$

Express the quadratic form $x_1^2 - 2x_1x_3 - 6x_2^2 + 3x_2x_3 + x_2x_4 + 5x_3^2 - x_3x_4 + x_4^2$ with at least three different matrices.

31.5 Prove that congruence is an equivalence relation on the set $\mathfrak{A}_n$ of all real n by n matrices.

31.6 Express the following quadratic forms with symmetric matrices: $x_1^2 + \sqrt{2}\, x_1x_2 - 5x_2^2$; $3x_1^2 + 5x_1x_2 - 7x_1x_3 + x_2x_3 - 4x_2^2 - x_3^2$; $x_1x_2 + x_1x_3 + x_1x_4 + x_2x_3 + x_2x_4 + x_3x_4$.

31.7 (a) Let A be an m by n matrix. Show that AA' and $A'A$ are symmetric matrices. (b) Let A be an n by n matrix. Show that $A + A'$ is symmetric.

31.8 Let

$$B = \begin{bmatrix} 7 & \frac{7}{2} & 0 \\ \frac{7}{2} & 0 & \frac{1}{2} \\ 0 & \frac{1}{2} & 4 \end{bmatrix} \quad\text{and}\quad P = \begin{bmatrix} \frac{1}{\sqrt{7}} & 0 & 0 \\ 0 & 0 & \frac{1}{2} \\ \frac{-2}{\sqrt{29}} & \frac{4}{\sqrt{29}} & \frac{-1}{2\sqrt{29}} \end{bmatrix}.$$

Show that

$$PBP' = \begin{bmatrix} 1 & 0 & 0 \\ 0 & 1 & 0 \\ 0 & 0 & -1 \end{bmatrix}.$$

Hence show that $7x_1^2 + 7x_1x_2 + x_2x_3 + 4x_3^2 = y_1^2 + y_2^2 - y_3^2$, where $[x_1 \quad x_2 \quad x_3] = [y_1 \quad y_2 \quad y_3]P$.

32 Orthogonal reduction of real symmetric matrices

The key result in the theory of the reduction of real symmetric matrices by orthogonal equivalence is the fact that the characteristic roots of a real symmetric matrix are real. In order to prove this result, we utilize the following properties of complex numbers, which are probably familiar to the reader. Recall that if $c = x + iy$ is a complex number, then the *conjugate* of c is the complex number $\bar{c} = x - iy$.

(32.1) Let c and d be complex numbers. Then (a) $\overline{c + d} = \bar{c} + \bar{d}$; (b) $\overline{cd} = \bar{c}\bar{d}$; (c) $\bar{\bar{c}} = c$; (d) c is a real number if and only if $c = \bar{c}$; (e) $c\bar{c}$ is a nonnegative real number and $c\bar{c} = 0$ if and only if $c = 0$.

(32.2) Theorem. The characteristic roots of a real symmetric matrix are real.

PROOF. Let $A = [a_{i,j}]$ be a real symmetric n by n matrix, and let r be a characteristic root of A. Then $|A - r \cdot I_n| = 0$. Regard the matrix $A - r \cdot I_n$ as a matrix whose elements are complex numbers. (In fact, if r is not real, the diagonal elements of $A - r \cdot I_n$ are not real.) The results of Chapter Three on the solutions of systems of homogeneous equations still hold if the matrix of coefficients of the system has complex numbers as elements. Therefore, since $|A - r \cdot I_n| = 0$, the system of equations $(A - r \cdot I_n)X = \mathbf{O}$ has a nontrivial solution

$$X = C = \begin{bmatrix} c_1 \\ c_2 \\ \cdot \\ \cdot \\ \cdot \\ c_n \end{bmatrix},$$

where the c_i are complex numbers. The equation $(A - r \cdot I_n)C = \mathbf{O}$ implies $AC = r \cdot C$. Now consider the complex number

$$m = \sum_{i,j=1}^{n} \bar{c}_i a_{i,j} c_j = [\bar{c}_1 \quad \bar{c}_2 \quad \dots \quad \bar{c}_n] A \begin{bmatrix} c_1 \\ c_2 \\ \cdot \\ \cdot \\ \cdot \\ c_n \end{bmatrix},$$

where each $\bar{c}_i$ is the conjugate of c_i. We have

$$\bar{m} = \overline{\sum_{i,j=1}^{n} \bar{c}_i a_{i,j} c_j} = \sum_{i,j=1}^{n} \overline{\bar{c}_i a_{i,j} c_j} = \sum_{i,j=1}^{n} \bar{\bar{c}}_i \bar{a}_{i,j} \bar{c}_j = \sum_{i,j=1}^{n} c_i a_{i,j} \bar{c}_j,$$

using (a), (b), (c), and (d) of 32.1. Moreover,

$$\bar{m} = \sum_{i,j=1}^{n} c_i a_{i,j} \bar{c}_j = \sum_{j,i=1}^{n} c_i a_{i,j} \bar{c}_j = \sum_{j,i=1}^{n} \bar{c}_j a_{i,j} c_i = \sum_{j,i=1}^{n} \bar{c}_j a_{j,i} c_i = \sum_{i,j=1}^{n} \bar{c}_i a_{i,j} c_j = m,$$

since $a_{i,j} = a_{j,i}$ for all pairs i, j. However, by 32.1(d), $\bar{m} = m$ implies that m is a real number. Using the equation $AC = r \cdot C$, we find

$$m = [\bar{c}_1 \quad \bar{c}_2 \quad . \; . \; . \quad \bar{c}_n](AC) = [\bar{c}_1 \quad \bar{c}_2 \quad . \; . \; . \quad \bar{c}_n](r \cdot C)$$
$$= r([\bar{c}_1 \quad \bar{c}_2 \quad . \; . \; . \quad \bar{c}_n]C).$$

By 32.1(e) and the fact that at least one $c_i \neq 0$, the product $[\bar{c}_1 \quad \bar{c}_2 \quad . \; . \; . \; \bar{c}_n]C = \bar{c}_1 c_1 + \bar{c}_2 c_2 + \cdots + \bar{c}_n c_n = s$ is a positive real number. Thus, $m = rs$, and $r = m/s$, where m and $s \neq 0$ are real. Therefore r is real.

(**32.3**) **Theorem.** Let A be a real symmetric n by n matrix. There exists an orthogonal matrix P such that

$$P^{-1}AP = \begin{bmatrix} r_1 & 0 & \cdots & 0 \\ 0 & r_2 & & \cdot \\ \cdot & & \cdot & \cdot \\ \cdot & & \cdot & \cdot \\ \cdot & & \cdot & 0 \\ 0 & \cdots & 0 & r_n \end{bmatrix} = D,$$

where $r_1, r_2, \ldots, r_n$ are the characteristic roots of A.

PROOF. By Theorems 30.5 and 32.2, there exists an orthogonal matrix P such that

$$P^{-1}AP = \begin{bmatrix} r_1 & b^*_{1,2} & \cdots & b^*_{1,n} \\ 0 & r_2 & & b^*_{2,n} \\ \cdot & & \cdot & \cdot \\ \cdot & & \cdot & \cdot \\ \cdot & & \cdot & \cdot \\ & & & b^*_{n-1,n} \\ 0 & \cdots & 0 & r_n \end{bmatrix},$$

where $r_1, r_2, \ldots, r_n$ are the characteristic roots of A. Since A is symmetric and $P^{-1} = P'$, it follows that $P^{-1}AP$ is symmetric. Therefore, the elements above the diagonal of $P^{-1}AP$ must be 0, which proves the theorem.

(32.4) Corollary. Two real symmetric matrices are orthogonally equivalent if and only if they have the same characteristic roots.

PROOF. Let A and B be n by n real symmetric matrices. If A and B are orthogonally equivalent, then they are similar. By Theorem 28.4, they have the same characteristic roots. Conversely, if A and B have the same characteristic roots, they are orthogonally equivalent to the same diagonal matrix D, by Theorem 32.3. Thus, $P^{-1}AP = Q^{-1}BQ$ for orthogonal matrices P and Q. Therefore, $B = (QP^{-1})A(PQ^{-1}) = (PQ^{-1})^{-1}A(PQ^{-1})$, where PQ^{-1} is an orthogonal matrix. That is, B is orthogonally equivalent to A.

The method for constructing the orthogonal matrix P of Theorem 32.3 is a modification of the method discussed in Section 29 for finding a nonsingular matrix Q such that $Q^{-1}AQ$ is a diagonal matrix.

Let A be an n by n symmetric matrix, and suppose that A is the matrix of a linear transformation L of $\mathcal{V}_n$ into itself with respect to the basis $E^{(n)}$. By Theorem 32.3, there exists an orthogonal matrix $P = [p_{i,j}]$ such that $AP = PD$, where D is a diagonal matrix with the characteristic values of L on the diagonal. Therefore, for $j = 1, 2, \ldots, n$,

$$A\begin{bmatrix} p_{1,j} \\ p_{2,j} \\ \cdot \\ \cdot \\ \cdot \\ p_{n,j} \end{bmatrix} = P\begin{bmatrix} 0 \\ \cdot \\ \cdot \\ \cdot \\ 0 \\ r_j \\ 0 \\ \cdot \\ \cdot \\ \cdot \\ 0 \end{bmatrix} = r_j \cdot \begin{bmatrix} p_{1,j} \\ p_{2,j} \\ \cdot \\ \cdot \\ \cdot \\ p_{n,j} \end{bmatrix}. \qquad (32\text{-}1)$$

The columns of P can be regarded as vectors in $\mathcal{V}_n$. Hence, by (32-1), the jth column of P is a characteristic vector of L, which belongs to the characteristic value r_j, for $j = 1, 2, \ldots, n$. Since P is an orthogonal matrix, these characteristic vectors form an orthonormal basis of $\mathcal{V}_n$. (By Example 1, Section 9, the n-tuple space $\mathcal{V}_n$ is a Euclidean vector space.) Conversely, suppose that $P = [p_{i,j}]$ is an n by n matrix whose columns form an orthonormal basis of $\mathcal{V}_n$ such that the jth column of P is a characteristic vector of L belonging to the characteristic value r_j, for $j = 1, 2, \ldots, n$.

Then equation (32-1) is satisfied, which implies that $P^{-1}AP = D$.

Example 1. Let

$$A = \begin{bmatrix} 53/18 & 2/9 & 1/18 \\ 2/9 & 19/9 & -2/9 \\ 1/18 & -2/9 & 53/18 \end{bmatrix}.$$

Then $|A - x \cdot I_3| = -(x-3)^2(x-2)$. Thus, the characteristic roots of A are 3, 3, 2. According to the preceding discussion, there is an orthonorm al basis of $\mathcal{V}_3$ consisting of characteristic vectors of the linear transformation detern ined by A, two of which belong to the repeated root 3 and one that belongs to 2. For the repeated root 3, the system of equations for the characteristic vectors is

$$\begin{bmatrix} -1/18 & 2/9 & 1/18 \\ 2/9 & -8/9 & -2/9 \\ 1/18 & -2/9 & -1/18 \end{bmatrix} \begin{bmatrix} x_1 \\ x_2 \\ x_3 \end{bmatrix} = \begin{bmatrix} 0 \\ 0 \\ 0 \end{bmatrix},$$

which is equivalent to the system

$$\begin{bmatrix} 1 & -4 & -1 \\ 0 & 0 & 0 \\ 0 & 0 & 0 \end{bmatrix} \begin{bmatrix} x_1 \\ x_2 \\ x_3 \end{bmatrix} = \begin{bmatrix} 0 \\ 0 \\ 0 \end{bmatrix}.$$

This system has the solution $\langle x_1, x_2, x_3 \rangle = \langle 4r + s, r, s \rangle$ for any real numbers r and s. Selecting $r = 0$, $s = 1$ and $r = -1/2$, $s = 1$, we obtain the orthogonal vectors $\langle 1, 0, 1 \rangle$ and $\langle -1, -1/2, 1 \rangle$. Then $(1/\sqrt{2}) \cdot \langle 1, 0, 1 \rangle$ and $(2/3) \cdot \langle -1, -1/2, 1 \rangle$ are orthogonal unit vectors. For the characteristic root 2, the system of equations for the characteristic vectors is

$$\begin{bmatrix} 17/18 & 2/9 & 1/18 \\ 2/9 & 1/9 & -2/9 \\ 1/18 & -2/9 & 17/18 \end{bmatrix} \begin{bmatrix} x_1 \\ x_2 \\ x_3 \end{bmatrix} = \begin{bmatrix} 0 \\ 0 \\ 0 \end{bmatrix}.$$

The solution of this system is $\langle x_1, x_2, x_3 \rangle = \langle -r, 4r, r \rangle$, for any real number r. Choosing $r = 1/3\sqrt{2}$, we obtain a characteristic unit vector $(1/3\sqrt{2}) \cdot \langle -1, 4, 1 \rangle$ belonging to 2. This vector is orthogonal to the characteristic vectors that belong o 3 (see Exercise 32.1). Thus, the set of vectors $\{(1/\sqrt{2}) \cdot \langle 1, 0, 1 \rangle, (2/3) \cdot \langle -1, -1/2 \quad \rangle,$ $(1/3\sqrt{2}) \cdot \langle -1, 4, 1 \rangle\}$ is an orthonormal basis of $\mathcal{V}_3$ of the type described in he preceding paragraph. Therefore, the orthogonal matrix

$$P = \begin{bmatrix} \frac{1}{\sqrt{2}} & -\frac{2}{3} & -\frac{1}{3\sqrt{2}} \\ 0 & -\frac{1}{3} & \frac{2\sqrt{2}}{3} \\ \frac{1}{\sqrt{2}} & \frac{2}{3} & \frac{1}{3\sqrt{2}} \end{bmatrix}$$

is a matrix such that

$$P^{-1}AP = \begin{bmatrix} 3 & 0 & 0 \\ 0 & 3 & 0 \\ 0 & 0 & 2 \end{bmatrix}.$$

Example 1 illustrates the general method for finding an orthogonal matrix P that reduces a symmetric matrix A to diagonal form. If $r = r_{i_1} = r_{i_2} = \cdots = r_{i_s}$ is a repeated characteristic root of A, then the matrix of coefficients of the homogeneous system of equations whose solutions are the characteristic vectors belonging to r has rank $n - s$ (see Exercise 32.3). Then the dimension of the subspace of $\mathcal{V}_n$ consisting of the solutions of this system of equations is $n - (n - s) = s$ (see Theorem 12.4). By Theorem 9.6, this subspace has an orthonormal basis. Thus, there are s mutually orthogonal characteristic vectors that belong to r. Since characteristic vectors belonging to distinct characteristic roots are orthogonal (see Exercise 32.1), we can find an orthonormal basis of $\mathcal{V}_n$ of the type required to construct the orthogonal matrix P.

We now apply Theorem 32.3 to quadratic mappings and forms.

(32.5) **Theorem.** Let $\mathcal{B}$ be a quadratic mapping of a Euclidean vector space $\mathcal{E}$ that has a symmetric matrix A with respect to an orthonormal basis $\{\mathbf{U}_1, \mathbf{U}_2, \ldots, \mathbf{U}_n\}$ of $\mathcal{E}$. There exists an orthonormal basis $\{\mathbf{W}_1, \mathbf{W}_2, \ldots, \mathbf{W}_n\}$ of $\mathcal{E}$ such that for $\mathbf{U} = a_1 \cdot \mathbf{W}_1 + a_2 \cdot \mathbf{W}_2 + \cdots + a_n \cdot \mathbf{W}_n \in \mathcal{E}$,

$$\mathcal{B}(\mathbf{U},\mathbf{U}) = r_1a_1^2 + r_2a_2^2 + \cdots + r_na_n^2,$$

where $r_1, r_2, \ldots, r_n$ are the characteristic roots of A.

PROOF. By Theorem 32.3, there is an orthogonal matrix P such that

$$P^{-1}AP = D = \begin{bmatrix} r_1 & 0 & \cdots & 0 \\ 0 & r_2 & & \vdots \\ \vdots & & \ddots & \vdots \\ \vdots & & & 0 \\ 0 & \cdots & 0 & r_n \end{bmatrix},$$

where $r_1, r_2, \ldots, r_n$ are the characteristic roots of A. Let the orthogonal matrix P^{-1} be the matrix of a change of basis from $\{\mathbf{U}_1, \mathbf{U}_2, \ldots, \mathbf{U}_n\}$ to a new basis $\{\mathbf{W}_1, \mathbf{W}_2, \ldots, \mathbf{W}_n\}$. Then the matrix of $\mathcal{B}$ with respect to this new basis is $P^{-1}A(P^{-1})' = P^{-1}AP = D$. Therefore

$$\mathcal{B}(\mathbf{U}, \mathbf{U}) = [a_1 \quad a_2 \quad \ldots \quad a_n]D\begin{bmatrix} a_1 \\ a_2 \\ \cdot \\ \cdot \\ \cdot \\ a_n \end{bmatrix} = r_1a_1^2 + r_2a_2^2 + \cdots + r_na_n^2.$$

(32.6) Theorem. Let $\sum_{i,j=1}^{n} x_ia_{i,j}x_j$ be a real quadratic form, where $A = [a_{i,j}]$ is a symmetric matrix with characteristic roots $r_1, r_2, \ldots, r_n$. There exists an orthogonal matrix Q such that

$$\sum_{i,j=1}^{n} x_ia_{i,j}x_j = r_1y_1^2 + r_2y_2^2 + \cdots + r_ny_n^2,$$

where $[x_1 \quad x_2 \quad \ldots \quad x_n] = [y_1 \quad y_2 \quad \ldots \quad y_n]Q$.

The proof of Theorem 32.6 is a direct application of Theorem 32.3 and is left as an exercise (Exercise 32.6).

Example 2. Let $\sum_{i,j=1}^{3} x_ia_{i,j}x_j$ be the quadratic form with the matrix $A = [a_{i,j}]$ of Example 1. Let P be the orthogonal matrix obtained in Example 1 such that

$$P^{-1}AP = \begin{bmatrix} 3 & 0 & 0 \\ 0 & 3 & 0 \\ 0 & 0 & 2 \end{bmatrix}.$$

Let $Q = P^{-1} = P'$, and let $[x_1 \quad x_2 \quad x_3] = [y_1 \quad y_2 \quad y_3]Q$. Then

$$\sum_{i,j=1}^{3} x_ia_{i,j}x_j = [x_1 \quad x_2 \quad x_3]A\begin{bmatrix} x_1 \\ x_2 \\ x_3 \end{bmatrix} = [y_1 \quad y_2 \quad y_3]QAQ'\begin{bmatrix} y_1 \\ y_2 \\ y_3 \end{bmatrix}$$

$$= [y_1 \quad y_2 \quad y_3]P^{-1}AP\begin{bmatrix} y_1 \\ y_2 \\ y_3 \end{bmatrix} = [y_1 \quad y_2 \quad y_3]\begin{bmatrix} 3 & 0 & 0 \\ 0 & 3 & 0 \\ 0 & 0 & 2 \end{bmatrix}\begin{bmatrix} y_1 \\ y_2 \\ y_3 \end{bmatrix}$$

$$= 3y_1^2 + 3y_2^2 + 2y_3^2.$$

Example 3. A central quadric surface, $ax^2 + bxy + cy^2 + dxz + eyz + fz^2 = k$, is said to be *referred to principal axes* if a new rectangular Cartesian coordinate system is chosen so that the equation of the quadric surface is $r_1\bar{x}^2 + r_2\bar{y}^2 + r_3\bar{z}^2 = k$. The lengths of the *semiaxes* of the quadric surface are $\sqrt{|k/r_i|}$, $i = 1, 2, 3$. The orthogonal matrix P that reduces the symmetric matrix

$$A = \begin{bmatrix} a & \frac{b}{2} & \frac{d}{2} \\ \frac{b}{2} & c & \frac{e}{2} \\ \frac{d}{2} & \frac{e}{2} & f \end{bmatrix}$$

of the quadratic form $ax^2 + bxy + cy^2 + dxz + eyz + fz^2$ to diagonal form defines a change of coordinates $[\bar{x} \quad \bar{y} \quad \bar{z}] = [x \quad y \quad z]P$ to a new rectangular Cartesian coordinate system. Thus, to find the equation of the quadric surface when referred to principal axes, it is sufficient to find the characteristic roots r_1, r_2, r_3 of the matrix A. Similar remarks apply to central conics in a plane.

The quadric surface $\frac{53}{18}x^2 + \frac{4}{9}xy + \frac{19}{9}y^2 + \frac{1}{9}xz + (-\frac{4}{9})yz + \frac{53}{18}z^2 = k$ has as the matrix of its quadratic form, the matrix A of Example 1. Hence, there is a new rectangular Cartesian coordinate system defined by $[\bar{x} \quad \bar{y} \quad \bar{z}] = [x \quad y \quad z]P$, where P is the orthogonal matrix obtained in Example 1, such that the equation of the quadric surface is $3\bar{x}^2 + 3\bar{y}^2 + 2\bar{z}^2 = k$. The lengths of the semiaxes are $\sqrt{|k/3|}$, $\sqrt{|k/3|}$, and $\sqrt{|k/2|}$. In this case, if $k > 0$, the surface is an ellipsoid, if $k = 0$, the surface consists of a single point, and if $k < 0$, the surface is imaginary.

Exercises

32.1 Prove that characteristic vectors belonging to distinct characteristic roots of a symmetric matrix A are orthogonal.

32.2 In Example 1, use matrix multiplication to check that

$$P^{-1}AP = \begin{bmatrix} 3 & 0 & 0 \\ 0 & 3 & 0 \\ 0 & 0 & 2 \end{bmatrix}.$$

***32.3** Prove that if r is a characteristic root of an n by n symmetric matrix A that is repeated s times, then the matrix $A - r \cdot I_n$ has rank $n - s$.

32.4 Find an orthogonal matrix P such that $P^{-1}AP$ is a diagonal matrix for the following symmetric matrices A:

$$\begin{bmatrix} 4 & 0 & 0 \\ 0 & -3 & 1 \\ 0 & 1 & 2 \end{bmatrix}; \qquad \begin{bmatrix} 0 & 0 & 0 & 1 \\ 0 & 0 & 2 & 0 \\ 0 & 2 & 0 & 0 \\ 1 & 0 & 0 & 0 \end{bmatrix}; \qquad \begin{bmatrix} 1 & \frac{3}{\sqrt{2}} & \frac{-3}{\sqrt{2}} \\ \frac{3}{\sqrt{2}} & \frac{-1}{2} & \frac{-3}{2} \\ \frac{-3}{\sqrt{2}} & \frac{-3}{2} & \frac{-1}{2} \end{bmatrix}.$$

32.5 Refer the following conics and quadric surfaces to principal axes and find their semiaxes:

$10x^2 + 4xy + 7y^2 = 100;$ $\quad x^2 + 5xy - 11y^2 = 4;$

$-x^2 - 2\sqrt{3}\,xz - 4yz + 3z^2 = 25;$ $\quad x^2 - 2y^2 + 6yz + 4z^2 = 1.$

32.6 Prove Theorem 32.6.

33 Congruent reduction of real symmetric matrices

In this section we find a set of canonical matrices for real symmetric matrices under the relation of congruence. Let $D_t^{(s)}$ be an n by n diagonal matrix, with $0 \leq s \leq t \leq n$, such that the first s diagonal elements are 1, the next $t - s$ diagonal elements are -1, and the remaining $n - t$ diagonal elements are 0. For example, if $n = 2$,

$$D_0^{(0)} = \begin{bmatrix} 0 & 0 \\ 0 & 0 \end{bmatrix}, \quad D_1^{(0)} = \begin{bmatrix} -1 & 0 \\ 0 & 0 \end{bmatrix}, \quad D_1^{(1)} = \begin{bmatrix} 1 & 0 \\ 0 & 0 \end{bmatrix},$$

$$D_2^{(0)} = \begin{bmatrix} -1 & 0 \\ 0 & -1 \end{bmatrix}, \quad D_2^{(1)} = \begin{bmatrix} 1 & 0 \\ 0 & -1 \end{bmatrix}, \quad \text{and} \quad D_2^{(2)} = \begin{bmatrix} 1 & 0 \\ 0 & 1 \end{bmatrix}.$$

If $n = 3$, there are ten $D_t^{(s)}$ matrices.

(33.1) **Theorem.** Let A be a real symmetric n by n matrix. There exists a nonsingular matrix P such that $PAP' = D_t^{(s)}$, where t is the rank of A and s is the number of positive characteristic roots of A.

PROOF. By Theorem 32.3, there exists an orthogonal matrix Q_1 such that $Q_1^{-1}AQ_1 = D$, where D is the diagonal matrix with the characteristic roots $r_1, r_2, \ldots, r_n$ of A on the diagonal. Clearly, the rank of D is equal to the number of nonzero characteristic roots. Moreover, A is equivalent to D. Therefore, if A has rank t, then D has rank t and there are exactly t nonzero characteristic roots. We may assume that $r_1, r_2, \ldots, r_s$ are positive, $r_{s+1}, r_{s+2}, \ldots, r_t$ are negative, and $r_{t+1}, r_{t+2}, \ldots, r_n$ are zero. Let Q_2 be the n by n diagonal matrix that has $1/\sqrt{r_i}$ for $i = 1, 2, \ldots, s$ in the first s positions on the diagonal, $1/\sqrt{-r_i}$ for $i = s + 1, s + 2, \ldots, t$ in the next $t - s$ diagonal positions, and 1 in the remaining places on the diagonal. Then Q_2 is nonsingular and symmetric. We have $Q_2DQ_2' = Q_2DQ_2 = D_t^{(s)}$, where t is the rank of A and s is the number of positive characteristic roots of A. Let $P = Q_2Q_1^{-1}$. Then $P' = (Q_1^{-1})'Q_2' = Q_1Q_2'$, since Q_1 is orthogonal. Therefore,

$$PAP' = Q_2Q_1^{-1}AQ_1Q_2' = Q_2DQ_2' = D_t^{(s)}.$$

Example 1. Let A be the matrix of Example 1, Section 32. Then the matrix Q_1 of Theorem 33.1 is

$$\begin{bmatrix} \frac{1}{\sqrt{2}} & \frac{-2}{3} & \frac{-1}{3\sqrt{2}} \\ 0 & \frac{-1}{3} & \frac{2\sqrt{2}}{3} \\ \frac{1}{\sqrt{2}} & \frac{2}{3} & \frac{1}{3\sqrt{2}} \end{bmatrix}, \quad \text{and} \quad Q_1^{-1}AQ_1 = \begin{bmatrix} 3 & 0 & 0 \\ 0 & 3 & 0 \\ 0 & 0 & 2 \end{bmatrix}.$$

The matrix Q_2 of Theorem 33.1 is the diagonal matrix

$$\begin{bmatrix} \frac{1}{\sqrt{3}} & 0 & 0 \\ 0 & \frac{1}{\sqrt{3}} & 0 \\ 0 & 0 & \frac{1}{\sqrt{2}} \end{bmatrix}.$$

Therefore,

$$P = Q_2Q_1^{-1} = \begin{bmatrix} \frac{1}{\sqrt{3}} & 0 & 0 \\ 0 & \frac{1}{\sqrt{3}} & 0 \\ 0 & 0 & \frac{1}{\sqrt{2}} \end{bmatrix} \begin{bmatrix} \frac{1}{\sqrt{2}} & 0 & \frac{1}{\sqrt{2}} \\ \frac{-2}{3} & \frac{-1}{3} & \frac{2}{3} \\ \frac{-1}{3\sqrt{2}} & \frac{2\sqrt{2}}{3} & \frac{1}{3\sqrt{2}} \end{bmatrix}$$

$$= \begin{bmatrix} \frac{1}{\sqrt{6}} & 0 & \frac{1}{\sqrt{6}} \\ \frac{-2}{3\sqrt{3}} & \frac{-1}{3\sqrt{3}} & \frac{2}{3\sqrt{3}} \\ \frac{-1}{6} & \frac{2}{3} & \frac{1}{6} \end{bmatrix}.$$

Then, for this matrix P,

$$PAP' = \begin{bmatrix} 1 & 0 & 0 \\ 0 & 1 & 0 \\ 0 & 0 & 1 \end{bmatrix} = D_3^{(3)}.$$

The number of positive characteristic roots of a real symmetric matrix A is called the *index* of A. Theorem 33.1 yields the following results for quadratic mappings and forms.

(33.2) Theorem. Let $\mathcal{B}$ be a quadratic mapping of a vector space $\mathcal{V}$ that has a symmetric matrix A with respect to a basis $\{\mathbf{U}_1, \mathbf{U}_2, \ldots, \mathbf{U}_n\}$ of $\mathcal{V}$. There exists a basis $\{\mathbf{W}_1, \mathbf{W}_2, \ldots, \mathbf{W}_n\}$ of $\mathcal{V}$ such that for $\mathbf{U} = a_1 \cdot \mathbf{W}_1 + a_2 \cdot \mathbf{W}_2 + \cdots + a_n \cdot \mathbf{W}_n \in \mathcal{V}$,

$$\mathcal{B}(\mathbf{U}, \mathbf{U}) = a_1^2 + \cdots + a_s^2 - a_{s+1}^2 - \cdots - a_t^2,$$

where t is the rank of A and s is the index of A.

PROOF. By Theorem 33.1, there is a nonsingular matrix P such that $PAP' = D_t^{(s)}$, where t is the rank of A and s is the index of A. Let P be the matrix of a change of basis from $\{\mathbf{U}_1, \mathbf{U}_2, \ldots, \mathbf{U}_n\}$ to a new basis $\{\mathbf{W}_1, \mathbf{W}_2, \ldots, \mathbf{W}_n\}$. Then the matrix of $\mathcal{B}$ with respect to the new basis is $PAP' = D_t^{(s)}$. Therefore,

$$\mathcal{B}(\mathbf{U}, \mathbf{U}) = [a_1 \quad a_2 \quad \cdots \quad a_n] D_t^{(s)} \begin{bmatrix} a_1 \\ a_2 \\ \cdot \\ \cdot \\ a_n \end{bmatrix}$$

$$= a_1^2 + \cdots + a_s^2 - a_{s+1}^2 - \cdots - a_t^2.$$

(33.3) Theorem. Let $\sum_{i,j=1}^{n} x_i a_{i,j} x_j$ be a real quadratic form, where $A = [a_{i,j}]$ is a symmetric matrix with rank t and index s. There exists a nonsingular matrix P such that

$$\sum_{i,j=1}^{n} x_i a_{i,j} x_j = y_1^2 + \cdots + y_s^2 - y_{s+1}^2 - \cdots - y_t^2,$$

where $[x_1 \quad x_2 \quad \cdots \quad x_n] = [y_1 \quad y_2 \quad \cdots \quad y_n]P$.

The proof of Theorem 33.3 is left as an exercise (Exercise 33.2).

Example 2. Let $\sum_{i,j=1}^{3} x_i a_{i,j} x_j$ be the quadratic form with matrix $A = [a_{i,j}]$, where A is the matrix of Example 1, Section 32. Then, A has rank 3 and index 3. Let P be the matrix of Example 1 of this section, so that $PAP' = D_3^{(3)}$. Then

$$\sum_{i,j=1}^{3} x_i a_{i,j} x_j = y_1^2 + y_2^2 + y_3^2,$$

where $[x_1 \quad x_2 \quad x_3] = [y_1 \quad y_2 \quad y_3]P$.

To prove that for a given n, the set of n by n $D_t^{(s)}$ matrices is a set of canonical matrices for real symmetric matrices under the relation of congruence, we must show that a symmetric matrix A is congruent to exactly one $D_t^{(s)}$ matrix. This result is a consequence of the following theorem.

(33.4) Theorem. If $D_t^{(s)}$ and $D_v^{(u)}$ are congruent, then $t = v$, and $s = u$.

PROOF. If $D_t^{(s)}$ and $D_v^{(u)}$ are congruent, then they are equivalent. Hence $t =$ rank of $D_t^{(s)} =$ rank of $D_v^{(u)} = v$. If $t = 0$, then $s = u = 0$, since $0 \leq s \leq t$ and $0 \leq u \leq v = t$. Therefore, we may suppose that $t > 0$. Assume that $s \neq u$, say $s < u$. We will find that this assumption leads to a contradiction, which will prove the theorem. Consider the quadratic form

$$x_1^2 + \cdots + x_s^2 - x_{s+1}^2 - \cdots - x_t^2$$

with matrix $D_t^{(s)}$. By hypothesis, there is a nonsingular matrix $P = [p_{i,j}]$ such that $PD_t^{(s)}P' = D_v^{(u)} = D_t^{(u)}$. Hence,

$$x_1^2 + \cdots + x_s^2 - x_{s+1}^2 - \cdots - x_t^2 \\ = y_1^2 + \cdots + y_u^2 - y_{u+1}^2 - \cdots - y_t^2, \tag{33-1}$$

where $[x_1 \ x_2 \ \ldots \ x_n] = [y_1 \ y_2 \ \ldots \ y_n]P$. We will now determine values for the x's and y's that show that (33-1) is impossible. Select $y_{u+1} = \cdots = y_n = 0$. Then the equations connecting the x's and the y's are

$$\begin{aligned} x_1 &= p_{1,1}y_1 + \cdots + p_{u,1}y_u \\ &\cdots \\ x_s &= p_{1,s}y_1 + \cdots + p_{u,s}y_u \\ x_{s+1} &= p_{1,s+1}y_1 + \cdots + p_{u,s+1}y_u \\ &\cdots \\ x_n &= p_{1,n}y_1 + \cdots + p_{u,n}y_u. \end{aligned}$$

If we set $x_1 = \cdots = x_s = 0$, then the first s equations become a homogeneous system to solve for $y_1, y_2, \ldots, y_u$. Since $s < u$, it follows from Corollary 12.3, that there is a nontrivial solution $y_1 = a_1$, $y_2 = a_2, \ldots,$ $y_u = a_u$. Then

$$x_{s+1} = p_{1,s+1}a_1 + \cdots + p_{u,s+1}a_u = b_{s+1}, \ldots, \\ x_n = p_{1,n}a_1 + \cdots + p_{u,n}a_u = b_n$$

are determined by the last $n - s$ equations. Substituting in (33-1), we obtain

$$-b_{s+1}^2 - \cdots - b_t^2 = a_1^2 + \cdots + a_u^2. \tag{33-2}$$

Since not every a_i is zero, the right-hand side of equation (33-2) is positive. However, the left-hand side of this equation is less than or equal to zero. This contradiction proves the theorem.

Now, if a symmetric matrix A is congruent to $D_t^{(s)}$ and $D_v^{(u)}$, then since congruence is an equivalence relation, $D_t^{(s)}$ is congruent to $D_v^{(u)}$. By Theorem

33.4, $t = v$ and $s = u$. That is, $D_t^{(s)} = D_v^{(u)}$. Hence, each symmetric matrix is congruent to exactly one $D_t^{(s)}$ matrix. Theorem 33.4 leads to one other important result:

(33.5) Corollary. Let A and B be real symmetric n by n matrices. Then A is congruent to B if and only if A and B have the same rank and index.

PROOF. Suppose rank of A = rank of $B = t$ and index of A = index of $B = s$. By Theorem 33.1, A is congruent to $D_t^{(s)}$ and B is congruent to $D_t^{(s)}$. Therefore A is congruent to B. Conversely, assume that A is congruent to B. By Theorem 33.1, A is congruent to $D_t^{(s)}$, where t is the rank of A and s is the index of A. Similarly, B is congruent to $D_v^{(u)}$, where v is the rank of B and u is the index of B. We have $D_t^{(s)}$ is congruent to A, A is congruent to B, and B is congruent to $D_v^{(u)}$. Therefore, $D_t^{(s)}$ is congruent to $D_v^{(u)}$. By Theorem 33.4, $t = v$ and $s = u$. Hence, A and B have the same rank and index.

The theory of the reduction of a real symmetric matrix A to canonical form and the application of this theory to the simplification of quadratic mappings and forms is now complete. However, the construction of a nonsingular matrix P such that $PAP' = D_t^{(s)}$ by the method of the proof of Theorem 33.1 is lengthy, since it involves first reducing A to diagonal form by orthogonal equivalence (see Example 1, Section 32). Fortunately, there is a simpler way to construct P.

Let E denote an elementary transformation matrix of any type, and let A be a symmetric matrix. The matrix EAE' is congruent to A. Moreover, E' is an elementary transformation matrix that performs the same elementary transformation on the columns of A as E performs on the rows. For example, if

$$A = \begin{bmatrix} 1 & -\frac{1}{2} & -3 \\ -\frac{1}{2} & \frac{5}{2} & 6 \\ -3 & 6 & 5 \end{bmatrix} \quad \text{and} \quad E = I_3^{(1,3,3)},$$

then

$$EAE' = \begin{bmatrix} 1 & -\frac{1}{2} & 0 \\ -\frac{1}{2} & \frac{5}{2} & \frac{9}{2} \\ 0 & \frac{9}{2} & -4 \end{bmatrix}.$$

That is, the first row of A is multiplied by 3 and added to the third row, and then the first column of A is multiplied by 3 and added to the third column. Since A is symmetric, a sequence of these *elementary congruence transformations* that reduces A to a $D_t^{(s)}$ matrix can be found. Continuing this example, where we now denote the matrix E by E_1, we have

$$E_2E_1AE_1'E_2' = \begin{bmatrix} 1 & 0 & 0 \\ 0 & \frac{9}{4} & \frac{9}{2} \\ 0 & \frac{9}{2} & -4 \end{bmatrix}, \quad \text{where} \quad E_2 = I_3^{(1,2,\frac{1}{2})};$$

$$E_3E_2E_1AE_1'E_2'E_3' = \begin{bmatrix} 1 & 0 & 0 \\ 0 & 1 & 3 \\ 0 & 3 & -4 \end{bmatrix}, \quad \text{where} \quad E_3 = {}^{(\frac{2}{3})}I_3^{(2)};$$

$$E_4E_3E_2E_1AE_1'E_2'E_3'E_4' = \begin{bmatrix} 1 & 0 & 0 \\ 0 & 1 & 0 \\ 0 & 0 & -13 \end{bmatrix}, \quad \text{where} \quad E_4 = I_3^{(2,3,-3)};$$

$$E_5E_4E_3E_2E_1AE_1'E_2'E_3'E_4'E_5' = \begin{bmatrix} 1 & 0 & 0 \\ 0 & 1 & 0 \\ 0 & 0 & -1 \end{bmatrix} = D_3^{(2)}, \quad \text{where} \quad E_5 = {}^{(1/\sqrt{13})}I_3^{(3)}.$$

Thus, $PAP' = D_3^{(2)}$, where $P = E_5E_4E_3E_2E_1$. Moreover, the matrix P can be computed by performing the sequence of elementary transformations on the identity matrix I_n. In this example,

$$P = \begin{bmatrix} 1 & 0 & 0 \\ \dfrac{1}{3} & \dfrac{2}{3} & 0 \\ \dfrac{2}{\sqrt{13}} & \dfrac{-2}{\sqrt{13}} & \dfrac{1}{\sqrt{13}} \end{bmatrix}.$$

The $D_t^{(s)}$ matrix obtained by this reduction must be the same as the one obtained by the more complicated procedure of Theorem 33.1, since we have proved that each symmetric matrix is congruent to exactly one $D_t^{(s)}$ matrix.

Example 3. Let

$$A = \begin{bmatrix} 1 & -6 & -3 \\ -6 & 40 & 19 \\ -3 & 19 & 10 \end{bmatrix}.$$

Then A is carried to a $D_t^{(s)}$ matrix by the following sequence of elementary congruence transformations:

$$A \xrightarrow{\text{Type II}} \begin{bmatrix} 1 & 0 & -3 \\ 0 & 4 & 1 \\ -3 & 1 & 10 \end{bmatrix} \xrightarrow{\text{Type II}} \begin{bmatrix} 1 & 0 & 0 \\ 0 & 4 & 1 \\ 0 & 1 & 1 \end{bmatrix}$$

$$\xrightarrow{\text{Type II}} \begin{bmatrix} 1 & 0 & 0 \\ 0 & 4 & 0 \\ 0 & 0 & \frac{3}{4} \end{bmatrix} \xrightarrow{\text{Type III}} \begin{bmatrix} 1 & 0 & 0 \\ 0 & 1 & 0 \\ 0 & 0 & \frac{3}{4} \end{bmatrix} \xrightarrow{\text{Type III}} \begin{bmatrix} 1 & 0 & 0 \\ 0 & 1 & 0 \\ 0 & 0 & 1 \end{bmatrix} = D_3^{(3)}.$$

The matrix P such that $PAP' = D_3^{(3)}$ is

$$P = \begin{bmatrix} 1 & 0 & 0 \\ 3 & \frac{1}{2} & 0 \\ \sqrt{3} & \frac{-1}{2\sqrt{3}} & \frac{2}{\sqrt{3}} \end{bmatrix}.$$

A quadratic form $\sum_{i,j=1}^{n} x_i a_{i,j} x_j$ is *positive definite* if all of its values are positive except for $x_1 = x_2 = \cdots = x_n = 0$. The form is called *positive semidefinite* if all of its values are greater than or equal to zero. As a consequence of Theorem 33.3, a form is positive definite if and only if $s = t = n$ and is positive semidefinite if and only if $s = t$. For example, the quadratic form of Example 2 is positive definite.

Exercises

33.1 List the ten $D_t^{(s)}$ matrices for $n = 3$.

33.2 Prove Theorem 33.3.

33.3 Find a nonsingular matrix P such that $PAP' = D_t^{(s)}$ for the following matrices A. Also, determine the rank and index of each matrix.

$$\begin{bmatrix} -5 & -\frac{1}{2} & -\frac{2}{3} \\ -\frac{1}{2} & 0 & 6 \\ -\frac{2}{3} & 6 & 1 \end{bmatrix}; \quad \begin{bmatrix} 4 & -1 & 6 & 2 \\ -1 & 3 & 0 & 5 \\ 6 & 0 & -1 & 1 \\ 2 & 5 & 1 & -7 \end{bmatrix}; \quad \begin{bmatrix} 1 & 1 & 1 & 1 \\ 1 & 1 & 1 & 1 \\ 1 & 1 & 1 & 1 \\ 1 & 1 & 1 & 1 \end{bmatrix}.$$

33.4 Find a nonsingular matrix P such that each of the following quadratic forms has the expression $y_1^2 + \cdots + y_s^2 - y_{s+1}^2 - \cdots - y_t^2$, where

$$[x_1 \quad x_2 \quad \ldots \quad x_n] = [y_1 \quad y_2 \quad \ldots \quad y_n]P:$$

(a) $x_1x_2 + 2x_1x_3 + 4x_1x_4 + x_2x_3 + x_4^2$;
(b) $x_1^2 + 2x_1x_2 + x_2^2 + 2x_1x_3 + 2x_2x_3 + x_3^2$;
(c) $2x_1^2 + 8x_1x_2 - 12x_1x_3 + 7x_2^2 - 24x_2x_3 + 15x_3^2$.

Are any of these forms positive definite? Are any of them positive semidefinite?

Answers to Selected Exercises

Section 1

1.3 $\langle 2, 5\rangle$, $\langle -1, \pi\rangle$, $\langle 1/2, \sqrt{2}\rangle$.

1.4 (i), (iii).

1.6 $[0] = \{km \mid k \in Z\}$, $[1] = \{km + 1 \mid k \in Z\}$, . . . , $[m - 1] = \{km + m - 1 \mid k \in Z\}$.

Section 2

2.6 (a) First show that the three vectors have the same length. Then show that they have the same direction (or are the zero vector) by considering the following cases: $[\overrightarrow{PQ}] = [\overrightarrow{0}]$; $[\overrightarrow{PQ}] \neq [\overrightarrow{0}]$ and either $r = 0$ or $s = 0$; $[\overrightarrow{PQ}] \neq [\overrightarrow{0}]$ and $r > 0$, $s > 0$; $[\overrightarrow{PQ}] \neq [\overrightarrow{0}]$ and $r > 0$, $s < 0$; $[\overrightarrow{PQ}] \neq [\overrightarrow{0}]$ and $r < 0$, $s > 0$; $[\overrightarrow{PQ}] \neq [\overrightarrow{0}]$ and $r < 0$, $s < 0$.

2.8 If $r \neq 0$ and $[\overrightarrow{PQ}] \neq [\overrightarrow{0}]$, then the length of $r \cdot [\overrightarrow{PQ}]$ is $|r|\,|PQ| \neq 0$.

2.10 If θ is the angle between $\overrightarrow{OP}$ and $\overrightarrow{OQ}$, the component of the force in the direction of the displacement is $|OP| \cos \theta$.

Section 3

3.1 Show that $k_1 \cdot [\overrightarrow{PQ}] + k_2 \cdot [\overrightarrow{RS}] = [\overrightarrow{0}]$, where k_1 and k_2 are not both zero, if and only if one of the vectors is a scalar multiple of the other. Show that this latter statement holds if and only if the vectors are collinear.

3.3 Let $[\overrightarrow{OX}]$ have unit length so that $|OP| = |x|$ and $|OQ| = |y|$. Show that $[\overrightarrow{OP}] \circ [\overrightarrow{OQ}] = xy$ by considering the cases $xy = 0$, $xy > 0$, and $xy < 0$.

3.6 $\langle -231/5, -73/5\rangle$, $\langle 69/5, 49/10\rangle$, $\langle -3, 26\rangle$.

3.7 $\sqrt{106}$, $\sqrt{2305/10}$, $\sqrt{58690/5}$, $\sqrt{21445/10}$, $\sqrt{685}$. 29.1°, 178.8°, 197.5°, 19.5°, 96.6°.

3.8 (a) $2\sqrt{2}$, $\cos \theta = 1$; (b) 0, $\cos \theta = 0$; (c) $(3 + 4\sqrt{3})/4$, $\cos \theta = (3 + 4\sqrt{3})/13$; (d) $14\sqrt{5}$, $\cos \theta = 7\sqrt{5}/27$; (e) -37, $\cos \theta = -1$.

3.9 Introduce a rectangular Cartesian coordinate system in a plane containing $[\overrightarrow{PQ}]$ and $[\overrightarrow{RS}]$. Then use Exercise 3.4 and Theorem 3.4.

Section 4

4.3 $\langle -7, -\sqrt{2}/2, 15 + 5\sqrt{2}\rangle$, $\langle -1 + \sqrt{2}, -13/2, -2 + \sqrt{3}\rangle$, $\langle -6, -126, 18 + 18\sqrt{3}\rangle$, $\langle (1 + 14\sqrt{2})/2, 0, (-73 + \sqrt{3})/2\rangle$.

4.4 Show that $[\overrightarrow{EF}] - [\overrightarrow{GH}] = (-3) \cdot ([\overrightarrow{AB}] - [\overrightarrow{CD}])$. $1 \cdot ([\overrightarrow{OX}] - [\overrightarrow{OY}]) + 1 \cdot ([\overrightarrow{OY}] - [\overrightarrow{OZ}]) + 1 \cdot ([\overrightarrow{OZ}] - [\overrightarrow{OX}]) = [\overrightarrow{0}]$, and use Exercise 3.11.

4.6 $\langle -7 + 2\sqrt{5}, (1 - 2\sqrt{2})/2, 2\rangle$, $\langle -5 - 2\sqrt{5}, (1 + 2\sqrt{2})/2, -12\rangle$, $\langle -16 + 8\sqrt{5}, 1 - 4\sqrt{2}, 18\rangle$.

4.7 $\frac{1}{2}\sqrt{301 - 112\sqrt{5} - 4\sqrt{2}}$, $\frac{1}{2}\sqrt{765 + 80\sqrt{5} + 4\sqrt{2}}$, $\sqrt{933 - 256\sqrt{5} - 8\sqrt{2}}$.

$$\cos\alpha = \frac{-7 + 2\sqrt{5}}{l}, \qquad \cos\beta = \frac{1 - 2\sqrt{2}}{2l}, \qquad \cos\gamma = \frac{2}{l},$$

where $l = \frac{1}{2}\sqrt{301 - 112\sqrt{5} - 4\sqrt{2}}$;

$$\cos\alpha = \frac{-5 - 2\sqrt{5}}{l}, \qquad \cos\beta = \frac{1 + 2\sqrt{2}}{2l}, \qquad \cos\gamma = -\frac{12}{l},$$

where $l = \frac{1}{2}\sqrt{765 + 80\sqrt{5} + 4\sqrt{2}}$;

$$\cos\alpha = \frac{-16 + 8\sqrt{5}}{l}, \qquad \cos\beta = \frac{1 - 4\sqrt{2}}{l}, \qquad \cos\gamma = \frac{18}{l},$$

where $l = \sqrt{933 - 256\sqrt{5} - 8\sqrt{2}}$.

4.8 (a) 50, $\cos\theta = \dfrac{25}{7\sqrt{13}}$; (b) 0, $\cos\theta = 0$; (c) 11, $\cos\theta = \dfrac{330}{19\sqrt{785}}$; (d) -78, $\cos\theta = -1$.

4.11 $[\overrightarrow{PQ}] = ([\overrightarrow{PQ}] - (t/r^2) \cdot [\overrightarrow{RS}]) + (t/r^2) \cdot [\overrightarrow{RS}]$.

Section 5

5.1 (a) $(-7/4, 19/6)$; (b) $(-31/10, 73/15)$; (c) $\left(\dfrac{-9 + \sqrt{2}}{2\sqrt{2}}, \dfrac{17 + \sqrt{2}}{3\sqrt{2}}\right)$.

5.3 $(1/3, 1/3, 1/3)$.

5.6 (a) $k_1 = -10/7$, $k_2 = 9/14$; (b) $k_1 = -8/7$, $k_2 = -11/14$; (c) $k_1 = 1/7$, $k_2 = -3/14$; (d) $k_1 = 2/7$, $k_2 = 1/14$.

5.7 $\langle 6, 6\sqrt{2}, 6\sqrt{3}\rangle$.

5.9 $x_P = 1 + k$, $y_P = -5 + 12k$, $z_P = 6 - 16k$.

Section 6

6.1 The coordinates of **I**, **J**, and **K** are $\langle -3/7, -5/7, -4/7\rangle$, $\langle 1/7, -3/7, -1/7\rangle$, and $\langle 9/7, 8/7, 5/7\rangle$, respectively.

6.3 (b), (c).

Section 7

7.3 $\langle -9/2, (3 - 6\sqrt{3})/2, 1/6, (-9 + 4\sqrt{2})/2\rangle$, $\langle -3\sqrt{3} + \sqrt{6}, 2\sqrt{6}, (9\sqrt{3} - 4\sqrt{2} - 18\sqrt{6})/18, \sqrt{2}\rangle$, $\langle -4, -1 - \sqrt{3}, 31/18, \sqrt{2}\rangle$.

7.5 (a), (c).

7.7 The set of all vectors coplanar with **U** and **W** is the set of all linear combinations of **U** and **W**.

7.12 (a) Let $\mathcal{S}_i$ be the subspace of $\mathcal{V}_4$ spanned by the single vector $\langle a_1, a_2, a_3, a_4\rangle$, where $a_i = 1$ and $a_j = 0$ if $j \neq i$, for $i = 1, 2, 3, 4$. Then $\mathcal{V}_4$ is the direct sum of the subspaces $\mathcal{S}_1, \mathcal{S}_2, \mathcal{S}_3, \mathcal{S}_4$. (There are other solutions.)

Section 8

8.1 (a), (d).

8.3 (a) Show that $r_1 \cdot \langle 2, -1/2, 1\rangle + r_2 \cdot \langle 3, 2, 1\rangle + r_3 \cdot \langle 0, 1, 1\rangle = \langle 0, 0, 0\rangle$ implies $r_1 = r_2 = r_3 = 0$.

8.6 (a) Let $\{\mathbf{U}_1, \mathbf{U}_2, \ldots, \mathbf{U}_k\}$ be a basis of $\mathcal{S} \cap \mathcal{T}$. By Exercise 8.5, there are vectors $\mathbf{U}_{k+1}, \ldots, \mathbf{U}_l$ and $\mathbf{V}_{k+1}, \ldots, \mathbf{V}_m$ such that $\{\mathbf{U}_1, \ldots, \mathbf{U}_k, \mathbf{U}_{k+1}, \ldots, \mathbf{U}_l\}$ is a basis of $\mathcal{S}$ and $\{\mathbf{U}_1, \ldots, \mathbf{U}_k, \mathbf{V}_{k+1}, \ldots, \mathbf{V}_m\}$ is a basis of $\mathcal{T}$. Show that $\{\mathbf{U}_1, \ldots, \mathbf{U}_k, \mathbf{U}_{k+1}, \ldots, \mathbf{U}_l, \mathbf{V}_{k+1}, \ldots, \mathbf{V}_m\}$ is a basis of $\mathcal{S} + \mathcal{T}$.

Section 9

9.3 Let $\{\mathbf{U}_1, \mathbf{U}_2, \ldots, \mathbf{U}_k\}$ be an orthonormal basis of $\mathcal{S}$. There are vectors $\mathbf{U}_{k+1}, \ldots, \mathbf{U}_n$ such that $\{\mathbf{U}_1, \ldots, \mathbf{U}_k, \mathbf{U}_{k+1}, \ldots, \mathbf{U}_n\}$ is an orthonormal basis of $\mathcal{V}$. If $\mathbf{V} \in \mathcal{V}$, then $\mathbf{V} = \sum_{i=1}^{k} a_i \cdot \mathbf{U}_i + \sum_{i=k+1}^{n} a_i \cdot \mathbf{U}_i$, where $\sum_{i=1}^{k} a_i \cdot \mathbf{U}_i \in \mathcal{S}$. Show that $\sum_{i=k+1}^{n} a_i \cdot \mathbf{U}_i \in \mathcal{T}$. Hence, $\mathcal{V} = \mathcal{S} + \mathcal{T}$. Then show that $\mathcal{S} \cap \mathcal{T} = \{\mathbf{0}\}$.

9.4 (a) Take care of the case $\mathbf{U} = \mathbf{0}$ or $\mathbf{V} = \mathbf{0}$. Otherwise, $\mathcal{G}(x \cdot \mathbf{U} + \mathbf{V}, x \cdot \mathbf{U} + \mathbf{V}) = x^2\mathcal{G}(\mathbf{U}, \mathbf{U}) + 2x\mathcal{G}(\mathbf{U}, \mathbf{V}) + \mathcal{G}(\mathbf{V}, \mathbf{V}) \geq 0$, where $\mathcal{G}(\mathbf{U}, \mathbf{U}) > 0$. Use the fact that $Ax^2 + Bx + C \geq 0$ $(A > 0)$ for all x if and only if $B^2 - 4AC \leq 0$.
(b) Show that $|\mathbf{U} + \mathbf{V}| \leq |\mathbf{U}| + |\mathbf{V}|$ if and only if $\mathcal{G}(\mathbf{U}, \mathbf{V}) \leq \sqrt{\mathcal{G}(\mathbf{U}, \mathbf{U})\mathcal{G}(\mathbf{V}, \mathbf{V})}$ and use (a).

9.5 (a) $\{(1/\sqrt{39}) \cdot \langle 3, -5, 2, 1\rangle\}$; (b) $\{(1/\sqrt{53}) \cdot \langle 1, 6, 0, 4\rangle, (1/\sqrt{125557}) \cdot \langle 102, -77, 318, 90\rangle\}$; (c) $\{(1/\sqrt{3}) \cdot \langle 1, 0, 1, 1\rangle, (1/\sqrt{6}) \cdot \langle 0, 2, 1, -1\rangle, (1/\sqrt{22}) \cdot \langle 10/3, 4/3, -3, -1/3\rangle\}$.

Section 10

10.1 (a) $x_1 = 0, x_2 = 0, x_3 = 0$; (b) inconsistent; (c) $x_1 = (10 - 2r)/11$, $x_2 = (-25 + 5r)/11$, $x_3 = r$, where r is any real number; (d) inconsistent.

10.4 Multiply $\mathbf{U}_3^{(5)}$ by -466, obtaining $\mathbf{U}_1^{(4)}, \mathbf{U}_2^{(4)}, \mathbf{U}_3^{(4)}$. Multiply $\mathbf{U}_2^{(4)}$ by 30 and add to $\mathbf{U}_3^{(4)}$, obtaining $\mathbf{U}_1^{(3)}, \mathbf{U}_2^{(3)}, \mathbf{U}_3^{(3)}$. Multiply $\mathbf{U}_2^{(3)}$ by $1/3$, obtaining $\mathbf{U}_1^{(2)}, \mathbf{U}_2^{(2)}, \mathbf{U}_3^{(2)}$. Multiply $\mathbf{U}_1^{(2)}$ by 4 and add to $\mathbf{U}_3^{(2)}$, obtaining $\mathbf{U}_1^{(1)}, \mathbf{U}_2^{(1)}, \mathbf{U}_3^{(1)}$. Multiply $\mathbf{U}_1^{(1)}$ by $1/2$, obtaining $\mathbf{U}_1, \mathbf{U}_2, \mathbf{U}_3$.

Section 11

11.2 (a) $k = 2, m_1 = 1, m_2 = 4$; (b) $k = 3, m_1 = 1, m_2 = 2, m_3 = 3$; (c) $k = 3, m_1 = 1, m_2 = 2, m_3 = 3$; (d) $k = 3, m_1 = 1, m_2 = 2, m_3 = 3$.

Section 12

12.1 (a) Inconsistent; (b) $x_1 = 64/55$, $x_2 = -69/55$, $x_3 = -28/55$, $x_4 = 8/5$; (c) inconsistent; (d) $x_1 = 3/2$, $x_2 = 25/8$, $x_3 = -1/8$.

12.2 (a) $x_1 = -3r$, $x_2 = -r$, $x_3 = r$, where r is any real number. The solution space is spanned by $\langle -3, -1, 1\rangle$. (b) Trivial solution. Solution space is $\{\langle 0, 0, 0\rangle\}$. (c) $x_1 = -r$, $x_2 = r$, $x_3 = r$, where r is any real number. The solution space is spanned by $\langle -1, 1, 1\rangle$. (d) Trivial solution. Solution space is $\{\langle 0, 0, 0\rangle\}$.

12.3 (b) and (c).

12.5 A basis of $\mathfrak{J}$ is $\{\langle 21, 14, 0, 0, 12\rangle, \langle 3, 2, 12, 0, 0\rangle, \langle 3, 4, 0, 6, 0\rangle\}$. (There are others.)

Section 13

13.4 Compute $[\mathbf{V} - P_{\mathbf{U}}(\mathbf{V})] \circ \mathbf{U}$.

13.7 Let $\mathbf{U}$ and $\mathbf{W}$ have coordinates $\langle a, b, c\rangle$ and $\langle d, e, f\rangle$, respectively. Let $m = a^2 + b^2 + c^2$ and $n = d^2 + e^2 + f^2$. Then

$$x' = \left(\frac{na^2 + md^2}{mn}\right)x + \left(\frac{nab + mde}{mn}\right)y + \left(\frac{nac + mdf}{mn}\right)z$$

$$y' = \left(\frac{nab + mde}{mn}\right)x + \left(\frac{nb^2 + me^2}{mn}\right)y + \left(\frac{nbc + mef}{mn}\right)z$$

$$z' = \left(\frac{nac + mdf}{mn}\right)x + \left(\frac{nbc + mef}{mn}\right)y + \left(\frac{nc^2 + mf^2}{mn}\right)z$$

If $\mathbf{U} = \mathbf{I}$ and $\mathbf{W} = \mathbf{J}$, then $x' = x$, $y' = y$, $z' = 0$.

Section 14

14.4 $L^{-1}(\{\mathbf{0}\}) = \{\mathbf{0}\}$ if and only if the system of equations $ax + by = 0$, $cx + dy = 0$ has only the trivial solution. This is the case if and only if $ad - bc \neq 0$.

14.7 Prove that isomorphic vector spaces have the same dimension.

14.8 (a) If $\{\mathbf{U}_1, \mathbf{U}_2, \ldots, \mathbf{U}_n\}$ is a basis of $\mathfrak{V}$, then $\{L(\mathbf{U}_1), L(\mathbf{U}_2), \ldots, L(\mathbf{U}_n)\}$ spans $L(\mathfrak{V})$.
(b) Let $\{\mathbf{U}_1, \mathbf{U}_2, \ldots, \mathbf{U}_k\}$ be a basis of $L^{-1}(\{\mathbf{0}\})$ such that $\{\mathbf{U}_1, \ldots, \mathbf{U}_k, \mathbf{U}_{k+1}, \ldots, \mathbf{U}_n\}$ is a basis of $\mathfrak{V}$. Show that $\{L(\mathbf{U}_{k+1}), \ldots, L(\mathbf{U}_n)\}$ is a basis of $L(\mathfrak{V})$.

Section 15

15.2 Let the vector $\mathbf{U}$ have coordinates $\langle a, b\rangle$.

$$\left\langle \left(\frac{a^2}{a^2+b^2} + \cos\varphi\right)x + \left(\frac{ab}{a^2+b^2} - \sin\varphi\right)y, \left(\frac{ab}{a^2+b^2} + \sin\varphi\right)x + \left(\frac{b^2}{a^2+b^2} + \cos\varphi\right)y \right\rangle,$$

$$\langle 3x\cos\varphi - 3y\sin\varphi, 3x\sin\varphi + 3y\cos\varphi\rangle,$$

$$\left\langle -\frac{5a^2}{a^2+b^2}x - \frac{5ab}{a^2+b^2}y, -\frac{5ab}{a^2+b^2}x - \frac{5b^2}{a^2+b^2}y \right\rangle,$$

$$\left\langle \frac{a^2 \cos \varphi - ab \sin \varphi}{a^2 + b^2} x + \frac{ab \cos \varphi - b^2 \sin \varphi}{a^2 + b^2} y, \frac{a^2 \sin \varphi + ab \cos \varphi}{a^2 + b^2} x + \frac{ab \sin \varphi + b^2 \cos \varphi}{a^2 + b^2} y \right\rangle,$$

$$\left\langle \frac{a^2 \cos \varphi + ab \sin \varphi}{a^2 + b^2} x + \frac{-a^2 \sin \varphi + ab \cos \varphi}{a^2 + b^2} y, \frac{ab \cos \varphi + b^2 \sin \varphi}{a^2 + b^2} x + \frac{-ab \sin \varphi + b^2 \cos \varphi}{a^2 + b^2} y \right\rangle,$$

$$\langle -x \cos \varphi + y \sin \varphi, -x \sin \varphi - y \cos \varphi \rangle,$$

$$\left\langle \left(\frac{7a^2}{a^2 + b^2} + 2 \cos \varphi\right) x + \left(\frac{7ab}{a^2 + b^2} - 2 \sin \varphi\right) y, \left(\frac{7ab}{a^2 + b^2} + 2 \sin \varphi\right) x + \left(\frac{7b^2}{a^2 + b^2} + 2 \cos \varphi\right) y \right\rangle.$$

15.6 $M(\mathcal{V}_5)$ contains $\langle 1, 1, 1, 1 \rangle$ and $ML(\mathcal{V}_3)$ does not contain this vector. $L^{-1}(\{\mathbf{0}\}) = \{\mathbf{0}\} = (ML)^{-1}(\{\mathbf{0}\})$. ML is a nonsingular transformation of $\mathcal{V}_3$ into $\mathcal{V}_4$. M is a singular transformation of $\mathcal{V}_5$ into $\mathcal{V}_4$. ML is not an isomorphism of $\mathcal{V}_3$ onto $\mathcal{V}_4$.

Section 16

16.1

$$M: \begin{bmatrix} 1 & 0 & 0 & 0 & 0 \\ 0 & 1 & 0 & 0 & 0 \\ 0 & 0 & 1 & 0 & 0 \\ 0 & 0 & 0 & 1 & 0 \end{bmatrix}, \quad ML: \begin{bmatrix} 1 & -1 & 0 \\ 0 & 0 & 0 \\ 1 & 0 & -1 \\ 0 & 1 & 0 \end{bmatrix}.$$

16.2

$$L: \begin{bmatrix} 1 & 2 & 0 & 0 & 0 \\ 0 & 0 & 0 & 0 & 0 \\ 0 & 0 & 0 & 1 & -1 \\ 0 & 0 & 0 & 0 & 0 \\ 0 & 0 & 1 & 0 & 0 \end{bmatrix}, \quad M: \begin{bmatrix} 1 & 0 & 0 & 0 & 0 \\ 1 & 1 & 0 & 0 & 0 \\ 1 & 1 & 1 & 0 & 0 \\ 0 & 0 & 0 & 5 & 0 \\ 0 & 0 & 0 & 0 & -1 \end{bmatrix}, \quad L + M: \begin{bmatrix} 2 & 2 & 0 & 0 & 0 \\ 1 & 1 & 0 & 0 & 0 \\ 1 & 1 & 1 & 1 & -1 \\ 0 & 0 & 0 & 5 & 0 \\ 0 & 0 & 1 & 0 & -1 \end{bmatrix},$$

$$10 \cdot L: \begin{bmatrix} 10 & 20 & 0 & 0 & 0 \\ 0 & 0 & 0 & 0 & 0 \\ 0 & 0 & 0 & 10 & -10 \\ 0 & 0 & 0 & 0 & 0 \\ 0 & 0 & 10 & 0 & 0 \end{bmatrix}, \quad ML: \begin{bmatrix} 1 & 2 & 0 & 0 & 0 \\ 1 & 2 & 0 & 0 & 0 \\ 1 & 2 & 0 & 1 & -1 \\ 0 & 0 & 0 & 0 & 0 \\ 0 & 0 & -1 & 0 & 0 \end{bmatrix}, \quad LM: \begin{bmatrix} 3 & 2 & 0 & 0 & 0 \\ 0 & 0 & 0 & 0 & 0 \\ 0 & 0 & 0 & 5 & 1 \\ 0 & 0 & 0 & 0 & 0 \\ 1 & 1 & 1 & 0 & 0 \end{bmatrix}.$$

16.5 See Section 13 for the description of $P_{\mathbf{U}}$ in terms of the coordinates $\langle a, b \rangle$ of $\mathbf{U}$.

16.6 $\langle 11, 6, 17, -2 \rangle$, $\langle 3, 2, 3, 0 \rangle$, $\langle -14, -10, -11, -1 \rangle$, $\langle -1, 0, -4, 1 \rangle$, $\langle -\sqrt{2} + 3\sqrt{3}, 2\sqrt{3}, -4\sqrt{2} + 3\sqrt{3}, \sqrt{2} \rangle$.

Section 17

17.3
$$\begin{bmatrix} 5/2 & -16/15 & 3 & 51/10 \\ 38/5 & -7 & 33/10 & 13 \end{bmatrix}, \quad \begin{bmatrix} 1/2 & -26/15 & -1 & 51/10 \\ 38/5 & -10 & 13/10 & -21 \end{bmatrix},$$
$$\begin{bmatrix} 5/2 & 7/5 & -3 & 49/10 \\ 32/5 & -7/2 & 37/10 & 6 \end{bmatrix}, \quad \begin{bmatrix} 5/2 & -16/15 & 3 & 51/10 \\ 38/5 & -7 & 33/10 & 13 \end{bmatrix},$$
$$\begin{bmatrix} 15+\sqrt{2} & \dfrac{42+\sqrt{2}}{3} & -25+2\sqrt{2} & 24 \\ 29 & \dfrac{-10+3\sqrt{2}}{2} & 22+\sqrt{2} & 55+17\sqrt{2} \end{bmatrix},$$
$$\begin{bmatrix} 30 & -28 & 20 & 102 \\ 152 & -170 & 46 & -80 \end{bmatrix}.$$

17.6 (a)
$$\begin{bmatrix} 0 & -1 & 2/5 & 6/5 & -1/5 \\ -2/5 & 0 & 0 & 3/5 & 0 \\ 0 & 2 & 3/5 & 2/5 & -1/5 \end{bmatrix},$$
(b)
$$\begin{bmatrix} -63 & 119 & -28 & 56 & 7 \\ 7 & 28 & 0 & -7 & 49 \\ -105 & -14 & -126 & -7 & 0 \end{bmatrix}.$$

17.8
$$[20 \quad 68 \quad -18 \quad 130], \quad \begin{bmatrix} 10 & 32 & -7 & 45 \\ -2 & -9 & 4 & -35 \\ 2 & 6 & -1 & 5 \\ 0 & 6 & -6 & 60 \end{bmatrix},$$
$$\begin{bmatrix} 57 & -2 \\ 16 & 3 \end{bmatrix}, \quad [2 \quad 7], \quad \begin{bmatrix} 339 & -11 \\ 98 & 23 \end{bmatrix}.$$

17.10 For the diagonal matrix $A = [a_{i,j}]$, write $a_{i,j} = a_{i,j}\delta_{i,j}$, where $\delta_{i,j} = 0$ if $i \neq j$ and $\delta_{i,j} = 1$ if $i = j$.

17.13 Suppose $AB = I_n$. Let L and M be linear transformations of $\mathcal{V}_n$ into $\mathcal{V}_n$ such that A is the matrix of L and B is the matrix of M. Then $LM = I_{\mathcal{V}_n}$. Show that M is nonsingular, hence an isomorphism of $\mathcal{V}_n$ onto $\mathcal{V}_n$. Then M^* exists, and $M^*M = MM^* = I_{\mathcal{V}_n}$. Show that $L = M^*$, and $ML = I_{\mathcal{V}_n}$. Then $BA = I_n$.

17.15 (a)
$$\begin{bmatrix} -1/7 & 2/7 \\ 0 & 1 \end{bmatrix},$$
(b)
$$\begin{bmatrix} -15/7 & 30/7 \\ 24/7 & -20/7 \end{bmatrix},$$
(c)
$$\begin{bmatrix} 1 & 0 & -2 \\ 3/4 & 1/4 & -3/2 \\ 0 & 0 & 1 \end{bmatrix}.$$

Section 18

18.1 (a) Row rank = 3; (b) Row rank = 2; (c) Row rank = 3.

18.2 (a) Nonhomogeneous system: $x_1 = (10 - 5r - 4s)/7$, $x_2 = (-2 + r - 16s)/14$, $x_3 = s$, $x_4 = (-2 - r)/2$, $x_5 = r$, where r and s are any real numbers. Homogeneous system: $x_1 = (-10r - 5s - 4t)/7$,

$x_2 = (2r + s - 16t)/14$, $x_3 = t$, $x_4 = (2r - s)/2$, $x_5 = s$, $x_6 = r$, where r, s, and t are any real numbers.
(b) Nonhomogeneous system: $x_1 = -12/5$, $x_2 = 3/10$. Homogeneous system: $x_1 = 12r/5$, $x_2 = -3r/10$, $x_3 = r$, where r is any real number.
(c) Nonhomogeneous system: inconsistent. Homogeneous system: $x_1 = x_2 = x_3 = 0$.

18.5 (a), (b), and (d).

18.7 (a) $x_1 = 1/16$, $x_2 = -5/16$; (b) $x_1 = -1$, $x_2 = -1$, $x_3 = 3$.

18.9
$$\left\{\left\langle \frac{-10r - 5s - 4t + 5}{7}, \frac{2r + s - 16t - 15}{14}, t, \frac{2r - s - 3}{2}, s, r\right\rangle \,\middle|\, r, s \text{ and } t \text{ any real numbers.}\right\}$$

18.10 Subspace spanned by $\langle 12/5, -3/10, 1\rangle$.

Section 19

19.1 (a) 2; (b) 3; (c) 2.

19.2 $\begin{bmatrix} -1 & 3 & -1 \\ 4 & -5 & 4 \\ 2 & -1 & 1 \end{bmatrix}$; **U** has coordinates $\langle 10, -7, 4\rangle$ and $\langle -2, -1, 6\rangle$ with respect to the first and second bases, respectively.

Section 20

20.1 $\begin{bmatrix} 16 & 11 & 1 \\ 9/2 & 7/2 & 3/2 \end{bmatrix}$.

20.2 $\{\langle 0, -1/3, -1\rangle, \langle 1, 0, -1\rangle, \langle 0, 0, 1\rangle\}$ and $\{\langle 1, 0, 0, 0\rangle, \langle 5, 1, 0, 0\rangle, \langle 4, 1/3, 1, 0\rangle, \langle -1, -1/3, 0, 1\rangle\}$.

20.6 $PAQ = B$ if and only if $Q'A'P' = B'$.

20.7 $\begin{bmatrix} 7/4 & 1/4 & 3/4 \\ 29/4 & 27/4 & 17/4 \\ -19/2 & -13/2 & -11/2 \end{bmatrix}$;

$L(\mathbf{E}_1^{(3)})$: $\langle 3, 1, 0\rangle$ and $\langle -1/4, 5/4, -1/2\rangle$; $L(\mathbf{E}_2^{(3)})$: $\langle 1, -1, 0\rangle$ and $\langle 1/4, 3/4, -3/4\rangle$; $L(\mathbf{E}_3^{(3)})$: $\langle 3, 0, 1\rangle$ and $\langle 1/2, 3/2, -2\rangle$.

20.10
$$AP = P\begin{bmatrix} k_1 & 0 & \cdots & 0 \\ 0 & k_2 & \cdot & \cdot \\ \cdot & \cdot & \cdot & \cdot \\ \cdot & \cdot & \cdot & \cdot \\ \cdot & & \cdot & 0 \\ 0 & \cdots & 0 & k_n \end{bmatrix}.$$

Section 21

21.1

$$\begin{bmatrix} 0 & 0 & 1 & 0 \\ 0 & 1 & 0 & 0 \\ 1 & 0 & 0 & 0 \\ 0 & 0 & 0 & 1 \end{bmatrix}, \quad \begin{bmatrix} 1 & 0 & 0 & 0 & 0 \\ 0 & 1 & 0 & 0 & 0 \\ 0 & 0 & 1 & 0 & 0 \\ 0 & \frac{1}{2} & 0 & 1 & 0 \\ 0 & 0 & 0 & 0 & 1 \end{bmatrix}, \quad \begin{bmatrix} 1 & 0 & 0 \\ 0 & \sqrt{2} & 0 \\ 0 & 0 & 1 \end{bmatrix}, \quad \begin{bmatrix} 0 & 1 & 0 \\ 1 & 0 & 0 \\ 0 & 0 & 1 \end{bmatrix},$$

$$\begin{bmatrix} 1 & 0 & 0 & 0 \\ 0 & 1 & 0 & 0 \\ 0 & 0 & 1 & 0 \\ 10 & 0 & 0 & 1 \end{bmatrix}. \quad \text{The inverses are} \quad \begin{bmatrix} 0 & 0 & 1 & 0 \\ 0 & 1 & 0 & 0 \\ 1 & 0 & 0 & 0 \\ 0 & 0 & 0 & 1 \end{bmatrix},$$

$$\begin{bmatrix} 1 & 0 & 0 & 0 & 0 \\ 0 & 1 & 0 & 0 & 0 \\ 0 & 0 & 1 & 0 & 0 \\ 0 & -\frac{1}{2} & 0 & 1 & 0 \\ 0 & 0 & 0 & 0 & 1 \end{bmatrix}, \quad \begin{bmatrix} 1 & 0 & 0 \\ 0 & \dfrac{1}{\sqrt{2}} & 0 \\ 0 & 0 & 1 \end{bmatrix}, \quad \begin{bmatrix} 0 & 1 & 0 \\ 1 & 0 & 0 \\ 0 & 0 & 1 \end{bmatrix}, \quad \begin{bmatrix} 1 & 0 & 0 & 0 \\ 0 & 1 & 0 & 0 \\ 0 & 0 & 1 & 0 \\ -10 & 0 & 0 & 1 \end{bmatrix}.$$

21.2

$$\begin{bmatrix} 7 & 5 & 1 \\ 2 & -1 & 0 \\ -3 & 4 & 2 \\ 1 & 3 & 1 \end{bmatrix}, \quad \begin{bmatrix} 2 & -\frac{1}{3} & 0 \\ 7 & \frac{5}{3} & 1 \\ -3 & \frac{4}{3} & 2 \\ 1 & 1 & 1 \end{bmatrix}, \quad \begin{bmatrix} \frac{1}{2} & \frac{2}{3} & -1 & 4 & \frac{3}{2} \\ -\frac{5}{3} & 0 & \frac{1}{3} & \frac{1}{6} & 2 \\ \frac{5}{3} & 2 & -3 & 0 & 1 \end{bmatrix},$$

$$\begin{bmatrix} -\frac{11}{2} & \frac{2}{3} & -1 & 4 & \frac{3}{2} \\ 1 & 0 & 1 & \frac{1}{2} & 6 \\ -\frac{49}{3} & 2 & -3 & 0 & 1 \end{bmatrix}, \quad \begin{bmatrix} 4 & -3 & 2 \\ 5 & 7 & 1 \\ -1 & 2 & 0 \\ 3 & 1 & 1 \end{bmatrix}, \quad \begin{bmatrix} -5 & 0 & -1 & \frac{1}{2} & 6 \\ \frac{1}{2} & \frac{2}{3} & 1 & 4 & \frac{3}{2} \\ \frac{5}{3} & 2 & 3 & 0 & 1 \end{bmatrix}.$$

21.5

$$\begin{bmatrix} 0 & 0 & 0 & \frac{1}{4} \\ 0 & 0 & \frac{1}{3} & 0 \\ 0 & \frac{1}{2} & 0 & 0 \\ 1 & 0 & 0 & 0 \end{bmatrix}, \quad \begin{bmatrix} \frac{10}{19} & -\frac{1}{19} & \frac{14}{19} \\ -\frac{2}{19} & \frac{4}{19} & \frac{1}{19} \\ -\frac{1}{19} & \frac{2}{19} & -\frac{9}{19} \end{bmatrix}, \quad \begin{bmatrix} 1 & 0 & 0 & 0 \\ -\frac{1}{2} & 3 & 0 & 0 \\ 2 & 0 & 1 & 0 \\ -\frac{1}{3} & 0 & 0 & 2 \end{bmatrix},$$

$$\begin{bmatrix} 0 & 1 & -1 \\ 1 & -1 & 0 \\ 0 & 0 & 1 \end{bmatrix}.$$

Section 22

22.4 3, 1, 1, 2.

Section 23

23.1

$$\begin{bmatrix} 1 & 0 & 0 & 0 & 0 \\ 0 & 1 & 0 & 0 & 0 \\ 0 & 0 & 1 & 0 & 0 \end{bmatrix}, \quad \begin{bmatrix} 1 & 0 & 0 & 0 & 0 \\ 0 & 1 & 0 & 0 & 0 \\ 0 & 0 & 1 & 0 & 0 \\ 0 & 0 & 0 & 1 & 0 \\ 0 & 0 & 0 & 0 & 1 \end{bmatrix}, \quad \begin{bmatrix} 1 & 0 & 0 & 0 \\ 0 & 0 & 0 & 0 \\ 0 & 0 & 0 & 0 \end{bmatrix}, \quad \begin{bmatrix} 1 & 0 \\ 0 & 1 \\ 0 & 0 \\ 0 & 0 \end{bmatrix}.$$

23.2 $s + 1$, where s is the minimum of m and n.

Section 24

24.1 0; 14; 6; 13.
24.2 Both have minus signs.
24.5 $-x^6 - x^5 + x^4 + 6x^3 - 4x^2 - x - 12$, 116, 1, $\frac{1}{210}$, $\sqrt{210}$.
24.7 t precedes $t - s$ smaller numbers and s is preceded by $t - s - 1$ larger numbers other than t.

Section 25

25.1 -1932, 0, $3(x + y)(y + z)(z + w) - (x + y)^3 - (y + z)^3 - (z + w)^3$.
25.2 144, 7500, 144, $\frac{1}{192}$, 1728.

Section 26

26.1 -364, -81, -47; -364, 81, -47.

Section 27

27.2 There are 40 three-rowed minors. Twenty-eight are zero, and there are two with each of the following values: 1, -1, 2, -2, 3, -3.

27.4

$$\begin{bmatrix} 39 & 18 & 3 \\ -30 & 0 & 15 \\ -6 & -27 & 3 \end{bmatrix}, \quad \begin{bmatrix} 0 & 0 & 0 & 1 \\ 2 & 1 & 0 & 0 \\ 1 & 0 & 0 & 0 \\ 0 & 0 & 1 & 0 \end{bmatrix}, \quad \begin{bmatrix} 0 & 0 & 0 & 0 \\ 0 & 0 & 0 & 0 \\ 0 & 0 & 0 & 0 \\ 0 & 0 & 0 & 0 \end{bmatrix}.$$

27.6 Use Theorem 27.2 and consider the two cases $|A| \neq 0$ and $|A| = 0$. Show that $|A| = 0$ implies $|A^{\text{adj}}| = 0$.
27.7 $x_1 = \frac{4}{15}$, $x_2 = \frac{1}{10}$, $x_3 = \frac{1}{2}$, $x_4 = \frac{2}{15}$; $x_1 = 3$, $x_2 = 1$, $x_3 = -3$; $x_1 = x_2 = x_3 = 0$.

Section 28

28.1 2, 3; $\langle r, 0, 0, 0\rangle$, $\langle -3s, s, 0, 0\rangle$.

28.2 $\langle (2 + 2\sqrt{2})r, r, 0\rangle$, $\langle (2 - \sqrt{2})s, s, 0\rangle$.

28.7 $(33 \pm \sqrt{633})/12$; 1, -1, i, $-i$; 1, $1 + 2i$, $1 - 2i$.

Section 29

29.2

$$Q^{-1} = \begin{bmatrix} 0 & 0 & -2/3 & 4/3 \\ 0 & 0 & 2/3 & -1/3 \\ -1/3 & 2/3 & 0 & 1/3 \\ 1/3 & 1/3 & -2 & 8/3 \end{bmatrix}.$$

29.3 The first and third matrices are similar to diagonal matrices.

29.4

$$\begin{bmatrix} 1 & -1 & 0 & 0 \\ 1 & 2 & 0 & 0 \\ -6 & 0 & 1 & -2 \\ 8 & 1 & -2 & 1 \end{bmatrix}, \quad \begin{bmatrix} 1 & 0 & -1 & 0 \\ 0 & 1 & 0 & -1 \\ 0 & 1 & 0 & 1 \\ 1 & 0 & 1 & 0 \end{bmatrix}.$$

(There are other solutions.)

Section 30

30.8

$$\begin{bmatrix} \frac{-3}{\sqrt{13}} & \frac{2}{\sqrt{13}\sqrt{14}} & \frac{2}{\sqrt{14}} \\ \frac{2}{\sqrt{13}} & \frac{3}{\sqrt{13}\sqrt{14}} & \frac{3}{\sqrt{14}} \\ 0 & \frac{-\sqrt{13}}{\sqrt{14}} & \frac{1}{\sqrt{14}} \end{bmatrix}, \quad \begin{bmatrix} \frac{-2}{\sqrt{13}} & \frac{3}{\sqrt{13}} \\ \frac{3}{\sqrt{13}} & \frac{2}{\sqrt{13}} \end{bmatrix}, \quad \begin{bmatrix} \frac{5}{\sqrt{86}} & \frac{3}{\sqrt{43}} & \frac{1}{\sqrt{2}} \\ \frac{6}{\sqrt{86}} & \frac{-5}{\sqrt{43}} & 0 \\ \frac{5}{\sqrt{86}} & \frac{3}{\sqrt{43}} & \frac{-1}{\sqrt{2}} \end{bmatrix}.$$

(There are other solutions.)

Section 31

31.2 If $\mathcal{B}$ is symmetric, then

$$[r_1 \quad r_2 \quad \cdots \quad r_n]A \begin{bmatrix} s_1 \\ s_2 \\ \cdot \\ \cdot \\ \cdot \\ s_n \end{bmatrix} = [s_1 \quad s_2 \quad \cdots \quad s_n]A \begin{bmatrix} r_1 \\ r_2 \\ \cdot \\ \cdot \\ \cdot \\ r_n \end{bmatrix}$$

for all r_i and s_j. By making suitable choices for $[r_1 \ r_2 \ \dots \ r_n]$ and $[s_1 \ s_2 \ \dots \ s_n]$, show that this implies that A is symmetric.

31.4 All three matrices are matrices of the quadratic form $-3x_1^2 + 8x_1x_2 + 4x_2x_3 + 4x_3^2$.

31.6
$$\begin{bmatrix} 1 & \frac{\sqrt{2}}{2} \\ \frac{\sqrt{2}}{2} & -5 \end{bmatrix}, \quad \begin{bmatrix} 3 & 5/2 & -7/2 \\ 5/2 & -4 & 1/2 \\ -7/2 & 1/2 & -1 \end{bmatrix}, \quad \begin{bmatrix} 0 & 1/2 & 1/2 & 1/2 \\ 1/2 & 0 & 1/2 & 1/2 \\ 1/2 & 1/2 & 0 & 1/2 \\ 1/2 & 1/2 & 1/2 & 0 \end{bmatrix}.$$

Section 32

32.1 Express the characteristic vectors **U** and **V** as n by 1 matrices U and V in terms of their coordinates. Then $\mathbf{U} \circ \mathbf{V} = U'V = V'U$. Let **U** belong to r and **V** belong to s. Show that $(AU)'V = (AV)'U$. Then show that $r \cdot U'V = s \cdot V'U$.

32.3 Let Q be a matrix such that $Q^{-1}AQ$ is in diagonal form. Use the fact that $Q^{-1}(A - r \cdot I_n)Q$ has the same rank as $A - r \cdot I_n$.

32.4
$$\begin{bmatrix} 1 & 0 & 0 \\ 0 & \frac{-5 + \sqrt{29}}{r} & \frac{2}{r} \\ 0 & \frac{2}{r} & \frac{5 - \sqrt{29}}{r} \end{bmatrix}, \quad \text{where} \quad r = \sqrt{58 - 10\sqrt{29}};$$

$$\begin{bmatrix} \frac{1}{\sqrt{2}} & \frac{-1}{\sqrt{2}} & 0 & 0 \\ 0 & 0 & \frac{1}{\sqrt{2}} & \frac{1}{\sqrt{2}} \\ 0 & 0 & \frac{1}{\sqrt{2}} & \frac{-1}{\sqrt{2}} \\ \frac{1}{\sqrt{2}} & \frac{1}{\sqrt{2}} & 0 & 0 \end{bmatrix}; \quad \begin{bmatrix} \frac{\sqrt{3}}{3} & 0 & \frac{\sqrt{6}}{3} \\ \sqrt{6} & -\frac{\sqrt{3}}{2} & -\frac{\sqrt{3}}{6} \\ \frac{\sqrt{2}}{2} & \frac{1}{2} & \frac{-1}{2} \end{bmatrix}.$$

(There are other solutions.)

32.5 $[(17 + \sqrt{553})/2]\bar{x}^2 + [(17 - \sqrt{553})/2]\bar{y}^2 = 100$; $\frac{3}{2}\bar{x}^2 - \frac{23}{2}\bar{y}^2 = 4$; $\bar{x}^2 + (1 + 3\sqrt{2})\bar{y}^2 + (1 - 3\sqrt{2})\bar{z}^2$; $-2\bar{x}^2 + (2 + \sqrt{6})\bar{y}^2 + (2 - \sqrt{6})\bar{z}^2$.

Section 33

33.3

$$\begin{bmatrix} 0 & 0 & 1 \\ 0 & \frac{1}{6} & -1 \\ \frac{12}{7\sqrt{15}} & \frac{1}{6\sqrt{15}} & \frac{1}{7\sqrt{15}} \end{bmatrix}, \quad \text{rank} = 3, \text{ index} = 1.$$

$$\begin{bmatrix} 0 & \frac{\sqrt{3}}{3} & 0 & 0 \\ \frac{\sqrt{3}}{r} & \frac{\sqrt{3}}{3r} & \frac{6\sqrt{3}}{r} & 0 \\ 0 & 0 & 1 & 0 \\ \frac{-29\sqrt{3}}{rs} & \frac{-208\sqrt{3}}{rs} & \frac{-55\sqrt{3}}{rs} & \frac{119\sqrt{3}}{rs} \end{bmatrix},$$

where $r = \sqrt{119}$, $s = 3\sqrt{662}$. Rank = 4, index = 2;

$$\begin{bmatrix} 1 & 0 & 0 & 0 \\ -1 & 1 & 0 & 0 \\ -1 & 0 & 1 & 0 \\ -1 & 0 & 0 & 1 \end{bmatrix}, \quad \text{rank} = 1, \text{ index} = 1.$$

(There are other solutions for the matrices.)

33.4

$$\begin{bmatrix} 0 & 0 & 0 & 1 \\ \frac{1}{2} & 0 & 2 & -1 \\ \frac{1}{2} & 0 & 0 & -1 \\ \frac{-1}{\sqrt{6}} & \frac{2}{\sqrt{6}} & \frac{-5}{\sqrt{6}} & \frac{2}{\sqrt{6}} \end{bmatrix}, \quad y_1^2 + y_2^2 - y_3^2 - y_4^2;$$

$$\begin{bmatrix} 1 & 0 & 0 \\ -1 & 1 & 0 \\ -1 & 0 & 1 \end{bmatrix}, \quad y_1^2, \text{ positive semidefinite;}$$

$$\begin{bmatrix} \frac{1}{\sqrt{2}} & 0 & 0 \\ -2 & 1 & 0 \\ \sqrt{3} & 0 & \frac{1}{\sqrt{3}} \end{bmatrix}, \quad y_1^2 - y_2^2 - y_3^2.$$

(There are other solutions for the matrices.)

Index

Addition:
of linear transformations, 85
of matrices, 95
of vectors, 7
Angle between vectors, 10
Associated homogeneous system, 72
Associated integer of an echelon form, 68
Associative law:
of matrix addition, 96
of matrix multiplication, 100
of multiplication of linear transformations, 87
of vector addition, 8
Augmented matrix, 106

Basis, 48
matrix of change of, 116
orthonormal, 53
Bilinear form, 183
value of, 183
Bilinear mapping, 181
matrix of, 182
Bilinearity condition, 51

Change of basis, matrix of, 116
Characteristic equation, 164
Characteristic polynomial, 164
Characteristic root, 164
Characteristic value, 162
Characteristic vector, 162
Coefficients of linear equations, 58
Coefficients, matrix of, 106
Cofactor, 156
Collinear vectors, 12
Column rank, 135
Column space, 135
Column transformation, elementary, 128, 129, 130
Commutative law of vector addition, 7
Complement, orthogonal, 56
Complete inverse image, 80
Components of a vector, 40
Congruence transformation, elementary, 199
Conjugate of a complex number, 188
Consistent linear equations, 58
Coordinate system, 14, 15, 24
Coplanar vectors, 14
Cramer's rule, 160

Determinant, 143
Determinantal rank, 158
Diagonal matrix, 104
Dimension of a vector space, 49
Dimensions of a matrix, 92
Direct sum, 44, 45
Directed line segment, 4
Direction angles, 27
Direction cosines, 28
Direction of a vector, 5

Echelon form, 64
associated integer of, 68
Elementary column transformation, 128, 129, 130
Elementary congruence transformation, 199
Elementary row transformation, 107
Elementary transformation matrix, 128, 129, 130
Elementary transformation of a set of vectors, 59
Equality of matrices, 92
Equivalence classes, 5, 6
Equivalence of directed line segments, 4
Equivalence, orthogonal, 175
Equivalence relation, 5, 6
Equivalent matrices, 122
Equivalent systems of linear equations, 58
Euclidean vector space, 52

Finite dimensional vector space, 49

Gram-Schmidt orthogonalization process, 55

Homogeneous system of linear equations, 70

Identity matrix, 101
Identity transformation, 87
Image of a subspace, 80
Image of a vector, 79
Inconsistent linear equations, 58
Index of a symmetric matrix, 196
Inner product, 10, 52
Inverse of a linear transformation, 87
Inverse of a matrix, 102
Inversion, 143
Isomorphism, 83

Kernel, 81
K-rowed minor, 157

Length of a vector, 5
Line, parametric equations of, 33
Line segment, direction of, 4
Linear combination, 35
Linear equations,
  coefficients of, 58
  consistent, 58
  equivalent systems of, 58
  homogeneous system of, 70
  inconsistent, 58
  row space of a system, 60
  solution of a system of, 58
Linear transformation, 76, 79
  inverse of, 87
  matrix of, 90
  nonsingular, 82
  rank of, 135
  singular, 82
Linear transformations,
  addition of, 85
  multiplication of, 86
  multiplication, associative law of, 87
  scalar multiplication of, 85
  sum of, 85
Linearly dependent set, 36, 45
Linearly independent set, 36, 45

Mapping,
  bilinear, 181
  quadratic, 182
  symmetric, 52
  zero, 85
Matrices,
  addition of, 95
  equality of, 92
  equivalent, 122
  scalar multiplication of, 96
  similar, 125
  subtraction of, 96
Matrix,
  augmented, 106
  of a bilinear mapping, 182
  of a change of basis, 116
  of coefficients, 106
  diagonal, 104
  dimensions of, 92
  inverse of, 102
  of a linear transformation, 90
  negative of, 96
  nonsingular, 102
  orthogonal, 173
  rank of, 137
  row rank of, 109
  row space of, 107
  scalar, 104
  singular, 102
  symmetric, 186
  symmetric, index of, 196
  transpose of, 104
  zero, 96
Matrix addition, 95
  associative law of, 96
Matrix multiplication, 99
  associative law of, 100
Minor, 154
Multiplication:
  of linear transformations, 86
  of matrices, 99

Negative of a matrix, 96
Negative of a vector, 8, 39
Nonsingular linear transformation, 82
Nonsingular matrix, 102
Nontrivial solution, 70
Null space, 81

Ordered pairs,
  scalar multiplication of, 16
  sum of, 16
Ordered triples,
  scalar multiplication of, 25
  sum of, 24
Orthogonal complement, 56
Orthogonal equivalence, 175
Orthogonal matrix, 173
Orthogonal projection of $\mathcal{E}_2$, 76
Orthogonal transformation, 172
Orthogonal vectors, 11, 53
Orthonormal basis, 53

Parametric equations of a line, 33
Positive definite, 52
Positive definite quadratic form, 201
Positive semidefinite quadratic form, 201
Principal axes, 193
Product:
  of linear transformations, 86
  of matrices, 99
Projection, 76, 78
Proper subspace, 42

Quadratic form, 184
Quadratic mapping, 182

Rank,
  column, 135
  determinantal, 158
  of a linear transformation, 135
  of a matrix, 137
  row, 109
Range space, 81
Rational canonical form, 141
Real vector space, 39
Relation, 6
Row by column rule, 99
Row rank, 109
Row space of a matrix, 107
Row space of a system of linear equations, 60
Row transformation, elementary, 107

Scalar matrix, 104
Scalar multiplication:
  of linear transformations, 85
  of matrices, 96
  of ordered pairs, 16
  of ordered triples, 25
  of vectors, 9, 39
Schwarz inequality, 56
Similar matrices, 125
Singular linear transformation, 82
Singular matrix, 102
Solution space, 71
Solution of a system of linear equations, 58
Solution vector, 71
Subspace, 42
  image of, 80
  proper, 42
  zero, 42
Subtraction:
  of matrices, 96
  of vectors, 9, 39
Sum of subspaces, 44, 45
Symmetric mapping, 52
Symmetric matrix, 186

Transpose of a matrix, 104
Triangle inequality, 56

Unit vector, 14, 52

Value of a bilinear form, 183
Value of a quadratic form, 184
Vector,
  components of, 40
  coordinates of, 16, 50
  direction of, 5
  image of, 79
  length of, 5
  negative of, 8, 39
  zero, 5, 39
Vector addition, 7
  associative law of, 8
  commutative law of, 7
Vector space, 39
  dimension of, 49
  Euclidean, 52
  finite dimensional, 49
  real, 39
Vectors,
  angle between, 10
  collinear, 12
  coplanar, 14
  elementary transformation of a set of, 59
  on a line, 12
  orthogonal, 11, 53
  in a plane, 14
  scalar multiplication of, 9, 39
  subtraction of, 9, 39
  sum of, 7, 39

Zero mapping, 85
Zero matrix, 96
Zero subspace, 42
Zero vector, 5, 39

5
B 6
C 7
D 8
E 9
F 0
G 1
H 2
I 3
J 4